Isaac Lea L.L.D.

Who assembled the original collection of gems that now bears his name in the United
States National Museum.

SMITHSONIAN INSTITUTION
UNITED STATES NATIONAL MUSEUM
Bulletin 118

HANDBOOK AND DESCRIPTIVE CATALOGUE OF THE COLLECTIONS OF GEMS AND PRECIOUS STONES IN THE UNITED STATES NATIONAL MUSEUM

BY

GEORGE P. MERRILL

Head Curator of Geology, United States National Museum

ASSISTED BY

MARGARET W. MOODEY AND EDGAR T. WHERRY

WASHINGTON
GOVERNMENT PRINTING OFFICE
1922

ADVERTISEMENT.

The scientific publications of the United States National Museum consist of two series, the *Proceedings* and the *Bulletins*.

The *Proceedings*, the first volume of which was issued in 1878, are intended primarily as a medium for the publication of original, and usually brief, papers based on the collections of the National Museum, presenting newly acquired facts in zoology, geology, and anthropology, including descriptions of new forms of animals, and revisions of limited groups. One or two volumes are issued annually and distributed to libraries and scientific organizations. A limited number of copies of each paper, in pamphlet form, is distributed to specialists and others interested in the different subjects as soon as printed. The dates of publication are recorded in the tables of contents of the volumes.

The *Bulletins*, the first of which was issued in 1875, consist of a series of separate publications comprising chiefly monographs of large zoological groups and other general systematic treatises (occasionally in several volumes), faunal works, reports of expeditions, and catalogues of type-specimens, special collections, etc. The majority of the volumes are octavos, but a quarto size has been adopted in a few instances in which large plates were regarded as indispensable.

Since 1902 a series of octavo volumes containing papers relating to the botanical collections of the Museum, and known as the *Contributions from the National Herbarium*, has been published as bulletins.

The present work forms No. 118 of the *Bulletin* series.

WILLIAM DEC. RAVENEL,
Administrative Assistant to the Secretary
In charge of the United States National Museum.

WASHINGTON, D. C., *January 23, 1922.*

PREFATORY NOTE.

In the annual report of the United States National Museum for 1900 (1902) there was published a descriptive catalogue of the collections of gems in the United States National Museum, as prepared by Mr. Wirt Tassin, then assistant curator in charge of the Division of Mineralogy, assisted by A. S. Eakle, subsequently professor of mineralogy in the University of California. As this catalogue has long been out of print, and as the collection has increased considerably since it appeared, a new edition has been decided upon. In this, however, a different method of treatment has been adopted, and the subject matter has been quite largely rewritten, so that it represents an essentially new work.

In order that just credit may be given to all concerned it may be well to state that the preparation of the catalogue was begun in 1916 by Dr. Edgar T. Wherry, then assistant curator in charge of the mineralogical collection. His resignation in 1917 caused a long delay, and meanwhile, during the occupancy of the building by the War Risk Bureau (October, 1917, to March, 1919), it was decided to entirely rearrange and recatalogue the collection which had been heretofore included with the general collection of minerals. This work, which involved as well the weighing and measuring of each individual stone, has been slow and laborious, but has been carried through in almost its entirety by Miss Margaret W. Moodey, the recorder for the department. In preparing the text so much of the edition of 1902 as was suitable has been retained (see particularly pp. 141–178), to which has been added the descriptive matter prepared by Doctor Wherry. Important additional matter is furnished in the accounts of the pegmatites and their associated minerals, that of southern California having been prepared by Dr. W. T. Schaller, for several years custodian of the collection. Other important additions are the references to the Gardner Williams collection of rocks from the diamond mines of South Africa, the list of gem names and the table for the identification of precious stones.

In addition to portraits of the founder and benefactor of the collection, and two colored plates illustrating gems in the collection, there have been added a number of plates showing typical localities from which gems are mined.

GEORGE P. MERRILL.

IV

TABLE OF CONTENTS.

LIST OF ILLUSTRATIONS.

HANDBOOK AND DESCRIPTIVE CATALOGUE OF THE COLLECTIONS OF GEMS AND PRECIOUS STONES IN THE UNITED STATES NATIONAL MUSEUM.

By George P. Merrill

Head Curator of Geology, United States National Museum

ASSISTED BY

Margaret W. Moodey and Edgar T. Wherry

1. HISTORY AND ARRANGEMENT OF THE COLLECTION.

In 1884 Prof. F. W. Clarke, then honorary curator of the Division of Mineralogy, prepared an exhibit of American precious stones as a part of the United States National Museum's contribution to the New Orleans exposition. The same collection was displayed at the Cincinnati exposition in the following year, after which it was returned to Washington and incorporated in the mineral collection of the museum. From 1886 to 1890 the growth of the collection was steady though slow. In 1891 the greater part of the collection of precious stones made by Dr. Joseph Leidy, of Philadelphia, was purchased by the museum and combined with what was already on hand to form an exhibit for the World's Columbian Exposition at Chicago in 1893, the whole being returned to Washington when that exposition closed.

The great popularity of these collections, as attested by the number of visitors and their equally numerous queries, impressed upon the Museum authorities the advisability of extending the series and building it up systematically, a work which, though at once undertaken, proceeded at first slowly and with difficulty owing to the expense involved. Fortunately this has to a considerable extent been alleviated through the magnanimity of a private individual. The collections are still, however, poorly balanced, lacking a satisfactory showing of the rarer and more highly priced stones, a single one of which, of suitable size for exhibition, would consume the available income for an entire year. It is not too much to hope and expect that this discrepancy, like the last, may also be remedied through individual action.

1

In 1894 Mrs. Frances Lea Chamberlain bequeathed to the museum a collection of precious stones which had been assembled by her father, Dr. Isaac Lea (pl. 1). Her husband, Dr. L. T. Chamberlain (pl. 2), who subsequently (1897) became honorary curator of the collection, added a large number of specimens, and on his death bequeathed a sum of money, the income of which is to be used for their further increase.

In addition, many specimens have been received throughout this period as gifts from individuals and transfers from the United States Geological Survey. These various collections have been combined, and are now exhibited as "The Isaac Lea Collection," although the individual stones are differentiated by label. The exhibit at present is comprised in a row of table cases, extending down the center of the Mineral Hall. (See pl. 3.) At the west end of this row, immediately to the right of the entrance to the hall, stands a large group of amethyst crystals from Brazil. In table cases fronting the windows on the south side of the hall are other series illustrating the properties of precious stones, their appearance in the rough as contrasted with the cut form; gem minerals in the matrix or as occurring in nature, and artificial and imitation stones. Finally, an upright case between the windows at the center of the hall contains many semiprecious stones—that is, stones used in the manufacture of small ornaments, rather than for personal adornment.

It may be added that in building up the collection an attempt has been made to show the possibilities of commonplace material; that there is a goodly number of stones, in themselves of little intrinsic value, which when properly cut and mounted are not merely beautiful, but have the additional value of being out of the line of the usual material sold in shops. In this connection particular attention may be called to the cabochons of silicified wood, obsidian, epidotic granite (unakite), and green feldspar (amazonstone).

Leander T. Chamberlain

Who, in memory of his wife, Frances Lea, endowed the Isaac Lea collection in the United
States National Museum.

2. NAMES AND PHYSICAL AND CHEMICAL PROPERTIES OF PRECIOUS STONES.

About 1,200 mineral species are now (1920) known to science, and of these somewhat less than one-tenth, or in round numbers 100, possess the properties of beauty and durability to such an extent that they are of importance, interest, and value as precious and semiprecious stones or gems. The present paper comprises descriptions of these minerals, lists of the cut stones of each represented in the collection, and notes on methods of identification, uses, etc. By way of introduction to the descriptive portion, brief definitions of the properties of the minerals and other explanatory notes are given; no attempt has been made, however, to make this a treatise on mineralogy, chemistry, or physics, and for further information concerning the various features discussed, reference should be made to works on those subjects.

Names.—The names of minerals have in part come down to us from the ancients, and in part been constructed by adding the suffix *ite* (from *ites*, similar to) or *lite* (from *lithos*, stone) to an appropriate root. As far as possible the names generally accepted by mineralogists have been adopted here.

Many stones, in addition to the standard names by which they are known to science, are also called by one or more synonyms, usually popular or trade names; the most important of these are added in each tabular description.

Chemical composition.—The chemical composition and formulas of the minerals are stated in a simple form. For the benefit of those unfamiliar with chemical terms it may be explained that the majority of mineral substances are compounds of two or more elements, in more or less definite proportions; and that these compounds are named by stating first the names of the elements forming the electro-positive or basic part of the compound, and then those of the elements forming the electro-negative or acidic part. The names of the negative elements are combined, usually in abbreviated form, and provided with significant suffixes, such as *ide* when a single element is concerned, and *ate* when oxygen is also present.

The formulas of the compounds are derived by placing the symbols of the elements together, with subscript figures to indicate the number of atoms of each represented. For definitions of the various chemical terms, and additional details, the reader is referred to textbooks of chemistry. The following table shows the elements that may be present in important amounts in precious stones, with their symbols:

3

Metals forming the bases of precious stones.

Aluminum	Al	Manganese	Mn
Barium	Ba	Mercury (*hydrargyrum*)	Hg
Beryllium (or glucinum)	Be	Nickel	Ni
Calcium	Ca	Potassium (*kalium*)	K
Cerium	Ce	Sodium (*natrium*)	Na
Chromium	Cr	Tin (*stannum*)	Sn
Cobalt	Co	Titanium	Ti
Copper (*cuprum*)	Cu	Uranium	U
Hydrogen	H	Vanadium	V
Iron (*ferrum*)	Fe	Yttrium	Y
Lead (*plumbum*)	Pb	Zinc	Zn
Lithium	Li	Zirconium	Zr
Magnesium	Mg		

Nonmetals forming the acid portions of precious stones.

Boron	B	Oxygen	O
Carbon	C	Phosphorus	P
Chlorine	Cl	Silicon	Si
Columbium	Cb	Sulphur	S
Fluorine	F		

Crystallization.—When a chemical compound passes from the liquid or gaseous state into the solid condition, cohesion and chemical affinity tend to draw its atoms together, and if these become grouped in a regular manner solids bounded by plane surfaces result; these are known as crystals. Six crystal systems (one of them consisting of two subsystems) are recognized, as follows: 1, Isometric, or cubic, comprising those crystals developed exactly alike in the six directions in space (front, back, right, left, up, and down), at right angles to one another; these have the general aspect of spheres, regularly flattened at an even number of equal intervals, and include the cube, regular octahedron, rhombic dodecahedron, etc., as well as combinations of these simple forms. 2, Tetragonal, comprising those crystals developed according to two different patterns, one repeated four times in directions at equal intervals in a plane, the other twice in the directions at right angles to that plane, all being at right angles to one another. The crystals of this system are made up of pinacoids, prisms, and pyramids. 3, Hexagonal, comprising crystals developed according to two different patterns, one repeated six times in directions at intervals lying 60° apart in a plane, and the other twice in the directions at right angles to that plane; the forms are like those of the tetragonal system. Trigonal (a subsystem of the hexagonal), comprising crystals developed according to two different patterns, one repeated three times at intervals lying 120° apart in a plane, and the other twice in the directions at right angles to that plane. 4, Orthorhombic system comprising those crystals developed according to three different patterns, each repeated twice, in opposite directions, all again at right angles; the crystals of this system are made up of combinations of pinacoids, prisms, domes, and pyramids. 5, Monoclinic, system, comprising crystals developed like the orthorhombic, but with the patterns reappearing in one plane twice at angles less, and twice at angles greater, than right angles; the forms are like those of the preceding system. 6, Triclinic system, comprising crystals developed like the two preceding systems, but with none of the patterns repeated exactly at right angles to one another; the forms are essentially the same as those of the two preceding systems.

In addition, a few minerals have their atoms irregularly arranged, and consequently are without crystal form; to these the term amorphous is applied.

Color.—The color of an object expresses the character of the ligh reflected or transmitted by it. The principal terms used in describing it are: White, gray, black, violet, blue, green, yellow, red, and brown. There are also many intermediate hues, best described by a combination of terms, as blue-green, etc. Colors may be divided into two classes:

1. Essential or idiochromatic colors, due to the chemical elements which make up a compound. They are definite and characteristic for each substance and only disappear when it is decomposed. The principal elements yielding colors in the order of their most frequent occurence in precious stones are:

Elements.	Valence.	Colors produced.
Iron	ferrous, Fe^{ii}	green.
	ferric, Fe^{iii}	red, brown, yellow.
	both together	blue, black.
Chromium	chromic, Cr^{iii}	green, violet, red.
	negative, Cr^{vi}	red, yellow.
Vanadium	V^{iii} and V^{v}	red, brown, yellow.
Manganese	manganous, Mn^{ii}	red, pink.
	manganic, Mn^{iii}	violet.
Copper	cuprous, Cu^{i}	red.
	cupric, Cu^{ii}	blue, green.
Titanium	titanic, Ti^{iii}	violet, blue.
Nickel	nickelous, Ni^{ii}	green.
Cobalt	cobaltous, Co^{ii}	red, blue.
Uranium	uranic, U^{vi}	greenish-yellow.
Molybdenum	negative, Mo^{vi}	yellow, red.
Neodymium	neodymic, Nd^{iii}	red-violet.
Cerium	cerous, Ce^{iii}	brown.

2. Nonessential or allochromatic colors, due to impurities or foreign constituents in a substance. They may vary widely from one specimen to another and may be of three different types: 1, Produced by evident, distinct particles, which in themselves show essential colors. Thus, finely divided ferric oxides are frequently inclosed in other

minerals, and render them yellow, brown, or red.   2, Disperse colors, due to submicroscopic inclusions, and varying with their shape, size, or arrangement.   These colors are thought to have been developed, in part at least, by exposure in the earth to radio-active substances, slight decomposition having thereby been effected, and traces of the constituent elements set free.   Heating usually destroys these colors, since it causes the free elements to reunite, but exposure to radiant energy of various kinds often restores them.   3, Internal reflection colors, due to symmetrically arranged inclusions, or to lamellae of extreme thinness, producing interference of light.

A special color phenomenon remains to be considered.   Some minerals transmit light of different colors in different directions, and are said to be pleochroic.   The most striking instance of this among precious stones is iolite, which is sometimes called "dichroite" because of this very property; in one direction it appears intense blue, in another somewhat paler blue, and in the third pale yellow.   In many cases, however, the difference in color is less striking, and special means must be used in order to detect it.   An instrument, called a dichroscope, is sometimes used for this purpose.   It consists of a metal tube containing a cleavage piece of Iceland spar; at one end it is pierced with a small square hole, and at the other has a magnifying lens to serve as an eyepiece; the hole appears double when viewed through the latter.   When a pleochroic stone is placed in front of the square hole, the two images of the hole will be differently colored.

Another method of observing pleochroism makes use of the polarizing nicol prism in the microscope.   The stone is placed on the stage, and the polarizer introduced; the stone is observed in one position and again after turning the stage through 90°; one of the pleochroic colors will be seen in each of these positions.

It should be noted that isometric minerals, which are isotropic between crossed nicols, show no pleochroism; tetragonal, hexagonal, and trigonal ones may show two colors, while those of the three remaining crystal systems in general show three colors.

Luster.—The luster or brilliancy of a mineral is a physical phenomenon connected with the manner in which light is refracted by it; the principal types are metallic, adamantine, and vitreous, but in addition some minerals of fundamentally vitreous luster possess certain peculiarities of structure, and as a result exhibit lusters resembling those of familiar substances, as waxy, greasy, silky, etc.

Hardness.—On the hardness of a mineral is dependent its resistance to scratching or abrasion.   It is usually described by reference to a standard scale of 10 minerals, which are, beginning with the softest— 1, talc; 2, gypsum; 3, calcite; 4, fluorite; 5, apatite; 6, orthoclase or microcline; 7, quartz; 8, topaz or beryl; 9, corundum (ruby or sapphire); and 10, diamond.   Each of these will scratch all preceding in the series and be scratched by all following. In general only those minerals which possess a hardness greater than 6 in this scale—that is, which will at least scratch orthoclase—are sufficiently durable to be used as precious stones.

Specific gravity.—The specific gravity of a substance is its weight compared with an equal bulk of pure water; thus, the statement that diamond has a specific gravity of 3.5 means that it is three and one-half times as heavy as water. This property is characteristic of many precious stones and is of considerable value in their identification. It is determined by weighing the stone first in air and then suspended in water. The first weight, divided by the difference between the two, gives the value desired. For details as to the apparatus used for this purpose, books on mineralogy or physics must be consulted.

Optical properties. Index of refraction.—When light passes obliquely from one transparent substance to another, its direction is, in general, altered at their boundary. The well-known phenomenon of the apparent bending of a stick thrust into water is an illustration of this. The extent to which light entering minerals from the air is shifted is called their index of refraction; in mathematical terms this is the ratio between the sine of the angle of incidence and that of the angle of refraction. In amorphous minerals and in those crystallizing in the isometric system, the index of refraction is the same in all directions; in those crystallizing in the systems derived from a revolution ellipsoid—namely, the hexagonal, trigonal, and tetragonal—there are two different indices; and in those crystallizing in the remaining systems there are three. The last two groups are said to possess double refraction, which in the first is the difference between the two indices; in the second, the difference between the largest and smallest.

In a few minerals, notably in Iceland spar (transparent calcite), the double refraction is so strong that an object observed through the mineral appears double; in most cases, however, the double refraction is too slight to be rendered visible in this manner, and special means must be employed for its recognition; polarized light (light the vibration of which is limited to a definite plane) is generally used for this purpose. For details of the phenomena connected with polarized light, books on optical mineralogy must be consulted. It may be mentioned here, however, that it is most conveniently obtained by causing ordinary light to traverse prisms of Iceland spar so constructed that only one of the two rays into which the light is split is actually transmitted. The light emerging from such a prism (called a "nicol" after its inventor) is vibrating in a single plane; and if two nicols are disposed so that the planes are at right angles no light will be able to traverse the system. A substance with single refraction placed between them is without effect on this extinction of the light and is said to be *isotropic*. But a substance possessing double refraction will, in all but one or two directions, cause light to be transmitted and is then described as *anisotropic*. The latter is also subdivided on the basis of number of optic axes (directions along which polarized light is not affected), crystals derived from revolution-ellipsoids having one such axis and being termed *uniaxial*, while those not so derivable have two and are termed *biaxial*. There is still another feature which is usually stated in connection with aniso-tropic crystals—the optical sign. When the greatest index of refrac-tion is shown in the direction of the optic axis, in uniaxial crystals, or in the acute angle between the two optic axes in biaxial ones, the sign is described as plus (+); and in reverse case it is minus (−).

MINERAL HALL, UNITED STATES NATIONAL MUSEUM

3. DESCRIPTIVE CATALOGUE OF THE COLLECTIONS.

The arrangement of the gem names in this catalogue is alphabetical throughout so far as practicable. Under each mineral or gem is given in tabular form some of the more striking qualities of a descriptive or determinative nature, followed by remarks on the mode of occurrence and such other miscellaneous information as it is thought will be of value. In the catalogue proper the material is arranged in the following order: Name, locality, cut, color, weight, measurements, and catalogue number. The weights are given in the newly introduced metro-carats. The specimens are listed by localities, alphabetically, and under each locality are arranged in the order of decreasing weights, except where several stones are described together, these being placed at the end of the list for that particular locality.

Adularia.—See under Feldspar.
Agate.—See under Chalcedony.
Alabaster.—See under Gypsum.
Albite.—See under Feldspar (Moonstone).
Alexandrite.—See under Chrysoberyl.
Almandite.—See under Garnet.
Amazonstone.—See under Feldspar.

AMBER.

Synonym.—Succinite.
Composition.—A resinous substance, containing carbon, hydrogen, and oxygen.
Crystallization.—Amorphous.
Color.—Yellow, orange-yellow, brown-yellow, or rarely red.
Luster.—Resinous; transparent to translucent.
Hardness.—2.5; too soft for extensive use as a precious stone.
Optical properties.—Mean refractive index 1.54; is isotropic excepting when in a condition of strain.
Specific gravity.—1.07; noticeably light.

Amber is a poor conductor of heat and electricity, becoming electrified when rubbed on cloth so that it will attract small bits of paper. It can be distinguished from imitations such as rosin and celluloid by being less inflammable, though it burns readily with a rich yellow flame, yielding an aromatic odor. Heated to 150° C. it begins to soften and melts at about 250°. From most minerals it may be distinguished by its extreme lightness and its solubility in alcohol.

9

It occurs in sediments of the later geological periods, representing the fossil resin of the tree *Pinus succinifera* and other plants; sometimes contains insects which became embedded in the material while it was soft and in a pitch-like condition. It is used chiefly for beads, earrings, and other similar ornaments. The value of the crude material is but a few cents an ounce.

LIST OF SPECIMENS.

COAST OF THE BALTIC SEA.

Two cuff buttons; pale yellow; opaque... No. 674
Breastpin of 3 facetted beads and pendant; light yellow-brown............ No. 675
Necklace of 50 facetted beads: light yellow-brown......................... No. 676
Bracelet of 16 rectangular links, 20 by 15 mm. average size, and buckle;
    alternating pale yellow and clouded amber. Isaac Lea collection........ No. 1641

INDIA (BURMA).

Heart-shaped cabochon; yellow-brown; 8.2 carats; 20 by 7 mm.............. No. 673

ITALY (SICILY).

Ten polished pieces; light and dark brown; various sizes and shapes; total
    weight, 92.5 carats.. No. 671
Pendant; brown; 19.3 carats; 45 by 18 by 10 mm. Isaac Lea collection.. No. 672

LOCALITY NOT RECORDED.

Necklace of 62 facetted beads, graduated sizes; yellow-brown; William H.
    Forwood bequest... No. 677

Amethyst.—See under Quartz.

ANDALUSITE.

Variety.—Chiastolite or macle.

Composition.—Aluminum orthosilicate, $Al_2O(SiO_4)$.

Crystallization.—Orthorhombic.

Color.—Gray when pure; often showing brown-green, or yellow-green, and rarely brown, pink, or violet hues, owing to the presence of impurities of unknown nature; rather strongly pleochroic, green to yellow or even to red.

Luster.—Vitreous; transparent to translucent.

Hardness.—7.5; a durable stone.

Specific gravity.—3.20 ± 0.05.

Optical properties.—Mean refractive index, 1.64; double refraction moderate, 0.01; biaxial, negative.

Chiastolite contains symmetrically arranged carbonaceous matter yielding in polished specimens a black cross on gray background. It may be distinguished from tourmaline and other similar minerals by its pleochroism, specific gravity, and optical properties. It occurs in metamorphic rocks, especially mica schist.

Uses.—Clear andalusite is cut facetted; chiastolite is cut cabochon and used for scarfpins, and ranks as a curiosity rather than a gem.

Step brilliant, rectangular girdle; brown-green; 1.39 carats; 11 by 6 by 3 mm.. No. 568
Brilliant, rectangular girdle; dark green; 1.03 carats; 7 by 6 by 4 mm...... No. 566
Step, rectangular girdle; brown-green; 0.83 carat; 10 by 4.5 by 2 mm....... No. 569
Step brilliant, square girdle; brown-green; 0.72 carat; 6 by 3.5 mm........ No. 567

Aquamarine.—See under Beryl.

Aragonite.—See under Calcite and Aragonite.

AXINITE.

Composition.—Iron calcium aluminum hydrous boro-silicate, $FeCa_2Al_2(OH)(BSi_4O_{15})$.

Crystallization.—Triclinic; habit wedge-shaped.

Color.—Brown; sometimes violet, violet-brown, or yellow-brown; essential, due to the iron, and to manganese which may replace it; strongly pleochroic, green to brown to blue.

Luster.—Brilliant-vitreous; transparent.

Hardness.—6.5; a fairly durable stone.

Specific gravity.—3.30 ± 0.05.

Optical properties.—Mean refractive index 1.68; double refraction weak, 0.009; optically biaxial, negative.

Axinite may be distinguished from tourmaline and other similar minerals by its pleochroism, specific gravity, and optical properties. It occurs in veins, chiefly in metamorphic rocks and is in little demand as a precious stone, because of unattractive colors and brittleness. Value purely arbitrary.

Step-brilliant, square girdle; violet-brown; 1.59 carats; 7.5 by 4.5 mm.... No. 581

AZURITE.

Composition.—Hydrous copper carbonate, $Cu_3(OH)_2(CO)_2$.

Crystallization.—Monoclinic.

Color.—Dark blue, characteristic of many compounds of copper.

Luster.—Vitreous; translucent to opaque.

Hardness.—4; too soft for extensive use as a precious stone.

Specific gravity.—3.80 ± 0.05.

Optical properties.—Mean refractive index 1.9; double refraction very strong, 0.20; biaxial, positive.

The mineral dissolves readily in hydrochloric acid with effervescence to a yellow solution. It may as a rule be distinguished from other blue precious stones by its intense color, softness, and solubility. It occurs in veins and pockets and has been derived from sulphide ores through decomposition by surface water, as has malachite, with which it is very commonly associated. Used for ornaments, scarfpins, etc.; the value as a gem is little more than the cost of cutting. (See under Malachite.)

BENITOITE.

Composition.—Barium titano-silicate, $BaTiSi_3O_9$.
Crystallization.—Hexagonal (trigonal), holohedral.
Color.—Pale to deep blue; pleochroic.
Luster.—Vitreous.
Hardness.—6.5.
Specific gravity.—3.64 – 3.67.
Optical properties.—Refractive index 1.757 to 1.804. Double refraction strong and positive. High index of refraction and marked pleochroism are distinguishing features of the mineral. So far as at present known it occurs only in natrolite veins cutting serpentine. It is usually cut as brilliant, more rarely cabochon. A limited supply of this mineral has as yet been found (pl. 4). It is, therefore, little used, though of good quality.

LIST OF SPECIMENS.
UNITED STATES.
California.

San Benito County:
Two gems, brilliant, circular girdle; blue and violet blue; 0.95 and 0.87 carats, 5.7 by 4.5 and 5.5 by 4 mm. Isaac Lea collection .... No. 1180.

BERYL.

Varieties.—Common, aquamarine, emerald, morganite (vorobievite), and golden beryl.
Composition.—Beryllium aluminum metasilicate, $Be_3Al_2(SiO_3)_6$.
Crystallization.—Hexagonal; habit usually prismatic, rarely tabular.
Color.—Colorless when pure; often showing green, blue, yellow, or pink hues, and in part named accordingly: Pale blue, green-blue, or blue-green, aquamarine; intense green, emerald; yellow, orange-yellow, or brown-yellow, golden-beryl; and pink, morganite, or vorobievite. Slightly pleochroic, if deeply colored.
Luster.—Vitreous; transparent.
Hardness.—8 (less when altered); a durable stone.
Specific gravity.—2.75 ± 0.10.
Optical properties.—Mean refractive index 1.58; double refraction weak, 0.005; uniaxial, negative. With the microspectroscope emerald yields two absorption bands in the orange, which form a characteristic distinction from green tourmaline, green corundum,

BENITOITE MINE, NEAR SAN BENITO, CALIFORNIA

and imitation emerald (green glass). Other varieties of beryl show
no spectrum. Other distinctive characters are color, slight pleochroism, specific gravity, refractive index, and weak double refraction.

Beryl occurs chiefly in granitic pegmatites and related formations.
The famous emerald deposits of Muzo, Colombia, South America, are
in a limestone thought to have been metamorphosed by solutions
accompanying the intrusion of pegmatite dikes. All the transparent
varieties of beryl are of more or less value as precious stones; they
are usually cut facetted. The emerald is considered of greatest value,
though many of the aquamarine varieties are of great beauty.

LIST OF SPECIMENS.

BERYL, common, golden, and caesium.

BRAZIL.

Brilliant, circular girdle; colorless; 4.67 carats; 12.5 by 6 mm.............. No. 738
Step-brilliant, oval girdle; yellow-green; 1.269 carats; 9 by 6 by 3 mm.
    Isaac Lea collection.. No. 743
Step-brilliant, elliptical girdle; colorless; 0.895 carat; 9 by 5.5 by 3.5 mm.. No. 740

RUSSIA (ALABASHKA, URAL MOUNTAINS).

Step-brilliant; rectangular girdle; yellow; 17.46 carats; 18 by 14 by 10 mm. No. 714
Table, rectangular girdle; yellow; 9.27 carats; 16 by 13 by 7 mm........... No. 715
Step-brilliant, rectangular girdle; green-yellow; 3.126 carats; 10 by 8 by 6
    mm.. No. 718
Step-brilliant, rectangular girdle; yellow; 3.113 carats; 12 by 9 by 5 mm.. No. 716
Brilliant, rectangular girdle; pale yellow; 1.73 carats; 8 by 7 by 6 mm.... No. 717
Brilliant, circular girdle; pale yellow; 1.31 carats; 8 by 5 mm............ No. 719

SIBERIA.

Table, rectangular girdle; yellow-green; 21.46 carats; 31 by 16 by 6.5 mm.. No. 713

UNITED STATES.

Connecticut.

Litchfield County:
    Brilliant, circular girdle; yellow; 1.73 carats; 8 by 6 mm............. No. 1036
    Brilliant; circular girdle; brown-yellow; 1.47 carats; 7.5 by 6 mm.
        Gift of New England Mining Company............................. No. 780
    Brilliant, circular girdle; green-yellow; 1.09 carats; 7 by 5 mm. Gift
        of New England Mining Company................................. No. 782
    Brilliant, circular girdle; brown-yellow; 0.987 carat; 6.5 by 5 mm. Gift
        of New England Mining Company................................. No. 784

Maine.

Mount Apatite, Auburn, Androscoggin County:
    Brilliant, circular girdle; very pale pink; 1.19 carats; 6.5 by 5 mm .. No. 1836
Topsham, Sagadahoc County:
    Brilliant, circular girdle; green-yellow; 23.01 carats; 14.5 by 11 mm.
        (Set in gold band) .... No. 1031
    Brilliant, circular girdle; green-yellow; 5.25 carats; 12 by 7.5 mm.... No. 1032
    Brilliant, circular girdle; yellow-green; 4.155 carats; 11 by 7.5 mm.... No. 1035
    Brilliant, circular girdle; yellow-green; 3.275 carats; 10 by 7 mm...... No. 1033
    Brilliant, circular girdle; yellow-green; 1.88 carats; 8.5 by 5.5 mm.... No. 1034

Massachusetts.

Fitchburg, Worcester County:

Brilliant, rectangular girdle; yellow-green; 0.765 carat; 6.5 by 5 by
4 mm.. No. 787

North Carolina.

Yancey County, Ray's Mica Mine:

Brilliant, square girdle; colorless; 1.685 carats; 8 by 6 mm............ No. 759
Brilliant, circular girdle; colorless; 1.39 carats; 7 by 5 mm............ No. 760
Brilliant, circular girdle; colorless; 1.17 carats; 7 by 5 mm............ No. 763
Brilliant, circular girdle; colorless; 1.15 carats; 7 by 5 mm............ No. 761
Brilliant, square girdle; colorless; 1.1 carats; 7 by 5 mm.............. No. 764

Pennsylvania.

Avondale, Delaware County:

Step-brilliant, square girdle; yellow; 3.77 carats; 10 by 7 mm........ No. 792
Step-brilliant, rectangular girdle; yellow-green; 2.12 carats; 8 by 6 by
4 mm.. No. 793

BERYL, variety AQUAMARINE.

BRAZIL.

Step-brilliant, elliptical girdle; very pale green; 7.879 carats; 15 by 12.5
by 7 mm.. No. 737
Step-brilliant, oval girdle; pale green; 4.64 carats; 20 by 10 by 5 mm.
Isaac Lea collection.. No. 741
Step-brilliant, oval girdle; blue-green; 3.047 carats; 17 by 9 by 4 mm.
Isaac Lea collection.. No. 742
Step-brilliant, elliptical girdle; pale blue-green; 1.84 carats; 9.5 by 7 by
4 mm.. No. 739
Step-brilliant, oval girdle; pale blue-green; 0.565 carat; 8 by 5 by 3 mm.
Isaac Lea collection.. No. 744

CEYLON.

Step-brilliant, elliptical girdle; pale blue-green; 7.719 carats; 17 by 13 by
7 mm. Isaac Lea collection.. No. 732
Step-brilliant, rectangular girdle; pale blue-green; 7.324 carats; 12.5 by 11
by 8.5 mm. Isaac Lea collection.. No.   3
Step-brilliant, elliptical girdle; very pale green; 1.576 carats; 10 by 7 by
5 mm. Isaac Lea collection.. No. 733
Step-brilliant, elliptical girdle; pale green; 1.045 carats; 8 by 6 by 4 mm.
Isaac Lea collection.. No. 736
Step-brilliant, rectangular girdle; pale green; 1.02 carats; 8 by 6 by 4 mm.
Isaac Lea collection.. No. 735
Step-brilliant, elliptical girdle; pale green; 1.007 carats; 8 by 6 by 4 mm.
Isaac Lea collection.. No. 734

IRELAND (MOURNE MOUNTAIN).

Brilliant, circular girdle; light blue; 1.765 carats; 8 by 6 mm............ No. 745

JAPAN (SEKINOTSU, OMI).

Brilliant, circular girdle; very pale blue-green; 7.395 carats; 12 by 9 mm.... No. 1038
Brilliant, circular girdle; very pale blue-green; 5.69 carats; 11 by 9 mm...... No. 1039

SIBERIA

Step-brilliant, elliptical girdle; blue-green; 47.94 carats; 29 by 22 by 9 mm.
Isaac Lea collection... No. 709
Rose, elliptical girdle; blue-green; 40.4 carats; 27 by 23 by 13 mm.......... No. 693
Table, rectangular girdle; blue-green; 29.6 carats; 37 by 12 by 9 mm........ No. 695
Step-rose, elliptical girdle; blue-green; 22.49 carats; 26 by 17 by 9 mm...... No. 694
Step-brilliant, elliptical girdle; blue-green; 12.3 carats; 19 by 16 by 7 mm.... No. 696
Step-brilliant, elliptical girdle; light green; 10.25 carats; 16 by 12 by 7 mm.
Isaac Lea collection... No. 710
Step-brilliant, rectangular girdle; blue-green; 8.5 carats; 16 by 13 by 7 mm.. No. 698
Step-brilliant, rectangular girdle; blue-green; 8.2 carats; 14 by 12.5 by 6.5
mm.. No. 700
Table, square girdle; blue-green; 6.96 carats; 14 by 7 mm.................... No. 697
Step, rectangular girdle; blue-green; 6.38 carats; 19 by 8 by 6 mm........... No. 699
Step-brilliant, elliptical girdle; blue-green; 4.9 carats; 17 by 9 by 5 mm..... No. 702
Step-brilliant, rectangular girdle; blue-green; 4.7 carats; 17 by 8 by 5 mm... No. 703
Step-brilliant, octagonal girdle; very pale blue-green; 4.6 carats; 13 by 5 mm. No. 704
Step-brilliant, elliptical girdle; very pale green; 4.548 carats; 16 by 11 by 5
mm.. No. 701
Step-brilliant, rectangular girdle; blue-green; 3.97 carats; 12 by 9 by 5.5 mm. No. 705
Brilliant-rose, elliptical girdle; deep green-blue; 3.28 carats; 12 by 8 by 6 mm.
Isaac Lea collection... No. 711
Step-brilliant, rectangular girdle; blue-green; 2.95 carats; 10 by 9 by 5.5 mm. No. 707
Step-brilliant, elliptical girdle; blue-green; 2.45 carats; 11 by 9 by 5 mm.... No. 706
Step-brilliant, elliptical girdle; light green; 2.048 carats; 11 by 8 by 5 mm... No. 708
Step-brilliant, octagonal girdle; pale green; 1.95 carats; 9 by 5 mm. Isaac
Lea collection... No. 712

UNITED STATES.
Connecticut.

Litchfield County:
Briolette, heart-shaped girdle; blue-green; 40.44 carats; 20 by 21 by 16
mm.. No. 1037
Brilliant, circular girdle; very pale green; 1.48 carats; 8 by 6 mm. Gift
of New England Mining Company..................................... No. 781
Brilliant, circular girdle; pale green; 1.119 carats; 7 by 5 mm. Gift of
New England Mining Company.. No. 783
Portland, Middlesex County:
Brilliant, rectangular girdle; deep blue-green; 14.26 carats; 17 by 15 by
10 mm .... No. 779

Maine.

Paris, Oxford County:
Brilliant, rectangular girdle; colorless; 0.989 carat; 7 by 5.5 by 5 mm.. No. 791
Stoneham, Oxford County:
Brilliant, elliptical girdle; very pale blue-green; 3.135 carats; 10 by 9 by
7 mm... No. 789
Brilliant, rectangular girdle; pale blue-green; 1.045 carats; 7 by 6 by 5
mm... No. 790

Massachusetts.

Fitchburg, Worcester County:
Trap, rectangular girdle; pale green; 0.889 carat; 7 by 6 by 4 mm........ No. 786
Brilliant, circular girdle; pale yellow-green; 0.745 carat; 6 by 4 mm...... No. 788
Royalston, Worcester County:
Brilliant, rectangular girdle; deep blue-green; 8.37 carats; 14 by 13 by
9 mm.. No. 785

North Carolina.

Asheville, Buncombe County:

Step-brilliant, rectangular girdle; blue-green; 2.86 carats; 10 by 8 by
7 mm... No. 777

Mitchell County:

Cabochon, elliptical girdle; cloudy blue; 7.42 carats; 17 by 10 by 6 mm.
Gift of J. K. Bruner... No. 778

Brilliant, circular girdle; blue-green; 7.617 carats; 13 by 9 mm. Isaac
Lea collection... No. 746

Brilliant, circular girdle; blue-green; 5.124 carats; 11 by 8 mm. Isaac
Lea collection... No. 747

Brilliant, circular girdle; blue-green; 2.87 carats; 9 by 6.5 mm. Isaac
Lea collection... No. 748

Brilliant, circular girdle; blue-green; 2.036 carats; 8 by 6 mm. Isaac
Lea collection... No. 749

Brilliant, circular girdle; blue-green; 1.52 carats; 8 by 6 mm. Isaac
Lea collection... No. 750

Brilliant, circular girdle; blue-green; 1.115 carats; 7 by 5 mm.
Isaac Lea collection... No. 751

Brilliant, circular girdle; blue-green; 1.038 carats; 7 by 5 mm. Isaac
Lea collection... No. 752

Brilliant, circular girdle; blue-green; 0.88 carat; 6 by 4.5 mm. Isaac
Lea collection... No. 753

Brilliant, circular girdle; blue-green; 0.726 carat; 6 by 4 mm. Isaac
Lea collection... No. 754

Brilliant, circular girdle; blue-green; 0.66 carat; 6 by 4 mm. Isaac
Lea collection... No. 755

Brilliant, circular girdle; blue-green; 0.4 carat; 5 by 3 mm. Isaac
Lea collection... No. 756

Mount Mitchell, Yancey County:

Step-brilliant, rectangular girdle; deep green-blue; 9.55 carats; 14 by
12 by 10 mm. Isaac Lea collection.................................. No. 776

Yancey County, Ray's Mica Mine:

Brilliant, circular girdle; pale green-blue; 6.44 carats; 12 by 8 mm.. No. 775
Brilliant, circular girdle; pale blue-green; 2.035 carats; 9 by 5 mm.... No. 757
Brilliant, square girdle; pale green-yellow; 1.824 carats; 8 by 6 mm... No. 758
Brilliant, circular girdle; pale blue-green; 1.32 carats; 7 by 5 mm..... No. 762
Brilliant, circular girdle; pale green; 1.056 carats; 7 by 5 mm......... No. 765
Brilliant, circular girdle; pale blue-green; 0.999 carat; 6.5 by 5 mm... No. 766
Brilliant, circular girdle; pale blue-green; 0.87 carat; 6 by 5 mm...... No. 767
Brilliant, circular girdle; pale green; 0.72 carat; 6 by 4 mm.......... No. 768
Brilliant, circular girdle; pale green; 0.60 carat; 5 by 4 mm.......... No. 769
Brilliant, circular girdle; pale green; 0.51 carat; 5 by 4 mm.......... No. 770
Brilliant, circular girdle; pale green; 0.335 carat; 5 by 3 mm......... No. 771
Brilliant, circular girdle; very pale green; 0.26 carat; 4 by 3 mm...... No. 772
Brilliant, square girdle; green-blue; 0.205 carat; 3.5 by 2.5 mm....... No. 773
Brilliant, circular girdle; green-yellow; 0.175 carat; 3.5 by 2 mm..... No. 774

LOCALITY NOT RECORDED.

Step-brilliant, elliptical girdle; pale green; 4 carats; 12.5 by 10 by 6 mm.
Isaac Lea collection... No. 720

Step-brilliant, elliptical girdle; pale green; 3.365 carats; 12 by 9 by 5 mm.
Isaac Lea collection... No. 721

Step-brilliant, elliptical girdle; pale blue-green; 1.982 carats; 9 by 7 by
4 mm... No. 727

Step-brilliant, elliptical girdle; pale green; 1.737 carats; 10 by 7 by 4 mm.
Isaac Lea collection.. No. 722
Brilliant, circular girdle; pale green; 1.265 carats; 7 by 4 mm............. No. 728
Step-brilliant, elliptical girdle; pale green; 1.25 carats; 9 by 7 by 4 mm.
Isaac Lea collection.. No. 724
Step-brilliant, elliptical girdle; pale green; 1.18 carats; 9 by 7 by 3.5 mm.
Isaac Lea collection.. No. 723
Brilliant, circular girdle; pale green; 1.159 carats; 7 by 4 mm. Isaac Lea
collection... No. 726
Step-brilliant, rectangular girdle; 0.915 carat; 7 by 5 by 3 mm............. No. 730
Step-brilliant, elliptical girdle; 0.907 carat; 10 by 6 by 3 mm. Isaac Lea
collection... No. 725
Brilliant, circular girdle; pale green; 0.838 carat; 7 by 4 mm............. No. 729
Step-brilliant, elliptical girdle; blue-green; 0.26 carat; 6 by 4 by 2 mm.... No. 731

BERYL, variety EMERALD.

UNITED STATES.

North Carolina.

Cabochon of emerald matrix, elliptical girdle; green and white mottled;
3.1 carats; 12 by 8 by 5 mm. Gift of Passmore Gem Company.......... No. 1650
Mitchell County:
Cabochon of emerald matrix, elliptical girdle; green and white mottled; 38.15 carats; 28 by 21 by 9 mm.............................. No. 1574
Stony Point, Alexander County:
Twenty-five small gems, step, square and rectangular girdles; one step-
brilliant, circular girdle; bright green; total weight 5.96 carats; average size, 4 by 3.5 by 3 mm. Isaac Lea collection..................... No. 801

LOCALITY NOT RECORDED.

Step, elliptical girdle; pale green; 12 by 11 by 7 mm. Set in a ring....... No. 828
Step, rectangular girdle; green; 12 by 10 by 6 mm. Set in a ring.......... No. 829
Table, rectangular girdle; deep green; 1.405 carats; 8 by 6 by 4 mm....... No. 794
Step-brilliant, elliptical girdle; green; 0.697 carat; 6.5 by 6 by 3 mm...... No. 795
Step, rectangular girdle; green; 0.52 carat; 6 by 5 by 3 mm............... No. 796
Polished pebble, pear-shaped girdle; green; 4.87 carats; 14 by 7 mm...... No. 797
Three small stones, step-brilliant, one irregular, one rectangular, one square
girdle; green; total weight, 0.4 carat................................ Nos. 798 to 800

BERYLLONITE.

Composition.—Sodium beryllium phosphate, $NaBePO_4$.
Crystallization.—Orthorhombic.
Color.—Colorless.
Luster.—Vitreous; transparent.
Hardness.—6; not very durable.
Specific gravity.—2.85 ± 0.05.
Optical properties.—Mean refractive index, 1.56; double refraction
moderate, 0.01; optically biaxial, negative.

The mineral can be distinguished with certainty from other precious
stones which resemble it only by chemical tests. It occurs in pegmatite, like beryl and tourmaline, and was first discovered among the

disintegrated material of a granitic vein at Stoneham, Maine. It is not much used as a precious stone and is cut chiefly as a matter of scientific interest.

LIST OF SPECIMENS.

UNITED STATES.

Maine.

Stoneham, Oxford County:

Brilliant, square girdle; colorless; 5 carats; 11 by 8 mm .... No. 423
Step-brilliant, square girdle; colorless; 3.86 carats; 10 by 7 mm......... No. 424
Brilliant, square girdle; colorless; 3.338 carats; 9 by 7.5 mm........... No. 425

Bloodstone.—See under Chalcedony.

CALAMINE.

Composition.—Basic zinc metasilicate $(ZnOH)_2(SiO_3)$.

Crystallization.—Orthorhombic; hemimorphic; habit usually columnar-radiated.

Color.—White when pure, but often green or blue owing to the presence of admixed copper carbonates.

Luster.—Vitreous or somewhat silky; translucent.

Hardness.—5; not very durable.

Specific gravity.—3.45 ± 0.05.

Optical properties.—Mean refractive index 1.62; double refraction strong, 0.02; optically biaxial, positive.

Calamine may be distinguished from most other minerals which resemble it by softness and solubility, being readily attacked by dilute hydrochloric acid, with the formation of gelatinous silica. From smithsonite, which is likewise attacked, it is distinguished by lack of effervescence. It occurs as an alteration product of sulphide zinc ore in deposits above the permanent water level and it is sometimes cut cabochon and used for scarfpins, etc., but the value little exceeds the cost of cutting.

LIST OF SPECIMENS.

MEXICO (DISTRICT OF GALEANA, SIERRA MADRE, GUERRERO).

Cabochon, elliptical girdle; blue clouded with white; 26.43 carats; 23 by 17 by 12 mm.   Gift of Charles H. Beers...................................... No. 1252
Cabochon, elliptical girdle; blue banded with white; 16.49 carats; 23 by 13 by 6.5 mm.   Gift of Charles H. Beers..................................... No. 1253
Cabochon, elliptical girdle; blue mottled with white; 10.64 carats; 18 by 12.5 by 6 mm.   Gift of Charles H. Beers.................................. No. 1254
Cabochon, elliptical girdle; blue with curved lines of white; 8.79 carats; 16 by 13 by 5 mm.   Gift of Charles H. Beers............................. No. 1255
Cabochon, elliptical girdle; blue banded with white; 8.69 carats; 16 by 12 by 5 mm.   Gift of Charles H. Beers..................................... No. 1256
Cabochon, elliptical girdle; blue with curved lines of white; 4.825 carats; 15 by 11 by 3 mm.   Gift of Charles H. Beers............................. No. 1257

CALCITE and ARAGONITE.

Calcium carbonate occurs in nature under a great variety of forms which are mainly quite unsuited for gem purposes, though widely used in ornamentation (see under Coral and Supplemental Collections). Occasional forms are cut as souvenirs or as of local interest. A few such are here included.

LIST OF SPECIMENS.

SPAIN (ROCK OF GIBRALTAR.)

Polished plate of stalagmitic calcite; elliptical girdle; banded light and dark brown; 48.2 carats; 38 by 30 by 5 mm. Gift of Rev. Alexander McDonald. No. 368

UNITED STATES.

California.

Colusa County:
Cabochon, rectangular girdle, of aragonite; light and dark brown; 22.08 carats; 27 by 14 by 7 mm... No. 369

WEST INDIES.

Cameo, "Departure of the hunter"; elliptical girdle; white on light brown base; 49 by 39 mm (fig. 1)... No. 1506

Cameo, "Winged angel"; elliptical girdle; white on light brown base; 45 by 37 mm.. No. 1503

Cameo, "Return of the hunter";
elliptical girdle; white on
light brown base; 42 by 36 mm. No. 1504

Cameo, head of Jupiter; elliptical girdle; white on light
brown base; 35 by 30 mm... No. 1505

Cameo, kneeling child with
cross; elliptical girdle; white
on light brown base; 31 by 24
mm......................... No. 1502

Three cameos, carved heads,
two representing bacchantes
and one Flora; white; oval
girdles; 36 by 22, 20 by 17, 19
by 16 mm................. No. 1501

FIG. 1.—SHELL CAMEO.

Conch shell with cameo carving, white and pink........................... No. 1510
Conch shell bracelet in form of a serpent; white and pink.................... No. 1512
Conch shell brooch, carved cupid; pink.................................. No. 1511
Conch shell brooch; fish; brown and white............................... No. 1509

LOCALITY NOT RECORDED.

Cameo, two faces; rectangular; white on light brown base.................. No. 1519

Californite.—See under Vesuvianite.

Cameo.—See under Calcite and Aragonite (shell cameo), and Quartz, variety Onyx.

Carnelian.—See under Chalcedony.

Catalinite.—See under Quartz.

Cat's-eye.—See under Chrysoberyl and Quartz.

CHALCEDONY.

Varieties.—Here are included the cryptocrystalline and amorphous, often more or less impure, varieties of silica comprised under the names agate, bloodstone, carnelian, chrysoprase, jasper, prase, etc. The term agate includes the banded forms (fig. 2); carnelian, the red; chrysoprase, the green; bloodstone, a compact, dark, opaque variety with blood red spots; jasper, a great range of opaque impure forms of a red, yellow brown, or black color, the varying hues being due mainly to iron and manganese oxides. The silicified wood of the Arizona "Fossil Forest" is largely chalcedony in the cryptocrystalline form of jasper; onyx is a variety of agate with straight alter-

FIG. 2.—BANDED AGATE.

nating bands of light and dark; moss agate, a milky or colorless form with dendritic markings of manganese oxide resembling moss or other plant growth. Plasma and prase are green in color, and sard, or sardonyx, of a golden to blood red color.

These stones are cut only cabochon or flat, unfacetted forms, and are valued according to their varying beauty, common agate and jasper being the cheaper forms. The majority of agates sold in the shops are from Brazil, and are cut and artificially colored in Germany.

The moss agates of Wyoming are found, according to Mr. C. J. Hares, of the United States Geological Survey, scattered over the surface of the ground in several townships of Fremont County and along the Sweetwater Valley. The agate pebbles range in size from 2 inches or more in diameter and are usually well rounded. The good specimens are uncommon, being associated with a great many worthless pebbles such as black and red jaspers, quartzite or white milky quartz, or chalcedony. The agates range from an opaque white and gray to highly translucent gray with black, dark brown, reddish to yellow-brown dendritic markings. Those with the black and dark brown markings are the most common. They show great variation in size and delicacy of pattern. Some are small rounded tufts, too dense to show individual lines, and others are as much as 2 or 3 millimeters across, exhibiting very delicate moss-like or sea-weed-like markings. The original source of the gravel is supposed to have been the White River formation of the vicinity, which is of Oligocene age. (See further under Quartz.)

LIST OF SPECIMENS.

CHALCEDONY, common.

GERMANY.

Two gems, cabochon, one rectangular, one elliptical; pale cloudy gray; 41 by 29 by 5, 19 by 16 by 6 mm. Gift of George F. Kunz.................. No. 803

INDIA.

Six stones, cabochon, three elliptical, two elongated octagon, one pear-shaped; 36 by 27 by 8 to 18 by 15 by 6 mm............................. No. 802

UNITED STATES.

California.

Muroc, Kern County:
   Cabochon, pear-shaped girdle; colorless and white mottled; 34 by 20 by 6 mm.. No. 812
   Cabochon, pear-shaped girdle; gray and green, mottled; 28 by 21 by 8 mm... No. 813

Colorado.

Cabochon, elliptical girdle; translucent with red color; 2.8 carats; 11 by 7 by 5 mm. (St. Stephen stone). Gift of J. B. Endicott................... No 815

Virginia.

Fairfax, Fairfax County:
   Cabochon, circular girdle; pale cloudy gray; 10 by 7 mm.............. No. 804

LOCALITY NOT RECORDED.

Twelve stones, cabochon and tabular, elliptical girdles; cloudy brown-gray; 46 by 35 by 4 mm. to 20 by 15 by 3 mm........................... No. 807
Four variously cut stones, one cabochon and one ring, elliptical girdles; two pendant; pale gray; 25 by 20 by 6, 26 by 17 by 5, 42 by 12, 25 by 12 mm.. No. 546
Four stones, cabochon, elliptical girdle; artificially colored yellow, three banded; 38 by 29 by 8 mm. to 23 by 17 by 7 mm........................ No 543
Five stones, cabochon and table, elliptical and pear-shaped girdles; artificially colored yellow; 32 by 24 by 7 mm., 19 by 10 mm............... No. 806

Five stones, cabochon, tabular, elliptical, rectangular, and diamond-shaped girdles; artificially colored gray, gray-green, and red; 29 by 23 by 12 mm. to 24 by 18 by 5 mm.. No. 545

Four stones, cabochon, rectangular girdle; yellow, banded; 28 by 18 by 5 mm. to 23 by 11 by 3 mm... No. 805

Three stones, table, rectangular girdle; yellow; 23 by 18 by 6 mm., 22 by 20 by 6 mm., 18 by 15 by 6 mm... No. 544

Six intaglios, five rectangular, one square girdle; dark brown; average, 23 by 16 mm.. No. 809

Four stones, cabochon and table, elliptical, rectangular, pendant; gray; average size 20 by 15 by 3 mm. Isaac Lea collection.

Sixty-two stones, variously cut; pale gray.................................... No. 808

Pendant; gray background with carvings of turtle and frogs in brown. Isaac Lea collection.. No. 814

Finger ring, pale yellow, artificially colored; diameter, 22 mm. Isaac Lea collection .... No. 810

CHALCEDONY, variety AGATE.

BRAZIL.

Three circular disks; dark brown to black, with rings of pale blue and white (artificially colored); average diameter, 43 mm. Bequest of William H. Forwood... No. 429

GERMANY.

Oberstein:[1]

Table, rectangular girdle (charm); black and white banded; 29 by 25 by 9 mm.. No. 533

Cabochon, elliptical girdle; black and white banded; 29 by 25 by 10 mm... No. 521

Two pieces, tabular, rectangular girdle; brown and white banded; 29 by 25 by 5 mm., 28 by 25 by 5 mm.................................... No. 535

Button, circular; brown banded; 26 by 4 mm. Isaac Lea collection... No. 1481

Four pieces, cabochon, heart-shaped and elliptical girdles; brown, banded; 36 by 32 by 6 mm., 25 by 18 by 4 mm...................... No. 519

Four pieces, table, rectangular and elliptical girdles; dark brown, banded; 37 by 29 by 3 mm. to 29 by 23 by 7 mm.................... No. 520

Four pieces, table, rectangular girdle; brown, banded; 56 by 38 by 3.5 mm. to 40 by 26 by 3 mm.. No. 530

Four pieces, cabochon, three diamond-shaped, one elongated octagon girdles; various colors; 29 by 18 by 5 mm., 26 by 15 by 5 mm...... No. 522

Five slabs, rectangular; blue, green, and brown, banded, artificially colored; 73 by 30 mm. to 73 by 25 mm. Gift of George F. Kunz.... No. 1482

Five pieces, two cabochon, three tabular, elliptical girdle; gray and brown, banded, one dull red and brown; 30 by 24 by 6 mm., to 24 by 19 by 5 mm.. No. 534

Seven pieces, table, elliptical and circular girdles; dark brown, banded; 54 by 37 by 5 to 34 by 24 by 7 mm................................... No. 531

Nine pieces, cabochon and tabular, circular, elliptical, and diamond-shaped girdles; black or dark brown and white banded; various sizes... No. 536

Ten pieces, tabular, elliptical girdle; gray and red banded; 38 by 30 by 6 mm. to 26 by 18 by 2 mm....................................... No. 532

---

[1] It is probable that a considerable number of stones accredited to this locality were originally from other sources and taken to Oberstein for cutting.

Oberstein—Continued.

Ten pendant or club-shaped pieces; very dark brown to black, 66 to 35 mm. in length.. No. 524

Ten pieces, various cuts, pendant or pear-shaped girdles; brown, banded; 49 by 10 to 18 by 8 mm.................................... No. 523

ITALY.

Ring; gray and brown; 25 mm. diameter. Isaac Lea collection........... No. 1479

JAPAN.

Elliptical disk; pale red and white, banded; 25 by 20 by 4 mm........... No. 1480

UNITED STATES.

Lake Superior.

Tabular, elliptical girdle; gray mottled with red; 42 by 28 by 4 mm. Isaac Lea collection.. No. 1477

Two pieces, tabular, rectangular girdle; brown banded; 27 by 15 by 2 mm.. No. 1476

Michigan.

Agate Bay, Lake Superior:

Ellipsoid, white clouded with light brown; mounted as a charm; 25 by 21 by 17 mm. Isaac Lea collection.............................. No. 1478

LOCALITY NOT RECORDED.

Slab, rectangular; dark brown; 55 by 39 by 5 mm. Gift of George F. Kunz.. No. 1483

Table, rectangular girdle; blue, artificially colored; banded with white; 38 by 19 by 4 mm... No. 1484

Ring or armlet; red, yellow, and white banded; 87 mm. diameter........ No. 1642

Tabular, rectangular girdle; brown, banded with white; 82 by 36 by 4 mm.. No. 1485

Table, rectangular girdle; dark gray-brown and white, banded; 24 by 20 by 6 mm.. No. 1488

Disk, rectangular; red-brown and gray, banded; 39 by 21 by 2 mm........ No. 444

Three stones, cabochon, circular girdle; gray and white, red-brown and white; gray and black; 11 by 6, 8 by 5, and 8 by 4 mm.................. No. 453

Two slabs, rectangular girdle; pink, cloudy; 71 by 42 by 4 mm., 69 by 41 by 3 mm. Gift of Col. J. G. Totten...................................... No. 1486

Six stones, various cuts and colors.................................... No. 1487

Nine stones, various cuts; gray, banded; 41 by 14 by 2.5 mm. to 15 by 12 by 2 mm.. No. 516

Ten stones, various cuts; brown and red, mottled; 60 by 19 by 3 mm. to 27 by 9 mm.. No. 1489

Twelve stones, tabular, various girdles and colors..................... No. 518

Fourteen stones, various cuts and colors; 40 by 29 by 10 mm. to 23 by 10 by 3 mm. Isaac Lea collection...................................... No. 517

Three pendants, table, eliptical girdle; various colors, banded; 45 by 36 by 5 and 43 by 33 by 5 mm. Gift of A. E. Heighway..................... No. 1646

CHALCEDONY, variety BLOODSTONE.

INDIA.

Three stones, cabochon and tabular, rectangular girdle; blue-green with red spots; 42 by 14 by 5, 35 by 14 by 4, and 28 by 26 by 3 mm............. No. 1459

Two stones, club-shaped; one facetted, one round; blue-green mottled with yellow and red; 40 by 10 and 37 by 8 mm............................. No. 1460

Two pieces, one cabochon, fluted, one flat, elliptical girdle, engraved with the letter H; green with red spots; 19 by 15 by 4 and 21 by 14 by 3 mm.. No. 1462

Cabochon, circular girdle; dark green with red and yellow spots; 58 by 6 mm.
Gift of George F. Kunz... No. 1463
Cabochon, elliptical girdle; dark green with few red spots; 40 by 30 by 6 mm. No. 1464
Table, rectangular girdle; dark green with very few red spots; 25 by 18 by
5 mm.. No. 1465
Table, circular girdle; dark and pale yellow-green, few red spots; 25 by
3 mm.. No. 1466
Table, circular girdle; dark blue-green with red spots; 19 by 3 mm. (fig. 8,
pl. 7)... No. 1467
Two pieces, table, rectangular girdle; dark blue-green; few red spots; 19 by
12 and 5 by 3 mm... No. 1468
Cabochon, elliptical girdle; dark green with red markings; 41 by 35 by 5.5
mm. Gift of Mrs. Spencer F. Baird... No. 1469
Table, circular girdle; streaked dark blue-green and red; 27 by 2 mm....... No. 1470
Table, one elliptical and four shield-shaped girdles; dark green with few red
spots; 18 by 10 by 2 mm. and 10 by 10 by 2.5 mm. Isaac Lea collection.. No. 1471

CHALCEDONY, variety CARNELIAN.

GERMANY.

Bracelet of 6 buttons and 12 beads; red banded. Isaac Lea collection.... No. 1643
Oberstein:
    Table, rectangular girdle; red; 24 by 19 mm.......................... No. 503

PALESTINE.

Table, elliptical girdle; red; 15 by 13 by 3 mm. Has Hebrew characters
on it.. No. 502

LOCALITY NOT RECORDED.

Tabular, elliptical girdle; deep brown-red; 53 by 42 mm.................. No. 506
Tabular, circular girdle; red-brown; 50 by 5 mm.......................... No. 510
Brooch, circular girdle; red; 39 mm. diameter. Gift of A. E. Heighway.... No. 1648
Pin bar; red; 65 mm. long. Gift of A. E. Heighway...................... No. 1649
Three stones, cabochon, circular and elliptical girdles; red-brown; 20 by 3
and 19 by 11 by 5 mm... No. 527
Three stones, two disks, one table, rectangular girdles; red-brown; 44 by 34
by 3, 25 by 22 by 3, 18 by 15 by 5 mm...................................... No. 526
Six stones, various cuts and girdles; 20 by 16 by 7 to 18 by 15 by 4 mm.... No. 507
Six disks, elliptical girdle; brown-red; 55 by 44 by 11 to 31 by 25 by 7 mm.. No. 525
Six stones, tabular, elliptical and circular girdles; red, banded and mottled;
53 by 45 by 4 to 38 by 28 by 5 mm.. No. 509
Six stones, various cuts; red, mottled and banded......................... No. 511
Seven stones, tabular, rectangular girdle; red; 45 by 30 by 9 to 15 by 13 by
5 mm. Isaac Lea collection... No. 514
Seven stones, various fancy cuts; red...................................... No. 529
Eight stones, cabochon, elliptical girale; red; 33 by 25 by 7 to 15 by 12 by
7 mm. Isaac Lea collection... No. 512
Eight stones, engraved, various girdles; pale yellow-red to deep brown-red;
25 by 21 by 4 to 12 by 2 mm.. No. 528
Fourteen stones, elliptical disks; pale red to red-brown; 27 by 20 by 6 to
17 by 14 by 6 mm. Isaac Lea collection.................................... No. 513
Fourteen intaglios and one cameo; very pale to dark red; 14 by 11 by 3 to 6
by 2 mm. Isaac Lea collection... No. 508
Nineteen stones, various cuts; pale to deep red. Isaac Lea collection..... No. 515

CHALCEDONY, variety CHRYSOPRASE.

SILESIA.

Cabochon, circular girdle; pale green; 51.29 carats; 24 by 13 mm.......... No. 1429

Mixed cabochon, elliptical girdle; mottled green; two gems, 42.23 and 32.47 carats; 29 by 23 by 10 and 27 by 21.5 by 9 mm..................... No. 1424

Mixed cabochon, elliptical girdle; very pale green; 41.25 carats; 29 by 24 by 9 mm.. No. 1425

Two gems, one brilliant, one mixed cabochon, elliptical girdles; green; 28.33 and 8.05 carats; 26 by 20 by 7 and 18 by 14 by 5 mm............... No. 1426

Three gems, mixed cabochon, elliptical girdle; brown-green; 21.29, 13.53, and 5.29 carats; 24 by 18 by 8, 20 by 16 by 7, and 15 by 7 by 5 mm...... No. 1427

Eight gems, mixed cabochon, elliptical, pear-shaped and square girdles; total weight, 14.4 carats; 18 by 10 by 3 to 7 by 5 by 3 mm............... No. 1428

UNITED STATES.

Arizona.

Globe, Gila County:

Cabochon, elliptical girdle; dull green; 5.58 carats; 15 by 10 by 5 mm.; Isaac Lea collection.. No. 1800

California.

Visalia, Tulare County:

Cabochon, elliptical girdle; green; 10 carats; 20 by 14 by 5 mm. Isaac Lea collection (fig. 5, pl. 12)... No. 1801

Cabochon, circular girdle; green; 7.99 carats; 13 by 7 mm. Isaac Lea collection... No. 1802

Cabochon, elliptical girdle; green; 6.25 carats; 13 by 10 by 7 mm. Isaac Lea collection.. No. 1803

Cabochon, elliptical girdle; green; 4.97 carats; 12 by 9 by 7 mm. Isaac Lea collection.. No. 1804

Cabochon, elliptical girdle; green; 4.77 carats; 18 by 9 by 4 mm. Isaac Lea collection.. No. 1805

Cabochon, elliptical girdle; green; 4.175 carats; 12.5 by 9 by 6 mm.... No. 1423

Cabochon, circular girdle; green; 4.05 carats; 11 by 5 mm. Isaac Lea collection... No. 1806

Cabochon, circular girdle; green; 2.28 carats; 8 by 5 mm. Isaac Lea collection... No. 1807

Cabochon, circular girdle; green; 0.5 carats; 5 by 3 mm. Isaac Lea collection... No. 1808

CHALCEDONY, variety JASPER.

EGYPT (NILE RIVER).

Two pieces, one cabochon, elliptical girdle, and one rectangular slab; brown, mottled; 31 by 24 by 6 and 47 by 38 by 4 mm........................... No. 822

ENGLAND (HERTFORDSHIRE).

Cabochon, circular girdles; brown, mottled; breastpin, 35 mm. diameter, and two cuff buttons, 25 mm. diameter................................. No. 820

INDIA.

Two disks, elliptical girdles; one mottled blue-green, red, and brown, one red and green; 84 by 57 by 4 and 80 by 55 by 3.5 mm..................... No. 1645

SAXONY.

Ellipsoid, polished; red; 42 by 35 by 22 mm................................. No. 823

Tabular, elliptical girdle; green and red banded; 25 by 19 mm............ No. 821

LOCALITY NOT RECORDED.

Elliptical disk of "agate jasper"; red-brown with blue veins; 33 by 25 by
    4 mm. (fig. 10, pl. 7)... No. 816
Elliptical disk of "agate jasper"; brown-red; 32 by 26 by 3 mm............ No. 819
Two pieces, table, rectangular girdle; red; 25 by 16 by 2 mm............... No. 818
Three pieces, variously cut; brown; 43 by 31 by 3, 34 by 27 by 7, and 19 by
    16 by 5 mm... No. 817

CHALCEDONY, variety MOSS AGATE.

CHINA.

Table, elliptical girdle; gray with green inclusions; 37 by 29 by 2 mm.
    Isaac Lea collection... No. 437

INDIA.

Two elliptical disks; cloudy gray with brown inclusions; 51 by 35 by 3 and
    39 by 30 by 4.5 mm. (fig. 3)... No. 1490

FIG. 3.—MOSS AGATES.

Elliptical disk; gray with black inclusions; 47 by 31 by 3 mm. Isaac Lea
    collection (fig. 3)... No. 419
Table, elliptical girdle; gray with green inclusions; 44 by 33 mm......... No. 418
Ninety-one small stones, cabochon, various girdles; gray with brown and
    red inclusions.. No. 420

JAPAN.

Five stones, one tabular, four cabochon; elliptical and circular girdles; gray;
    34 by 22 by 3 to 10 by 5 mm. Isaac Lea collection...................... No. 427

UNITED STATES.

Kansas.

Eight small stones, cabochon, seven elliptical, one diamond-shaped girdle;
    cloudy gray with brown inclusions; total weight, 3.23 carats; 15 by 10 by
    3 to 12 by 8 by 2 mm.. No. 438

Montana.

Glendive, Dawson County:
Three gems, cabochon, elliptical girdles; cloudy gray with dark brown
inclusions; 46 by 20 by 8, 35 by 15 by 3.5, and 26 by 12.5 by 4 mm.
Isaac Lea collection .... No. 1491
Cabochon, pendant or pear-shaped girdle; cloudy gray with red-brown
and dark brown inclusions; 62 by 35 by 5 mm. Isaac Lea collection. No. 1492

Wyoming.

Fort Bridger, Uinta County:
Cabochon, elliptical girdle; cloudy gray with black inclusions; 4.45
carats; 16 by 12 by 3.5 mm... No. 432
Yellowstone National Park:
Table, rectangular girdle; cloudy gray with black inclusions; 6.22 carats;
19 by 13 by 2.5 mm. Isaac Lea collection........................... No. 431
Cabochon, elliptical girdle; cloudy gray, brown inclusions; two pieces,
7.66 and 7.42 carats; 20 by 14 by 4 mm............................. No. 426
One cabochon and two tabular cut pieces, elliptical girdles; cloudy
gray with brown inclusions; 16.46, 9.23, and 9.1 carats; 25 by 16 by
6 and 26 by 17 by 2 mm.. No. 428

LOCALITY NOT RECORDED.

An armlet; lead gray and green; 85 mm. diameter....................... No. 459
Pendant, table, elliptical girdle; gray with green inclusions; 45 by 35 by 5
mm. Gift of A. E. Heighway... No. 1647
Tabular, elliptical girdle; red-brown; 52 by 38 by 4 mm................ No. 454
Club-shaped piece; mottled red, brown, and gray; 43 by 10 mm........... No. 446
Tabular, elliptical girdle; mottled red, brown, and gray; 36 by 28 by 6 mm. No. 445
Tabular, elliptical girdle; mottled red, brown, and gray; 34 by 29 by 7 mm. No. 430
Cabochon, diamond-shaped girdle; red-brown; 27 by 20 by 5 mm.......... No. 443
Disk, elliptical; mottled red-brown and gray; 22 by 18 by 3 mm......... No. 448
Tabular, elliptical girdle; mottled red, green, and blue; 22 by 17 by 4 mm. No. 447
Cabochon, square girdle; gray and white; two pieces, 21 by 4 mm., which
have been ignited at red heat...................................... No. 433
Two disks; red and dull green; 26 by 16 by 2 mm....................... No. 455
Two rectangular disks; red-brown, mottled; 54 by 36 by 2 and 36 by 31 by
3 mm... No. 440
Four stones, various cuts and girdles; green......................... No. 441
Four pendants; gray and brown mottled; average size, 33 by 13 mm....... No. 442
Six small rectangular slabs; mottled red, brown, yellow, and gray; 60 by 34,
58 by 34, and 47 by 33 mm. Gift of George F. Kunz................... No. 435
Ten pieces, table and cabochon, elliptical girdles; dull gray with various
colored inclusions; 41 by 28 by 3 to 20 by 15 by 2 mm.............. No. 439
Thirteen small stones, cabochon, elliptical and rectangular girdles; cloudy
gray with dark inclusions; 29 by 21 to 15 by 12 mm. Isaac Lea collection. No. 434

CHALCEDONY, variety ONYX.

LOCALITY NOT RECORDED.

Cameo, elliptical girdle; white on gray base; 60 by 46 mm.............. No. 537
Elliptical piece; dark brown and white, banded; 45 by 33 by 13 mm. Gift
of George F. Kunz.. No. 541
Cameo, elliptical girdle; white on dark brown base; 37 by 28 mm........ No. 538
Cameo, elliptical girdle; white on light brown base; 34 by 25 mm....... No. 539

CHALCEDONY, variety PLASMA.

INDIA.

Three elliptical buttons; dark blue-green, mottled; average size, 42 by 33
by 7 mm.. No. 1473
Two pieces, cabochon, elliptical girdle; blue-green; 33 by 26 by 4 and 30 by
24 by 4 mm... No. 1474
Button, elliptical; gray-green, mottled; 26 by 19 by 6 mm.................. No. 1472
Disk, cabochon, elliptical girdle; dark green with white streaks; 53 by 40
by 5 mm.. No. 1475

CHALCEDONY, variety PRASE.

GERMANY.

Cabochon, elliptical girdle; gray-green; 24.26 carats; 18 by 13 by 11 mm... No. 1431

Saxony.

Cabochon-brilliant, elliptical girdle; dull green; 9.735 and 9.45 carats; 20 by
13 by 5 and 22 by 12 by 5 mm.. No. 1430

CHALCEDONY, variety SARDONYX.

LOCALITY NOT RECORDED.

Three pieces, elliptical girdles; red-brown, white, and brown, banded; 43 by
29 by 11, 26 by 19 by 8, and 20 by 15 by 7 mm.   Colored in Germany.
Gift of George F. Kunz... No. 540
Four intaglios, three red-brown on dark brown, one gray on red-brown; 23
by 16 to 18.5 by 4 mm.. No. 542

CHALCEDONY, variety SILICIFIED WOOD.

UNITED STATES.

Arizona.

Adamana, Apache County:
Thirty-six stones, cabochon, elliptical and circular girdles; mottled
brown, red, yellow, etc.; 52 by 42 by 9 to 16 by 10 by 5 mm. (figs. 4, 5,
pl. 7)... No. 824

Chlorastrolite.—See under Prehnite.

CHROMITE.

Composition.—Ferrous chromite, $FeCr_2O_4$.
Crystallization.—Isometric; habit octahedral; usually massive.
Color.—Black; streak pale brown.
Luster.—Sub-metallic.
Hardness.—5.5; rather soft for use as a precious stone.
Specific gravity.—4.5 ± 0.2.
Optical properties.—Refractive index extremely high; practically
opaque.
Methods of identification.—Distinguished from jet by its heaviness;
from hematite by its streak.

The mineral occurs in serpentinous rocks, and often accumulates
as a "chrome sand" in the beds of streams flowing over such rocks.

It is used rarely for beads and similar objects, being cut mostly
only as a matter of scientific interest; value not exceeding the cost
of cutting.

One double cabochon, four cabochon, circular girdle; black, polished; 1.435 grams; 6 mm. average diameter. Isaac Lea collection.................... No. 679

CHRYSOBERYL.

Varieties.—Alexandrite; cat's-eye or cymophane.

Composition.—Beryllium aluminate, $BeAl_2O_4$.

Crystallization.—Orthorhombic; habit tabular.

Color.—Pale yellow, green-yellow, yellow-green, dull green, and rarely brown-yellow or orange-brown; in artificial light, red, especially in the emerald green variety alexandrite; pleochroic, green to red, in deep colored varieties.

Luster.—Vitreous; in cat's-eye, silky.

Hardness.—8.5; a very durable stone.

Specific gravity.—3.60 ± 0.1.

Optical properties.—Mean refractive index 1.75; double refraction moderate, 0.01; optically biaxial, positive.

The variety cymophane, the true cat's-eye, shows minute laminations which yield a peculiar luster. Alexandrite shows with the microspectroscope a strong absorption band in the yellow and can be recognized by the red color in artificial light; pale colored varieties, including cat's-eye, can be distinguished from similar minerals by the high specific gravity and by optical properties. The mineral occurs in pegmatite and in mica gneiss. The chief commercial sources of chrysoberyl are Brazil and Ceylon. The variety alexandrite comes chiefly from the Takovaya stream in the Ekaterinburg district of Russia, though it has more recently been found in Ceylon. The mineral "was discovered in Russia on the very day on which the coming of age of the Czarevitch Alexander Nicolajevitch, afterwards Czar Alexander II, was celebrated, and in his honour it was named by the Finnish mineralogist Nils von Nordenskiöld."

Stones resembling chrysoberyl have been produced artificially, but their complete identity with the natural mineral remains to be proved. The peculiar property shown by alexandrite of changing color in artificial light renders it rather highly prized as a gem; cat's-eye is usually cut cabochon so as to bring out the luster.

Brilliant, square girdle; pale yellow-green; 6.329 carats; 11 by 7.5 mm..... No. 640
Brilliant, elliptical girdle; green-yellow; 2.5 carats; 10 by 7 by 5 mm....... No. 641
Trap-brilliant, elliptical girdle; green-yellow; 1.84 carats; 8 by 7 by 4 mm.. No. 642
Table, rectangular girdle; green-yellow; 0.99 carat; 7 by 5 by 3 mm........ No. 643
Step-brilliant, elliptical girdle; green-yellow; 0.965 carat; 7.5 by 6 by 3 mm. No. 644
Table, square girdle; pale green-yellow; 0.745 carat; 5 by 3 mm........... No. 645
Step-brilliant; irregular girdle; green-yellow; 0.495 carat; 5 by 3 mm...... No. 647
Step-brilliant, pentagonal girdle; green-yellow; 0.482 carat; 5 by 5 by 3 mm. No. 648

Step-brilliant, rectangular girdle; pale yellow; 0.46 carat; 6 by 5 by 2 mm.. No. 646
Thirteen small gems, step-brilliant, various girdles; green-yellow; total
    weight, 2.6 carats.. No. 649
Twenty-five small gems, various cuts; green-yellow; total weight, 2.777 carats.
    Isaac Lea collection... No. 662

CEYLON.

Brilliant, elliptical girdle; dark yellow-green; 5.1 carats; 10 by 9 by 7 mm.. No. 634
Step-brilliant, elliptical girdle (Indian cut); brown-yellow; 4.257 carats; 8
    by 6 by 9 mm... No. 638
Step-brilliant, rectangular girdle; dull yellow-green; 3.9 carats; 12 by 10 by
    4 mm.   Isaac Lea collection... No. 636
Step-brilliant, rectangular girdle; dark green-brown; 3.09 carats; 8 by 7 by
    6 mm.. No. 635
Step-brilliant, elliptical girdle; yellow-green; 1.9 carats; 7 by 6 by 5 mm.
    Isaac Lea collection.. No. 637
Brilliant-rose, circular girdle; orange-brown; 1.157 carats; 6.5 by 4 mm..... No. 639

CHRYSOBERYL, variety ALEXANDRITE.

RUSSIA (URAL MOUNTAINS).

Step-brilliant, rectangular girdle; green; 2.247 carats; 8 by 7 by 4 mm...... No. 691
Step, rectangular girdle; green; 1.07 carats; 6.5 by 5.5 by 3.5 mm. Isaac
    Lea collection.. No. 688
Trap, rectangular girdle; green; 0.43 carat; 5 by 4 by 3 mm. Isaac Lea
    collection.. No. 690
Step-brilliant, elliptical girdle; green; 0.378 carat; 6 by 5 by 2 mm. Isaac
    Lea collection.. No. 689

CHRYSOBERYL, variety CAT'S-EYE.

SIAM.

Seventeen cat's-eyes and 16 diamond chips mounted in a heavy gold ring.... No. 692

CHRYSOLITE.

Synonyms.—Olivine, peridot.

Composition.—Magnesium orthosilicate, Mg_2SiO_4.

Crystallization.—Orthorhombic.

Color.—Yellow-green, green-yellow, or rarely pure yellow; essential, due to ferrous iron replacing magnesium; very faintly pleochroic.

Luster.—Vitreous.

Hardness.—6.5; a fairly durable precious stone.

Specific gravity.—3.40 ± 0.2.

Optical properties.—Mean refractive index, 1.68; double refraction strong, 0.03; optically biaxial, positive.

Chrysolite, also known under the names olivine and peridot, is an abundant constituent of many igneous rocks, as the basalts, peridotites, and stony meteorites, but in most cases in the form of small granules only. When these rocks become disintegrated, the mineral, which is very refractory to weathering agencies, is set free and accumulates in the residual sand. The principal American sources are the Navajo Indian country of Arizona, and New Mexico. (See pl. 5.)

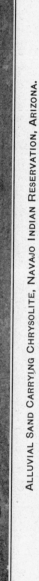

ALLUVIAL SAND CARRYING CHRYSOLITE, NAVAJO INDIAN RESERVATION, ARIZONA.

Step-brilliant, rectangular girdle; yellow-brown; 8.48 carats; 14 by 9 by 8 mm. Isaac Lea collection.. No. 555
Step-brilliant, elliptical girdle; pale yellow; 0.43 carat; 5.5 by 5 by 3 mm. Isaac Lea collection... No. 556

THE LEVANT.

Step, rectangular girdle; dark green; 18.5 carats; 20 by 16 by 7 mm........ No. 554
Step, rectangular girdle; yellow-green; 8.858 carats; 15 by 12 by 6 mm..... No. 553

UNITED STATES.

Arizona.

Navajo Indian Reservation:
  Brilliant, circular girdle; deep green; 3.93 carats; 10 by 7 mm........ No. 1181
  Brilliant, square girdle; dark green; 2.74 carats; 9 by 6 mm. Isaac Lea collection.. No. 557

New Mexico.

Fort Wingate, Bernalillo Connty:
  Brilliant, circular girdle; dark green; 1.65 carats; 8 by 6 mm......... No. 558
  Brilliant, circular girdle; dark green; 1.56 carats; 7.5 by 5.5 mm....... No. 560
  Brilliant, circular girdle; dark green; 1.48 carats; 8 by 5 mm......... No. 559
  Brilliant, circular girdle; dark green; 1.417 carats; 8 by 5 mm........ No. 562
  Brilliant, circular girdle; dark green; 1.226 carats; 7.5 by 5 mm....... No. 561
  Step-brilliant, rectangular girdle; green; 1.094 carats; 7 by 6 by 4 mm. No. 563

Chrysoprase.—See under Chalcedony.

Conch Shell.—See under Calcite and Aragonite.

CORAL.

Corals are composed of calcium carbonate and are formed as stony secretions within the body of the coral polyp. Of the many varieties known only those formed by the *Corallium rubrum* from the African coast of the Mediterranean are utilized for gem purposes. The material is dredged from a depth of 500 to 800 feet by means of metal dragnets. The colors vary from deep red through pink to greenish, brown, yellow, white, and black. The white, pink, and red varieties are utilized chiefly in the form of necklaces and bracelets.

LIST OF SPECIMENS.

Bracelet, red... No. 1515
Small chain of beads, red... No. 1516
Two roses, red.. Nos. 1517, 1518
Twenty-two spherical beads, white, 3 circular beads, pink; 4 rings, 5 leaf shaped, and 36 small branching pieces, red. Gift of H. P. Petersen.
Nos. 1843, 1844, 1845

CORUNDUM.

Varieties and synonyms.—Ruby, sapphire, oriental amethyst, oriental emerald, and oriental topaz.

Composition.—Aluminum sesquioxide, Al_2O_3 ; the aluminum may be partially replaced by chromium, iron, titanium, etc., yielding colored varieties.

Crystallization.—Hexagonal-trigonal, rhombohedral; habit usually pyramidal, with rounded edges, and with prominent basal plane. (See fig. 4.)

Color.—Colorless when pure; often showing more or less intense coloration, and named accordingly; ruby, the red variety colored by chromium; sapphire, blue, titanium; oriental amethyst, violet, chromium and titanium; oriental emerald, green, iron and titanium; and oriental topaz, yellow, iron. May also show silvery internal reflections, usually in the form of a six-rayed star, owing to symmet-

FIG. 4.—CORUNDUM CRYSTALS.

rically arranged inclusions (asteria); pleochroic from pale to deep tints.

Luster.—Rather dull and greasy in natural state; adamantine when cut; transparent to translucent.

Hardness.—9; will scratch every mineral except diamond; extremely durable.

Specific gravity.—4 ± 0.1; noticeably heavy.

Optical properties.—Mean refractive index, 1.76; double refraction weak, 0.008; uniaxial, negative.

The transparent corundums rank among the most valuable of gem stones, and include two recognized varieties, the red ruby and the blue sapphire. The ruby varies in hue from a rose to a deep carmine, the same crystal occasionally exhibiting different colors, the most approved tint being a "pigeon's blood" red. The sapphire, in general, includes corundums of any color except the red. Specifically, the name is limited in its use to the blue-colored specimens, the approved tints being royal blue, velvet blue, and cornflower blue. The sapphire occasionally exhibits a different color effect by natural light from that seen by artificial light, and as a rule is less brilliant by the latter.

Corundums of other colors are named according to their hues: Oriental emerald, the green-colored kinds, varying in tint from a lively green, exceeding that of the emerald, to a sea or blue-green. Oriental amethyst, purple or amethystine. Oriental topaz, yellow, rivaling the yellow diamond in brilliancy. Oriental hyacinth is hyacinthine in tint and is rare. Adamantine spar includes the hair-brown varieties.

The six-rayed star seen in many clouded corundums, especially when cut cabochon with the summits cutting the vertical axis of the prism, is due to numerous minute crystals or layers within the stone which reflect the incident light so as to produce the stellar effect. These rays are invariably white, though the specimen may be of any color, and may be best seen by artificial light. This chatoyancy, when marked, gives the asteria, or star stone, also known as the star ruby or star sapphire, as the case may be. Should the gem assume a fibrous texture, the chatoyancy affords the "cat's-eye" ray.

Corundum is associated with crystalline rocks as granular limestone or dolomite, gneiss, granite, mica, and chlorite schist. The finest sapphires are usually obtained from the beds of streams, either in modified hexagonal prisms or in rolled masses, accompanied by grains of magnetic iron ore and other heavy minerals.

The best rubies come from the mines of upper Burma, in an area about 30 miles square, of which Mogok is the center, where they are found in place in crystalline limestone; they occur also in gravel and in the soil of the hillsides. A similar locality exists in the marble hills of Sagyin, 16 miles north of Mandalay. Ruby mines have also been worked at Jagdalik, near Kabul, Afghanistan. Blue sapphires are brought from Ceylon.

The great corundum region of the United States extends from the Virginia line through North and South Carolina, across Georgia and into Alabama. Numerous localities are known in the crystalline rocks of the region, especially in Madison, Buncombe, Haywood, Jackson, Macon, and Clay Counties, North Carolina. Rubies rivaling those from Burma in color have been found in the Cowee district of this State, but the region affords no commercial supply. Fine gem sapphires are found on the river bars in the Upper Missouri near Helena, Montana. They are most abundant at Eldorado Bar, Frenchmans Bar, and Yogo Gulch, where they occur in a pyroxenite and as pebbles more or less rolled in the sands resulting from its disintegration. The Montana gems rarely exceed one-fourth to one-half inch in length and range in color from light green, light blue, steel blue, bluish red, light red, and intermediate shades; frequently the colors mentioned will appear red or assume a reddish tinge by artificial light. They are usually dichroic and often blue in one direction and red in another. (See pl. 6.)

Rubies of a high degree of perfection are now produced artificially and their manufacture has become a matter of trade importance. The artificial stone, in crystallization and composition, is identical with the natural.

CORUNDUM, variety RUBY.

CEYLON.

Step-brilliant, heart-shaped girdle; pale violet red; 6.84 carats; 13 by 10 by 7 mm. Isaac Lea collection...................................... No. 198

Step-brilliant, elliptical girdle; violet red; 4.193 carats; 11 by 7 by 6.5 mm. Isaac Lea collection..................................... No. 197

Step-brilliant, elliptical girdle; pale red; 3.5 carats; 10 by 7.5 by 6 mm. Isaac Lea collection...................................... No. 14

Step-brilliant, elliptical girdle; very pale red; 2.754 carats; 9 by 7.5 by 5 mm. Isaac Lea collection..................................... No. 16

Step-brilliant, elliptical girdle; violet-red; 1.265 carats; 6.5 by 6 by 5 mm. Isaac Lea collection..................................... No. 202

Step-brilliant, square girdle; deep red; 0.884 carat; 6 by 3 mm. Isaac Lea collection... No. 201

Step-brilliant, square girdle; deep red; 0.81 carat; 5 by 4 mm. Isaac Lea collection... No. 200

Step-brilliant, rectangular girdle; deep red; 0.81 carat; 6 by 5 by 4 mm. Isaac Lea collection..................................... No. 205

Step-brilliant, irregular girdle; deep red; 0.737 carat; 7.5 by 6 by 3 mm. Isaac Lea collection..................................... No. 203

Brilliant, elliptical girdle; pale red; 0.70 carat; 6 by 5 by 4 mm. Isaac Lea collection... No. 209

Step-brilliant, rectangular girdle; deep red; 0.64 carat; 5.5 by 4.5 by 3 mm. Isaac Lea collection..................................... No. 208

Step-brilliant, circular girdle; deep red; 0.627 carat; 5.5 by 3 mm. Isaac Lea collection... No. 206

Step-brilliant, elliptical girdle; deep red; 0.625 carat; 6 by 4.5 by 3 mm. Isaac Lea collection..................................... No. 207

Step-brilliant, rectangular girdle; pale, cloudy red; 0.44 carat; 5 by 4 by 2.5 mm. Isaac Lea collection................................ No. 69

One lot of 239 small gems of which 228 are cut and 11 uncut. Mostly step-brilliant, various girdles; red; total weight, 18.36 carats.................. No. 219

UNITED STATES.

Montana.

Brilliant, circular girdle; red-violet; 2.165 carats; 8 by 3 mm. Isaac Lea collection... No. 1019

Brilliant, circular girdle; very pale red; 1.215 carats; 6 by 4 mm. Isaac Lea collection... No. 1021

Table, rectangular girdle; red violet; 1.025 carats; 6.5 by 5 by 2 mm.   Isaac
Lea collection... No. 1020
Brilliant, elliptical girdle; red; 0.58 carat; 6 by 5 by 2.5 mm.   Isaac Lea
collection... No. 1022
Brilliant, circular girdle; red; 0.45 carat; 4 by 3.5 mm.   Isaac Lea collection. No. 1023
Rock Creek, Granite County:
    Ten gems, brilliant cut, circular girdle; red and violet-red; total weight,
    3.52 carats; 4 by 3 mm. to 3.5 by 2.5 mm .... No. 1026

North Carolina.

Corundum Hill, Macon County:
    Step-brilliant, rectangular girdle; red; 1.528 carats; 9 by 5 by 4 mm... No. 194
    Step-brilliant, square girdle; red; 0.89 carat ; 6 by 4 mm............... No. 195
    Step-brilliant, square girdle; red; 0.357 carat; 4 by 2.5 mm........... No. 196

LOCALITY NOT RECORDED.

Brilliant, square girdle; deep red; 1 carat; 5.5 by 5.5 by 4 mm.   Mounted in
a ring. Isaac Lea collection.. No. 218

CORUNDUM, variety RUBY (ASTERIA).

CEYLON.

Cabochon, circular girdle; red, mottled; 9.33 carats; 11 by 9 mm.   Isaac Lea
collection.. No. 210
Cabochon, circular girdle; cloudy red; 2.54 carats; 7 by 5 mm.   Isaac Lea
collection.. No. 199
Cabochon, circular girdle (irregular); 2.365 carats; 6 by 6 mm.   Isaac Lea
collection .... No. 213
Cabochon, circular girdle; red; 1.56 carats; 6.5 by 4 mm.   Isaac Lea collec-
tion.. No. 212
Cabochon, circular girdle; cloudy red; 1.364 carats; 6 by 5 mm.   Isaac Lea
collection .... No. 214
Cabochon, elliptical girdle; very cloudy red; 1.3 carats; 7 by 6 by 4 mm.
Isaac Lea collection.. No. 211
Cabochon, elliptical girdle; red; 1.284 carats; 7 by 6 by 4 mm.   Isaac Lea
collection.. No. 204
Cabochon, circular girdle; cloudy red; 1.157 carats; 6 by 5 mm.   Isaac Lea
collection.. No. 215

LOCALITY NOT RECORDED.

Cabochon, circular girdle; red; 1.569 carats; 7 by 4 mm.................. No. 216
Cabochon, circular girdle; red; 1.067 carats; 7 by 3 mm.................. No. 217

CORUNDUM, variety SAPPHIRE.

AUSTRALIA.

Queensland.

Step-brilliant, elliptical girdle; deep green-blue; 2.34 carats; 8 by 7 by 5
mm. Isaac Lea collection... No. 1822
Step-brilliant, elliptical girdle; deep green-blue; 2.11 carats; 7.5 by 7 by 5
mm. Isaac Lea collection .... No. 1823
Brilliant, circular girdle; deep green-blue; 0.8 carat; 6 by 3 mm.   Isaac
Lea collection .... No. 1825

CEYLON.

Step-brilliant, elliptical girdle; blue; 31.38 carats; 20 by 13 by 12 mm. The Shepard collection.. No. 1027

Step-brilliant, elliptical girdle; blue (dichroic); 28.76 carats; 18 by 12 by 15 mm. Isaac Lea collection... No.   1

Step-brilliant, rectangular girdle; blue-gray; 21.53 carats; 17 by 13.5 by 10 mm. Isaac Lea collection... No.   6

Step-brilliant, rectangular girdle; pale blue; 11.33 carats; 12 by 13 by 8.5 mm. Isaac Lea collection... No.   7

Step-brilliant, elliptical girdle; pale blue; 10.78 carats; 14 by 10 by 9 mm. Isaac Lea collection.. No.   5

Step-brilliant, rectangular girdle; pale blue; 6.936 carats; 12 by 11 by 6 mm. Isaac Lea collection... No.   10

Step-brilliant, elliptical girdle; deep blue; 6.595 carats; 14 by 10 by 4.5 mm. Isaac Lea collection... No.   4

Step-brilliant, circular girdle; violet-blue; 5.488 carats; 10 by 7 mm. Isaac Lea collection.. No.   8

Step-brilliant, elliptical girdle; violet-blue; 5.275 carats; 11 by 9 by 7 mm. Isaac Lea collection.. No.   13

Step-brilliant, oval girdle; pale blue; 4.526 carats; 10.5 by 8 by 6 mm. Isaac Lea collection.. No.   24

Step-brilliant, square girdle; deep blue; 4.057 carats; 10 by 5 mm. Isaac Lea collection.. No.   15

Step-brilliant, elliptical girdle (irregular); pale blue; 3.865 carats; 9 by 8 by 7 mm. Bequest, William H. Forwood.............................. No. 1028

Step-brilliant, elliptical girdle; pale green-blue; 3.27 carats; 10 by 8 by 5 mm. Isaac Lea collection... No.   22

Step-brilliant, oval girdle; blue; 2.96 carats; 8 by 7 by 6 mm. Isaac Lea collection... No.   20

Step-brilliant, square girdle; blue; 2.96 carats; 7 by 7 mm. Isaac Lea collection... No.   32

Step-brilliant, oval girdle; pale blue; 2.815 carats; 9 by 8 by 5 mm. Isaac Lea collection.. No.   19

Step-brilliant, rectangular girdle; very pale blue; 2.645 carats; 10 by 8 by 4.5 mm. Isaac Lea collection....................................... No.   17

Step-brilliant, rectangular girdle; gray-blue; 2.44 carats; 7.25 by 6.5 by 6 mm. Isaac Lea collection... No.   34

Step-brilliant, elliptical girdle; blue; 2.155 carats; 9 by 7 by 4 mm. Isaac Lea collection.. No.   23

Step-brilliant, circular girdle; blue; 2.014 carats; 7 by 6 mm. Isaac Lea collection... No.   28

Step-brilliant, square girdle; pale blue; 1.66 carats; 7 by 4 mm. Isaac Lea collection... No.   37

Step-brilliant, square girdle; violet-blue; 1.62 carats; 6 by 5 mm. Isaac Lea collection.. No.   57

Step-brilliant, elliptical girdle; blue; 1.614 carats; 8 by 6 by 3.5 mm. Isaac Lea collection.. No.   47

Step-brilliant, elliptical girdle; pale violet-blue; 1.577 carats; 8 by 5 by 5 mm. Isaac Lea collection... No.   49

Step-brilliant, circular girdle; blue; 1.536 carats; 7 by 4 mm. Isaac Lea collection... No.   64

Step-brilliant, elliptical girdle; blue-gray; 1.49 carats; 6 by 5 by 6 mm. Isaac Lea collection.. No.   40

Step-brilliant, irregular oval girdle; colorless with blue streaks; 1.445 carats; 6 by 6 by 5 mm. Isaac Lea collection.............................. No.   75

Step-brilliant, circular girdle; light blue; 1.42 carats; 7 by 4 mm. Isaac Lea collection.. No. 60

Step-brilliant, irregular girdle; colorless, blotched with blue; 1.355 carats; 7 by 6 by 4 mm. Isaac Lea collection.................................. No. 74

Step-brilliant, square girdle; light blue; 1.35 carats; 7 by 6.5 by 4 mm. Isaac Lea collection.. No. 44

Step-brilliant, irregular elliptical girdle; pale blue; 1.296 carats; 7 by 5 by 5 mm. Isaac Lea collection.. No. 78

Step-brilliant, elliptical girdle; colorless with blue streaks; 1.279 carats; 6.5 by 5 by 5 mm. Isaac Lea collection................................ No. 77

Step-brilliant, square girdle; blue; 1.25 carats; 6 by 4 mm. Isaac Lea collection... No. 66

Step-brilliant, elliptical girdle; colorless with blue blotches; 1.22 carats; 7 by 5.5 by 4 mm. Isaac Lea collection.............................. No. 63

Step-brilliant, circular girdle; very pale blue; 1.192 carats; 7 by 4 mm. Isaac Lea collection... No. 52

Step-brilliant, circular girdle; very pale blue; 1.157 carats; 6.5 by 4 mm. Isaac Lea collection... No. 56

Step-brilliant, rectangular girdle; pale blue; 1.15 carats; 6 by 4.5 by 5 mm. Isaac Lea collection.. No. 72

Step-brilliant, square girdle; pale blue; 1.105 carats; 6 by 4 mm. Isaac Lea collection... No. 79

Step-brilliant, elliptical girdle; pale blue; 1.043 carats; 7 by 5 by 4 mm. Isaac Lea collection... No. 84

Step-brilliant, elliptical girdle; deep blue; 1 carat; 7 by 6 by 3.5 mm. Isaac Lea collection.. No. 61

Step-brilliant, elliptical girdle; deep blue; 0.98 carat; 6 by 5 by 4 mm. Isaac Lea collection... No. 45

Step-brilliant, elliptical girdle (irregular); blue; 0.977 carat; 6.5 by 5 by 4 mm. Isaac Lea collection...................................... No. 90

Step-brilliant, rectangular girdle; deep blue; 0.962 carat; 6 by 5 by 4 mm. Isaac Lea collection.. No. 68

Step-brilliant, elliptical girdle; colorless, with blue blotches; 0.957 carat; 6 by 4.5 by 5 mm. Isaac Lea collection............................. No. 82

Step-brilliant, elliptical girdle; colorless, with blue streaks; 0.957 carat; 6 by 4.5 by 5 mm. Isaac Lea collection............................. No. 87

Step-brilliant, oval girdle; deep violet blue; 0.922 carat; 6.5 by 5 by 3.5 mm. Isaac Lea collection... No. 71

Step-brilliant, elliptical girdle; blue; 0.892 carat; 6 by 5 by 4 mm. Isaac Lea collection... No. 102

Step-brilliant, elliptical girdle; colorless, with blue streaks; 0.887 carat; 6.5 by 5 by 3.5 mm. Isaac Lea collection......................... No. 85

Step-brilliant, elliptical girdle; deep blue; 0.887 carat; 6.5 by 5 by 3 mm. Isaac Lea collection.. No. 88

Step-brilliant, elliptical girdle; colorless, with slight blue streaks; 0.855 carat; 6.5 by 5 by 3.5 mm. Isaac Lea collection .... No. 73

Step-brilliant, circular girdle; colorless, blotched with blue; 0.85 carat; 5 by 5 mm. Isaac Lea collection....................................... No. 101

Step-brilliant, irregular oval girdle; deep blue; 0.811 carat; 6.5 by 5 by 3 mm. Isaac Lea collection....................................... No. 92

Step-brilliant, rectangular girdle; light blue; 0.79 carat; 6 by 4 by 3.5 mm. Isaac Lea collection.. No. 81

Step-brilliant, elliptical girdle; blue; 0.77 carat; 5.5 by 5 by 4 mm. Isaac Lea collection... No. 109

Step-brilliant, elliptical girdle; colorless, with blue blotches; 0.749 carat; 6 by 5 by 3.5 mm.   Isaac Lea collection............................... No.   99

Step-brilliant, rectangular girdle; green-blue; 0.733 carat; 6 by 5 by 3.5 mm... No.   133

Step-brilliant, irregular oval girdle; violet-blue; 0.73 carat; 6 by 5 by 4 mm. Isaac Lea collection......:............................... No.   105

Step-brilliant, circular girdle; light blue; 0.735 carat; 5 by 4 mm. Isaac Lea collection... No.   97

Step-brilliant, elliptical girdle; pale blue; 0.72 carat; 6 by 5 by 4 mm. Isaac Lea collection...................................... No.   95

Step-brilliant, elliptical girdle; deep blue; 0.717 carat; 6 by 5 by 3 mm. Isaac Lea collection...................................... No.   106

Step-brilliant, oval girdle; violet-blue; 0.715 carat; 5.5 by 4 by 4 mm. Isaac Lea collection...................................... No.   51

Step-brilliant, elliptical girdle; pale violet-blue; 0.7 carat; 6 by 4 by 4.5 mm. Isaac Lea collection................................ No.   108

Step-brilliant, elliptical girdle; smoky blue; 0.68 carat; 5.7 by 5 by 3 mm. Isaac Lea collection...................................... No.   86

Step-brilliant, elliptical girdle; deep blue; 0.68 carat; 6 by 4.5 by 3.25 mm. Isaac Lea collection...................................... No.   91

Step-brilliant, elliptical-girdle; deep blue; 0.66 carat; 4.5 by 3 by 4.5 mm. Isaac Lea collection...................................... No.   124

Step-brilliant, irregular oval girdle; smoky blue; 0.65 carat; 5 by 4 by 3.5 mm. Isaac Lea collection................................ No.   123

Step-brilliant, rectangular girdle; pale blue; 0.64 carat; 6 by 5 by 3 mm. Isaac Lea collection......:............................... No.   93

Step-brilliant, elliptical girdle; blue; 0.588 carat; 5 by 4.5 by 3 mm. Isaac Lea collection... No.   12

Step-brilliant, elliptical girdle; light blue; 0.58 carat; 6 by 4.5 by 3 mm. Isaac Lea collection...................................... No.   103

Step-brilliant, irregular oval girdle; deep blue; 0.569 carat; 5.5 by 5 by 3 mm. Isaac Lea collection................................ No.   107

Step-brilliant, elliptical girdle; deep blue; 0.565 carat; 5 by 4.5 by 3.5 mm. Isaac Lea collection...................................... No.   110

Step-brilliant, elliptical girdle; smoky blue; 0.56 carat; 5 by 4 by 3.5 mm. Isaac Lea collection...................................... No.   125

Step-brilliant, rectangular girdle; smoky blue; 0.557 carat; 5.5 by 4 by 3 mm. Isaac Lea collection................................ No.   104

Step-brilliant, circular girdle; colorless, with blue at girdle; 0.555 carat; 5 by 3 mm. Isaac Lea collection......................... No.   126

Step-brilliant, elliptical girdle; colorless, with blue blotches; 0.505 carat; 4.5 by 4 by 3 mm. Isaac Lea collection................. No.   116

Step-brilliant, elliptical girdle; pale blue; 0.48 carat; 5 by 3.5 by 3 mm. Isaac Lea collection...................................... No.   115

Step-brilliant, oval girdle; almost colorless, blue at girdle; 0.475 carat; 4.5 by 4 by 3 mm. Isaac Lea collection.................... No.   119

Step-brilliant, elliptical girdle; deep blue; 0.46 carat; 4.5 by 3.5 by 3 mm. Isaac Lea collection...................................... No.   127

Step-brilliant, circular girdle; pale blue; 0.39 carat; 4 by 3 mm. Isaac Lea collection... No.   121

Step-brilliant, elliptical girdle; almost colorless, blue at girdle; 0.38 carat; 4.5 by 3.5 by 2.5 mm. Isaac Lea collection.............. No.   118

Step-brilliant, circular girdle; almost colorless, blue at girdle; 0.36 carat; 4 by 2 mm. Isaac Lea collection......................... No.   120

Step-brilliant, oval girdle; blue; 0.355 carat; 4 by 3.5 by 2.5 mm. Isaac Lea collection... No. 122

Step-brilliant, elliptical girdle; pale blue; 0.34 carat; 4.5 by 3.5 by 2 mm. Isaac Lea collection... No. 128

Step-brilliant, irregular oval girdle; deep blue; 0.33 carat; 4 by 2.5 by 2 mm. Isaac Lea collection... No. 114

Step-brilliant, circular girdle; deep blue; 0.325 carat; 3.5 by 3 mm. Isaac Lea collection... No. 117

Step-brilliant, various girdles; mostly blue; 18 gems, total weight, 5.135 carats; average, 3 by 3 by 2 mm... No. 136

SIBERIA (URAL MOUNTAINS).

Step-brilliant, elliptical girdle; deep blue; 1.189 carats; 7 by 6 by 4 mm.... No. 170

UNITED STATES.

Montana.

Brilliant, circular girdle; very pale blue; 3.15 carats; 8 by 5 mm. Isaac Lea collection.. No. 1011

Brilliant, circular girdle; very pale blue; 1.73 carats; 7.5 by 2.5 mm. Isaac Lea collection.. No. 1012

Brilliant, circular girdle; pale blue; 1.40 carats; 6 by 4 mm. Isaac Lea collection... No. 1013

Brilliant, circular girdle; blue; 1.31 carats; 6 by 4 mm. Isaac Lea collection... No. 1014

Brilliant, square girdle; blue; 1.156 carats; 6 by 5 mm...................... No. 158

Brilliant, circular girdle; blue; 0.93 carat; 5.5 by 4 mm. Isaac Lea collection... No. 1015

Brilliant, circular girdle; blue; 0.78 carat; 5 by 3 mm. Isaac Lea collection... No. 1016

Brilliant, circular girdle; blue; 0.535 carat; 4.5 by 3 mm. Isaac Lea collection... No. 1017

Brilliant, rectangular girdle; pale blue; 0.36 carat; 4 by 3 by 2.5 mm. Isaac Lea collection... No. 1018

Rock Creek, Granite County:

Brilliant, circular girdle; three gems, one green-blue, two very pale blue; total weight, 1.265 carats; 4 by 3 mm.......................... No. 1024

Yogo Gulch, Fergus County:

Step-brilliant, elliptical girdle; deep blue; two gems, 1.86 and 1.8 carats; 8 by 7 by 5 mm. Isaac Lea collection........................ No. 458

North Carolina.

Corundum Hill, Macon County:

Step-brilliant, rectangular girdle; dark green-blue; 3.865 carats; 11 by 8 by 6 mm.. No. 162

Step-brilliant, oval girdle; blue; 0.966 carat; 8 by 6 by 3 mm. Gift of Clarence S. Bement.. No. 169

Step-brilliant, rectangular girdle; deep blue and green; 0.782 carat; 5.5 by 4 by 4 mm... No. 166

CORUNDUM, variety SAPPHIRE (ASTERIA).

CEYLON.

Polished pebble; blue gray; 100.11 carats; 34 by 27 by 14 mm. Isaac Lea collection.. No. 30

Cabochon, circular girdle; blue; 68.77 carats; 24 by 14 mm. Isaac Lea collection.. No. 172

Cabochon, circular girdle; gray (banded); 50.5 carats; 25 by 10 mm. Isaac
Lea collection.. No. 171

Cabochon, circular girdle; violet; 50.349 carats; 22 by 13 mm. Isaac Lea
collection.. No. 173

Cabochon, circular girdle; light blue; 39.761 carats; 24 by 8 mm. Isaac
Lea collection... No. 174

Cabochon, circular girdle; gray blue; 28.3 carats; 18 by 10 mm. Isaac
Lea collection... No. 175

Cabochon, circular girdle; pale gray; 15.3 carats; 14 by 10 mm. Isaac Lea
collection.. No. 176

Cabochon, circular girdle; milky white; 10.2 carats; 11 by 9.5 mm.......... No. 185

Cabochon, circular girdle; gray-blue; 7.525 carats; 11 by 8 mm. Isaac
Lea collection... No. 179

Cabochon, circular girdle; milky white; 6.388 carats; 11 by 6.5 mm. Isaac
Lea collection... No. 178

Cabochon, elliptical girdle; light blue; 5.486 carats; 11 by 9 by 6 mm.
Isaac Lea collection... No. 180

Cabochon, circular girdle; light violet; 4.98 carats; 10 by 7 mm............. No. 186

Cabochon, irregular girdle (polished pebble); very pale blue-violet; 4.86
carats; 9 by 9 by 6 mm. Isaac Lea collection............................. No. 188

Cabochon, circular girdle; blue-gray; 4.48 carats; 9 by 7 mm............... No. 187

Cabochon, circular girdle; dark blue; 4.095 carats; 9 by 6 mm. Isaac Lea
collection.. No. 181

Cabochon, circular girdle; milky white; 3.019 carats; 9 by 5 mm. Isaac
Lea collection... No. 183

Cabochon, circular girdle; pale blue-gray; 2.336 carats; 8 by 5 mm. Isaac
Lea collection... No. 177

Cabochon, circular girdle; gray; 2.3 carats; 8 by 7 by 7 mm. Isaac Lea collection... No. 182

Cabochon, circular girdle; gray-blue; 2.288 carats; 7 by 5 mm............... No. 190

Cabochon, circular girdle; blue-gray; 1.66 carats; 6 by 6 mm. Isaac Lea collection... No. 184

Cabochon, irregular girdle; gray; 1 carat; 5 by 5 by 3 mm. Isaac Lea collection... No. 189

UNITED STATES.

North Carolina.

Ellijay, Macon County:

    Cabochon, circular girdle; bronze; 10.689 carats; 14 by 7 mm........... No. 191

    Cabochon, circular girdle; bronze; 4.67 carats; 10 by 5.5 mm............. No. 192

    Cabochon, elliptical girdle; bronze; 3.439 carats; 11 by 8 by 4 mm..... No. 193

CORUNDUM, variety WHITE SAPPHIRE.

CEYLON.

Cabochon, elliptical girdle; cloudy white; 3.57 carats; 12.5 by 7 by 5 mm.
Isaac Lea collection.. No. 25

Step-brilliant, square girdle; colorless; 0.85 carat; 6 by 3 mm. Isaac Lea
collection.. No. 65

Step-brilliant, rectangular girdle; colorless; 0.775 carat; 6 by 5 by 3.5 mm.
Isaac Lea collection.. No. 83

Step-brilliant, elliptical girdle; colorless; 0.707 carat; 6 by 5 by 4 mm.
Isaac Lea collection.. No. 94

Step-brilliant, elliptical girdle; colorless; 0.228 carat; 5 by 4 by 2 mm.
Isaac Lea collection... No. 113

CORUNDUM, variety ORIENTAL AMETHYST.

CEYLON.

Step-brilliant, elliptical girdle (Indian cut); blue-violet; 13.214 carats; 13
by 8 by 13 mm. Isaac Lea collection................................... No. 11
Step-brilliant, rectangular girdle; pale violet; 3.6 carats; 9 by 7 by 6 mm.
Isaac Lea collection... No. 27
Step-brilliant, circular girdle; violet; 2.4 carats; 8 by 5.5 mm. Isaac Lea
collection.. No. 21
Step-brilliant, square girdle; pale violet; 1.9 carats; 7 by 4 mm. Isaac Lea
collection.. No. 26
Step-brilliant, rectangular girdle; red violet; 1.459 carats; 7 by 5.5 by 5 mm.
Isaac Lea collection... No. 58
Step-brilliant, rectangular girdle; violet; 1.44 carats; 8.5 by 6 by 4 mm...... No. 130
Step-brilliant, elliptical girdle; violet; 1.4 carats; 8 by 6 by 4 mm. Isaac
Lea collection... No. 41
Step-brilliant, elliptical girdle; blue-violet; 1.23 carats; 8 by 6 by 4 mm.
Isaac Lea collection... No. 55
Step-brilliant; elliptical girdle; violet; 1.078 carats; 6.5 by 5 by 4 mm. Isaac
Lea collection... No. 80
Step-brilliant, rectangular girdle; red violet; 0.97 carat; 6 by 5 by 4 mm.
Isaac Lea collection... No. 70
Step-brilliant, irregularly rectangular girdle; violet; 0.826 carat; 8 by 7 by
2 mm. Isaac Lea collection.. No. 53
Brilliant, circular girdle; red violet; 0.5 carat; 5 by 4 mm. Gift of Clarence
S. Bement... No. 135
Step-brilliant, elliptical girdle; deep violet; 0.4 carat; 5 by 4 by 2 mm.
Isaac Lea collection... No. 129

CORUNDUM, variety ORIENTAL EMERALD.

CEYLON.

Step-brilliant, rectangular girdle; pale blue-green; 4.265 carats; 13 by 10 by
6 mm. Isaac Lea collection... No. 9
Step-brilliant, circular girdle; deep blue-green; 0.863 carat; 7 by 3.5 mm..... No. 131
Step-brilliant, elliptical girdle; deep blue-green; 0.657 carat; 6 by 5 by 3.5
mm... No. 132
Step-brilliant, square girdle; pale green; 0.4 carat; 4 by 3 mm. Isaac Lea
collection.. No. 112

UNITED STATES.

Montana.

Step-brilliant, rectangular girdle; pale green; 2.499 carats; 9 by 6 by 5 mm... No. 156
Step-brilliant, square girdle; blue-green; 0.813 carat; 5.5 by 4 mm. Gift of
Clarence S. Bement.. No. 157
Brilliant, circular girdle; blue-green; 0.7 carat; 5 by 4 mm.................... No. 160

North Carolina.

Corundum Hill, Macon County:
Step-brilliant, rectangular girdle; blue-green; 1.015 carats; 6.5 by 5 by
4 mm.. No. 165

CORUNDUM, variety ORIENTAL TOPAZ.

AUSTRALIA.

Queensland.

Brilliant, circular girdle; pale yellow; 2.44 carats; 8 by 4.5 mm. Isaac
Lea collection... No. 1824

CEYLON.

Step-brilliant, rectangular girdle; pale yellow; 7.6 carats; 12 by 10 by 7
mm. Isaac Lea collection... No. 2

Step-brilliant, elliptical girdle; pale orange-yellow; 3.307 carats; 9.5 by 7.5
by 5 mm. Isaac Lea collection.. No. 18

Step-brilliant, rectangular girdle; pale yellow; 3.277 carats; 10 by 7 by 6
mm. Isaac Lea collection... No. 33

Step-brilliant, elliptical girdle; pale yellow; 3.052 carats; 10 by 7 by 5 mm.
Isaac Lea collection... No. 31

Step-brilliant, elliptical girdle; pale yellow; 2.369 carats; 9 by 7.5 by 4.5
mm. Isaac Lea collection... No. 35

Step-brilliant, elliptical girdle; pale green-yellow; 2.336 carats; 9 by 8 by
5 mm. Isaac Lea collection... No. 29

Step-brilliant, irregular girdle; very pale yellow; 1.982 carats; 7.5 by 7 by
4.5 mm. Isaac Lea collection... No. 43

Step-brilliant, elliptical girdle; very pale yellow; 1.923 carats; 8 by 7 by
5 mm. Isaac Lea collection... No. 38

Step-brilliant, elliptical girdle; very pale yellow; 1.738 carats; 8 by 6 by 4
mm. Isaac Lea collection... No. 46

Step-brilliant, elliptical girdle; deep yellow; 1.518 carats; 8 by 4 by 6 mm.
Isaac Lea collection... No. 42

Step-brilliant, elliptical girdle; pale yellow; 1.46 carats; 7 by 5.5 by 4.5
mm. Isaac Lea collection... No. 39

Step-brilliant, elliptical girdle; very pale yellow; 1.37 carats; 7 by 6 by 4
mm. Isaac Lea collection... No. 50

Step-brilliant, oval girdle; very pale yellow; 1.277 carats; 7.5 by 5 by 4
mm. Isaac Lea collection... No. 48

Step-brilliant, elliptical girdle; very deep yellow; 1.27 carats; 7 by 6 by 4
mm. Isaac Lea collection... No. 54

Step-brilliant, elliptical girdle; very pale yellow; 1.18 carats; 6 by 5 by 5
mm. Isaac Lea collection... No. 76

Step-brilliant, elliptical girdle; very pale yellow; 1.105 carats; 6.5 by 5 by
4.5 mm. Isaac Lea collection... No. 59

Step-brilliant, elliptical girdle; pale yellow; 0.946 carat; 6 by 5 by 3 mm.
Isaac Lea collection... No. 67

Step-brilliant, elliptical girdle; very pale yellow; 0.917 carat; 6 by 5 by 4
mm. Isaac Lea collection... No. 62

Brilliant, square girdle; green-yellow; 0.889 carat; 6 by 4 mm. Gift of
Clarence S. Bement.. No. 134

Step-brilliant, elliptical girdle; pale yellow; 0.776 carat; 6 by 5 by 3 mm.
Isaac Lea collection... No. 89

Step-brilliant, square girdle; pale yellow; 0.747 carat; 5.5 by 3.25 mm.
Isaac Lea collection... No. 36

Step-brilliant, elliptical girdle; pale yellow; 0.742 carat; 6 by 5 by 3 mm.
Isaac Lea collection... No. 98

Step-brilliant, rectangular girdle; very pale yellow; 0.659 carat; 5.5 by 4.5
by 3.5 mm. Isaac Lea collection...................................... No. 96

SEMI-PRECIOUS STONES

FOR DESCRIPTION OF PLATE SEE PAGE VIII

North Carolina.

Rutherford County:

Uncut; pale yellow; 0.14 carat; 3 mm. diameter; flattened octahedron.

The Shepard collection.. No. 1002

Diopside.—See under Pyroxene.

Emerald.—See under Beryl.

EPIDOTE.

Composition.—Calcium aluminum iron orthosilicate, $Ca_2(Al,Fe)_3$ $(OH)(SiO_4)_3$.

Crystallization.—Monoclinic.

Color.—Brown, green, green-yellow, or green-brown, owing to the presence of iron; strongly pleochroic, green to brown.

Luster.—Vitreous.

Hardness.—6.5; fairly durable.

Specific gravity.—3.30 ± 0.10.

Optical properties.—Mean refractive index 1.75; double refraction strong, 0.04; optically biaxial, negative.

With the microspectroscope epidote shows an absorption band in the violet. The color of the mineral is its most distinctive quality. It occurs in metamorphic rocks and in veins, and is little used as a precious stone owing to its intense color.

LIST OF SPECIMENS.

TYROL.

Step, rectangular girdle; dark brown; 3.92 carats; 14 by 8 by 3 mm........ No. 579

Step, rectangular girdle; dark green; 0.74 carat; 8 by 4.5 by 2 mm........... No. 580

Essonite.—See under Garnet.

EUCLASE.

Composition.—Beryllium aluminum orthosilicate, $BeAl(OH)(SiO_4)$.

Crystallization.—Monoclinic.

Color.—Colorless when pure, but often colored pale green or blue by traces of iron.

Luster.—Vitreous.

Hardness.—7.5; very durable.

Specific gravity.—3.10 ± 0.05.

Optical properties.—Mean refractive index 1.66; double refraction moderate, 0.02; optically biaxial, positive.

The mineral can be distinguished only by its optical properties. Occurs in metamorphic rocks such as mica schist, but it is rare and not widely used as a gem.

LIST OF SPECIMENS.

BRAZIL.

Step-brilliant, square girdle; pale green; 1.06 carats; 7 by 4 mm............ No. 832

Fairy Stone.—See under Staurolite.

16002

FELDSPAR.

Varieties.—This name includes several varieties, which are distinguishable by their crystallization and chemical composition, comprising albite, containing sodium (Na); labradorite, sodium and calcium (Na+Ca); microcline, potassium (K); oligoclase, sodium and calcium (Na+Ca); and orthoclase, potassium (K); and in addition several varieties based on peculiarities of structure or color, as amazonstone, adularia, moonstone, perthite, and sunstone.

Composition.—Silicates of potassium or sodium; in part, combinations of silicates of sodium with ortho-silicates of calcium, the element aluminum being present throughout. $KAlSi_3O_8$, $NaAlSi_3O_8$, and $mNaAlSi_3O_8 + nCaAl_2(SiO_4)_2$.

Crystallization.—Monoclinic or triclinic.

Color.—Colorless when pure; sometimes colored pink or green by impurities of unknown nature; in addition, may show internal reflection colors of two types, the one due to the presence of innumerable minute laminae, the other due to inclusions of hematite.

Luster.—Vitreous; transparent to translucent.

Hardness.—6; not very durable.

Specific gravity.—2.5 to 2.7.

Optical properties.—Mean refractive index, 1.53, varying from one kind of feldspar to another; optically biaxial.

The feldspars are distinguished by their optical properties, moderate hardness, pronounced cleavage, and peculiar color phenomena.

They are cut for the most part cabochon, to bring out color effects, and are classed as semiprecious stones. Only exceptionally fine stones are worth more than the cost of cutting. They are shown to best advantage in the varieties moonstone, orthoclase, and amazonstone.

LIST OF SPECIMENS.

FELDSPAR, variety ADULARIA.

SWITZERLAND (ST. GOTTHARD).

Three cabochons, two elliptical, one rectangular girdle; colorless; 2.175, 2.09, and 0.685 carats; two 10 by 9 by 4 mm.; one 7 by 5 by 2 mm............ No. 405

FELDSPAR, variety AMAZONSTONE.

SIBERIA.

Rectangular slab; green; 110.45 carats; 72 by 40 by 4 mm.   Gift of Clarence S. Bement.. No. 387

Three gems, two cabochon, one double cabochon; elliptical girdle; green and blue-green; 9.13, 6.77, and 5.03 carats; 22 by 17 by 4 mm., 17 by 13 by 4 mm., 15 by 11 by 5 mm... No. 389

Cabochon, elliptical girdle; green; 5.79 carats; 18 by 13 by 3 mm.   Isaac Lea collection.. No. 388

UNITED STATES.

Colorado.

Pikes Peak, El Paso County:
    Cabochon, elliptical girdle; green; two stones, 29.5 and 29.28 carats; 28
    by 22 by 8 mm .... No. 39

Pennsylvania.

Media, Delaware County:
    Elliptical disk; blue-green with pale yellow bands; 4.18 carats; 17 by
    11 by 3 mm. Gift of Dr. Robert H. Lamborn .... No. 393
Mineral Hill, Delaware County:
    Cabochon, elliptical girdle; blue-green with pale yellow veins; 119.75
    carats; 45 by 34 by 12 mm. Isaac Lea collection .... No. 392

Virginia,

Amelia Courthouse, Amelia County:
    Cabochon, elliptical girdle; blue-green; 102.74 carats; 48 by 34 by 9 mm. No. 391
    Two cabochons, one circular, one elliptical girdle; green; 92.22 and
    44.96 carats; 34 by 11 and 49.5 by 19 by 6 mm. Isaac Lea collection
    (fig. 9, pl. 7) .... No. 1259
    Six balls; pale blue; total weight, 14.36 carats; 7 mm. diameter; Isaac
    Lea collection. .... No. 452

FELDSPAR, variety LABRADORITE.

LABRADOR.

Two knob-shaped pieces; dark gray-blue; 30.27 and 24.41 carats; 23 mm.
    diameter. Isaac Lea collection .... No. 396
Cabochon, rectangular girdle (intaglio); dark gray with blue and green
    color; 24.35 carats; 25 by 17 by 6 mm .... No. 408
Double cabochon, elliptical girdle; gray-brown; 19.18 carats; 26 by 20 by
    6 mm .... No. 406
Cabochon, circular girdle; dark gray-green; 18.75 carats; 20 by 6 mm. Isaac
    Lea collection .... No. 395
Circular disk; dark gray with blue and green color; 17.535 carats; 22 by 4 mm. No. 407
Cabochon, rectangular girdle; dark gray-blue; 15.74 carats; 24 by 15 by 5 mm. No. 397
Owl's head; dark gray-green; 4.59 carats; 12 mm. diameter .... No. 394

FELDSPAR, variety MOONSTONE.

(*Albite* and *Oligoclase.*)

CEYLON.

Double cabochon, long triangular girdle; colorless with pale blue internal
    color; 45.54 carats; 44 by 25 by 8 mm .... No. 409
Three cabochons, two elliptical and one circular girdle; colorless; 35.85,
    7.05, and 4.68 carats; 38 by 15 by 9, 14 by 11 by 6, and 12 by 5 mm. Isaac
    Lea collection. .... No. 398
Double cabochon, elliptical girdle; blue internal color; 12.55 carats; 15 by
    12 by 10 mm. .... No. 400
Four cabochons, elliptical girdle; colorless; 8.9, 5.7, 4.76, and 2.7 carats; 16
    by 12 by 8, 17 by 10 by 5, 16 by 9.5 by 4, and 13 by 8 by 4.5 mm .... No. 411
Cabochon, elliptical girdle; colorless; 5.47 carats; 21.5 by 9 by 4 mm .... No. 410
Cabochon, elliptical and circular girdles; colorless; lot of 110 gems, all small;
    total weight, 36.03 carats. .... No. 399

INDIA.

Cabochon, elliptical girdle; colorless; 5.12 carats. Bequest, William H. Forwood... No. 401

TYROL.

Cabochon, elliptical girdle; colorless with faint blue internal color; 14.79 carats; 22 by 14 by 8 mm... No. 417

UNITED STATES.
Colorado.

Cabochon, circular girdle; colorless; 0.95 carat; 7 by 3 mm................. No. 402

Pennsylvania.
Delaware County:
  Tabular, diamond-shaped girdle; light gray showing blue internal color; 54 by 30 by 17 mm... No. 1204
  Cabochon, elliptical and circular girdles; colorless; two gems, total weight, 0.57 carat; 6.5 by 4.5 by 2.5 and 4 by 2 mm. Isaac Lea collection.. No. 1205
Media, Delaware County:
  Cabochon, rectangular girdle; colorless; 13.245 carats; 22 by 10 by 7 mm. No. 1206

Virginia.
Amelia Courthouse, Amelia County:
  Cabochon, elliptical girdle; white with blue internal color; two gems, 84.05 and 61.9 carats; 46 by 30 by 8 and 37 by 25 by 9 mm............. No. 413
  Cabochon, elliptical girdle; white, opaque; 27.89 carats; 30 by 16 by 8 mm... No. 414
  Double cabochon, elliptical girdle; colorless; 14.09 carats; 18 by 14 by 10 mm... No. 416
  Double cabochon, elliptical girdle; white with blue internal color; 3.945 carats; 14 by 8 by 6 mm..................................... No. 415
  Cabochon, elliptical girdle; colorless; five gems, total weight, 23 carats; 16 by 11 by 5.5 to 10 by 8 by 4 mm................................. No. 412
Hanover County:
  Cabochon, elliptical girdle; colorless; 25.15 carats; 30 by 15 by 7.5 mm. Gift of Clarence S. Bement.. No. 1203

FELDSPAR, variety OLIGOCLASE.
UNITED STATES.
North Carolina.

Hawk mine, near Bakersville, Mitchell County:
  Step-brilliant, rectangular girdle; colorless; 6.03 carats; 14 by 10 by 6 mm. No. 404
  Brilliant, square girdle; colorless; 2.4 carats; 8.5 by 6 mm............... No. 403

FELDSPAR, variety ORTHOCLASE.
MADAGASCAR.

Brilliant, circular girdle; green-yellow; 60.96 carats; 26 by 18 mm. Isaac Lea collection.. No. 1838
Brilliant, elliptical girdle; green-yellow; 17.9 carats; 20 by 15 by 10 mm. Isaac Lea collection.. No. 1820
Brilliant, octagonal girdle; pale yellow; 4.7 carats; 11 by 11 by 6 mm. Isaac Lea collection .... No. 1821

FELDSPAR, variety PERTHITE.

CANADA (PERTH, ONTARIO).

Cabochon, elliptical girdle; brown; 100.47 carats; 45 by 35 by 10 mm. Isaac
Lea collection... No. 386
Cabochon, rectangular girdle; brown with white veins; 17.85 carats; 33 by 13
by 5 mm.. No. 385

FELDSPAR, variety SUNSTONE.

NORWAY.

Cabochon, circular girdle; red-brown; two pieces; 20 and 18.5 carats; 23 by 6
and 23 by 5.5 mm.. No. 1196
Cabochon, rectangular girdle; red-brown; 7.93 carats; 32 by 9 by 3 mm..... No. 1199
Four cabochons, one double cabochon, elliptical girdle; red-brown; 7.6
carats to 2.4 carats; 17 by 13 by 5 to 9 by 8 by 4 mm. Isaac Lea collection.. No. 1197
Double cabochon, elliptical girdle; red-brown; 5.26 carats; 14 by 11 by 5 mm.
Isaac Lea collection... No. 1198
Three cabochons, two elliptical, one square girdle; dark gray, blue internal
color; 11.08, 5.06, and 3.5 carats; 20 by 12 by 7, 14 by 10 by 4.5, and 11 by
4 mm.. No. 1200

UNITED STATES.

Pennsylvania.

Media, Delaware County:
Cabochon, elliptical girdle; two stones, one red-gray, one light gray;
56.37 and 19.67 carats; 43 by 32 by 6 mm. and 27 by 19 by 5.5 mm.... No. 1202
Tabular cabochon, rectangular girdle; gray with pale brown streaks;
6.77 carats; 19 by 11 by 3 mm. Gift of Dr. R. H. Lamborn.......... No. 1201

FLUORITE.

Synonym.—Fluor-spar.
Composition.—Calcium difluoride, CaF_2.
Crystallization.—Isometric.
Color.—Colorless when pure, but usually showing disperse colors
owing to the presence of submicroscopic particles of indeterminate
nature; may be a beautiful yellow, green, blue, violet, or pink.
Luster.—Vitreous; transparent to translucent.
Hardness.—4; too soft for ordinary use as a precious stone, but
can be used in ornaments, etc.
Specific gravity.—3.18 ± 0.05.
Optical properties.—Refractive index, 1.434; optically isotropic;
may show fluorescence or different colors when viewed by reflected
and transmitted light, but never pleochroism.

The mineral is distinguished by its softness, by its lack of double
refraction, and its easy and perfect octahedral cleavage. It occurs
in veins in many kinds of rocks, including the pegmatites.

It is used for paper weights, vases, and other ornaments, chiefly as curiosities, and is worth little more than the cost of cutting. Small faceted stones are sometimes cut from this mineral, but are not sold commercially.

LIST OF SPECIMENS.

UNITED STATES.

New Hampshire.

Chatham, Carroll County:
  Brilliant, circular girdle; green-blue; 1.875 carats; 7.5 by 5 mm.   Gift of
  Sumner Andrews... No. 358

Virginia.

Amelia Courthouse, Amelia County.
  Step-brilliant, rectangular girdle; very pale smoky brown; 5.047 carats;
  11 by 9 by 7 mm... No. 357

GADOLINITE.

Composition.—Beryllium iron yttrium orthosilicate, $Be_2FeY_2O_2$
$(SiO_4)_2$.

Crystallization.—Monoclinic.

Color.—Black.

Luster.—Submetallic or brilliant vitreous; practically opaque except in very thin splinters.

Hardness.—6.5; fairly durable.

Specific gravity.—4.40 ±0.05.

Optical properties.—Mean refractive index, 1.80; optically biaxial, positive.

Gadolinite can be distinguished from several minerals which it resembles only by chemical tests. It is sometimes cut brilliant, but its dark color prevents its extensive use as a precious stone, and it is worth little more than the cost of cutting.

LIST OF SPECIMENS.

UNITED STATES.

Texas.

Burnet, Llano County:
  Brilliant, circular girdle; black, opaque; 8.56 carats; 13 by 8 mm.   Isaac
  Lea collection.. No. 587

GARNET.

There are three prominent groups of garnet with several subdivisions under each, many of these grading into each other.   They are:
  1. Aluminum garnet:
        Grossularite.—Lime–aluminum garnet.
        Pyrope.—Magnesium–aluminum garnet.
        Almandite and rhodolite.—Iron–aluminum garnet.
        Spessartite.—Manganese–aluminum garnet.

OPEN CUT EMERALD MINE, NOW ABANDONED, NEAR SHELBY, NORTH CAROLINA.

2. Iron garnet: Andradite.—Calcium–iron garnet.

3. Chromium garnet: Ouvarovite.—Calcium–chromium garnet.

The lime–aluminum garnet has a hardness of 7, a specific gravity of 3.55 to 3.66, and a considerable color range. The several varieties are: Essonite (cinnamon stone or hyacinth), of which the specimens of a clear yellow-brown to deep gold tinged with brown are more commonly used as gems. Grossularite includes the pale green, yellow to nearly white, pale pink, red-orange, and brown kinds. Romanzovite is a brown variety; wiluite is yellow-green to greenish white; topazolite is deep to pale yellow; and succinite is amber-colored.

The principal magnesian garnet is the pyrope, meaning "fire-like," a deep red to nearly black stone, prized as a gem. It is among the hardest of the garnets, ranking 7.5 in the scale. Its specific gravity lies between 3.7 and 3.8.

The almandite, or carbuncle, and rhodolite are iron–aluminum garnets. Almandite varies in color from bright red to deep red of several tints, occasionally assuming an orange hue by artificial light. The color of the rhodolite lies between a violet-purple and a brown-red. These varieties have a hardness of about 7.5, with a specific gravity seldom less than 4, and occasionally as high as 4.3. Both are prized as gems.

Spessartite is a manganese–aluminum garnet, varying in specific gravity from 3.7 to 4.3, and has a hardness of about 7. The color varies from a red-brown, sometimes with a tinge of violet, to orange red. It often affords fine gems.

The calcium–iron garnet varies in specific gravity between 3.6 and 4 and in hardness from 5 to 7. The group includes a diversity of forms, varying widely in color and other respects, the more important of which are: Andradite, a yellow or orange-brown variety; demantoid, or Uralian emerald, a grass-green, emerald-green, or brown-green stone having a brilliant luster, and when cut exhibiting considerable fire, especially by artificial light; colophonite, a brown-black garnet, characterized by a resinous luster; and melanite, a black to yellow-brown kind.

The calcium–chromium garnet, ouvarovite, is almost invariably a fine emerald green color, and is harder than any of the other varieties, ranking nearly 8 in the scale.

Garnet is common in mica, hornblende, and chlorite schist, gneiss and granite, occurring also in limestone, serpentine, and volcanic rocks (fig. 6). The garnet of granite, gneiss, mica schist, and similar rocks is commonly almandite. Grossularite is common in limestones and crystalline schists. Pyrope belongs especially to peridotites and the serpentines derived from them; occurs also in basalts. Spessartite occurs in granitic rocks, in quartzite, in certain schists, and in some rhyolites. Iron garnets are common in eruptive rocks, occurring also as a product of contact metamorphism.   Demantoid occurs in serpentine.   The chrome garnets belong particularly to serpentine; found also in granular limestone.

The mineral is widely used as a semiprecious stone, although the color is in some cases so deep that it is not much in favor.   The most noted garnet region of the world is that some 60 kilometers north of Prague in Bohemia.   For many years this has been almost the only commercial source of the common ruby garnet found mounted in various and multiple forms in the jewelers' shops.

Of late years a great many very beautiful garnets have been brought in from the Indian Reservations in Arizona and New Mexico, where they are gathered from the loose sands and gravels which result from

FIG. 6.—GARNETS IN MATRIX.

a decomposition of boulders of garnetiferous gneiss which, according to Gregory,[1] have been brought from an unknown depth to the surface by igneous injections.   These are often of no mean quality and are popularly spoken of as Arizona rubies.   The principal localities are the Mule Ear and Moses Rock fields in southern Utah and the Garnet Ridge field in the adjoining portion of Arizona.

LIST OF SPECIMENS.

GARNET, variety ALMANDITE.

BOHEMIA.

Cabochon, irregular elliptical girdle; violet-red; 24.42 carats; 25 by 13 by 6 mm.   Isaac Lea collection... No. 969
Cabochon, elliptical girdle; violet-red; 23.2 carats; 24 by 13 by 7 mm. Isaac Lea collection.. No. 968

---

[1] Economic Geology, vol. 11, 1916, p. 224.

Cabochon, pear-shaped girdle; violet-red; 21.37 carats; 23 by 13 by 7 mm. Isaac Lea collection.. No. 970

Cabochon, elliptical girdle; violet-red; 15.347 carats; 18 by 12 by 6 mm. Isaac Lea collection... No. 971

Cabochon, elliptical girdle; violet-red; 10.79 carats; 15 by 12 by 6 mm. Isaac Lea collection.. No. 973

Rose-shell, elliptical girdle; brown-red; 9.13 carats; 15 by 13 by 5 mm. Isaac Lea collection... No. 972

Rose, square girdle; brown-red; 6.46 carats; 11 by 6 mm. Isaac Lea collection. No. 975

Cabochon, elliptical girdle; violet-red; 6.36 carats; 12 by 9 by 5 mm. Isaac Lea collection... No. 976

Rose-shell, circular girdle; brown-red; 6.08 carats; 13 by 4 mm. Isaac Lea collection.. No. 974

Cabochon, elliptical girdle; violet-red; 3.97 carats; 12 by 10 by 3 mm. Isaac Lea collection... No. 982

Step-brilliant, pear-shaped girdle; brown-red; 3.34 carats; 13 by 10 by 4 mm. Isaac Lea collection... No. 977

Step-brilliant, oval girdle; brown-red; 2.74 carats; 10 by 7.5 by 4 mm. Isaac Lea collection... No. 978

Step-brilliant, elliptical girdle; violet-red; 2.62 carats; 11 by 8.5 by 4 mm. Isaac Lea collection.. No. 979

Cabochon, elliptical girdle; violet-red; 2.49 carats; 12 by 8 by 2 mm. Isaac Lea collection... No. 984

Cabochon, irregular elliptical girdle; violet-red; 2 carats; 10 by 6 by 2.5 mm. Isaac Lea collection.. No. 986

Cabochon, elliptical girdle: violet-red; 1.66 carats; 8 by 7 by 2 mm. Isaac Lea collection... No. 985

Cabochon, elliptical girdle; violet-red; 1.65 carats; 8 by 6 by 3 mm. Isaac Lea collection... No. 983

Step, square girdle; brown-red; 1.63 carats; 7 by 3 mm. Isaac Lea collection. No. 980

Cabochon, elliptical girdle; violet-red; 1.58 carats; 8 by 6 by 3 mm. Isaac Lea collection... No. 989

Cabochon, circular girdle; violet-red; 1.43 carats; 7 by 3 mm. Isaac Lea collection.. No. 981

Brilliant, elliptical girdle; violet-red; 1.41 carats; 10 by 8 by 2 mm. Isaac Lea collection... No. 993

Cabochon, elliptical girdle; violet-red; 1.38 carats; 8 by 7 by 2 mm. Isaac Lea collection... No. 987

Cabochon, circular girdle; violet-red; 1.245 carats; 7 by 2 mm. Isaac Lea collection.. No. 988

Cabochon, elliptical girdle; violet-red; 1.06 carats; 8 by 6 by 2 mm. Isaac Lea collection... No. 992

Rose, pear-shaped girdle; deep red; 0.48 carat; 6 by 5 by 1.5 mm. Isaac Lea collection.. No. 990

CEYLON.

Cabochon, oval girdle; violet-red; 10.4 carats; 17 by 9 by 6 mm............... No. 920

Cabochon, elliptical girdle; violet-red; 10 carats; 16 by 10 by 7 mm.......... No. 919

Cabochon, oval girdle; violet-red; 8.96 carats; 15 by 9 by 6 mm. (polished pebble)... No. 921

Cabochon, elliptical girdle; violet-red; 8 carats; 16.5 by 8 by 6 mm........... No. 922

Brilliant, circular girdle; violet-red; 1.95 carats; 8 by 3 mm. Isaac Lea collection.. No. 924

Brilliant, elliptical girdle; violet-red; 1.59 carats; 8 by 7 by 2 mm. Isaac
Lea collection.. No. 923
Brilliant, pear-shaped girdle; violet-red; 1.33 carats; 8 by 6 by 3 mm. Isaac
Lea collection.. No. 934
Brilliant, elliptical girdle; violet-red; 1.23 carats; 8 by 7 by 2 mm. Isaac
Lea collection.. No. 930
Brilliant, elliptical girdle; violet-red; 1.13 carats; 8 by 7 by 2 mm. Isaac
Lea collection.. No. 925
Brilliant, elliptical girdle; violet-red; 0.99 carat; 8 by 6 by 1.5 mm. Isaac
Lea collection.. No. 931
Brilliant, elliptical girdle; violet-red; 0.67 carat; 5.5 by 5 by 2 mm. Isaac
Lea collection.. No. 932
Brilliant, square girdle; violet-red; 0.625 carat; 5 by 2 mm. Isaac Lea col-
lection.. No. 928
Brilliant, elliptical girdle; violet-red; 0.615 carat; 7 by 5 by 2 mm. Isaac
Lea collection.. No. 933
Brilliant, elliptical girdle; violet-red; 0.535 carat; 5.5 by 5 by 2 mm. Isaac
Lea collection.. No. 926
Brilliant, rectangular girdle; violet-red; 0.425 carat; 5 by 4 by 1.5 mm.
Isaac Lea collection .... No. 927
Brilliant, square girdle; violet-red; 0.4 carat; 4 by 2 mm. Isaac Lea col-
lection.. No. 929

CHINA (TUNGCHOW, SHANTUNG PROVINCE).

Cabochon, elliptical girdle; deep red; 19.416 carats; 23 by 15 by 8 mm ... No. 1207

INDIA.

Rose-shell, elliptical girdle; brown-red; 57.46 carats; 31 by 27 by 9 mm .. No. 833
Rose-shell, circular girdle; brown-red; 24.33 carats; 20 by 8 mm .... No. 834
Rose-shell, rectangular girdle; brown-red; 23.98 carats; 19 by 17 by 10 mm. No. 835
Rose, elliptical girdle; brown-red; 19.82 carats; 18 by 17 by 7 mm .... No. 838
Rose-shell, elliptical girdle; brown-red; 14.5 carats; 21 by 17 by 7 mm ... No. 836
Rose, circular girdle; brown-red; 14.387 carats; 15 by 7 mm .... No. 841
Rose, elliptical girdle; brown-red; 13.62 carats; 18 by 15 by 6 mm .... No. 839
Brilliant, elliptical girdle; violet-red; 12.8 carats; 15 by 13 by 7 mm ..... No. 840
Brilliant, irregular girdle; violet-red; 12.45 carats; 15 by 14 by 7 mm..... No. 845
Rose-shell, elliptical girdle; brown-red; 12.04 carats; 10 by 17 by 6 mm .. No. 837
Brilliant, rectangular girdle; brown-red; 11.045 carats; 13 by 12 by 8 mm. No. 855
Rose-shell, elliptical girdle; brown-red; 10.96 carats; 16 by 14 by 7 mm .. No. 842
Rose, elliptical girdle; brown-red; 10.09 carats; 15 by 13 by 6 mm........ No. 847
Rose, elliptical girdle; brown-red; 9.87 carats; 15.5 by 14 by 5 mm....... No. 844
Brilliant, irregular oval girdle; violet-red; 9.7 carats; 14 by 13 by 5 mm.. No. 848
Rose, pear-shaped girdle; brown-red; 9.375 carats; 16 by 13 by 5 mm .... No. 854
Rose-shell, circular girdle; brown-red; 9.167 carats; 15 by 7 mm.......... No. 843
Rose, pear-shaped girdle; brown-red; 9.147 carats; 17 by 12 by 5 mm..... No. 846
Rose-shell, elliptical girdle; brown-red; 9.04 carats; 14 by 13 by 6 mm... No. 853
Rose, pear-shaped girdle; brown-red; 8.3 carats; 21 by 11 by 5 mm....... No. 879
Rose, pear-shaped girdle; brown-red; 7.12 carats; 20 by 10 by 5 mm...... No. 880
Rose-shell, elliptical girdle; violet-red; 6.8 carats; 18 by 15 by 5 mm..... No. 878
Rose, circular girdle; brown-red; 6.46 carats; 11 by 4.5 mm.............. No. 856
Rose-shell, circular girdle; brown-red; 5.5 carats; 13 by 4.5 mm.......... No. 849
Step, rectangular girdle; brown-red; 5.35 carats; 13 by 10 by 5 mm ...... No. 859
Rose, circular girdle; brown-red; 4.96 carats; 12 by 4 mm................ No. 850
Rose-shell, circular girdle; brown-red; 4.769 carats; 13 by 5 mm.......... No. 882

Rose-shell, elliptical girdle; brown-red; 4.57 carats; 14 by 11 by 4 mm.... No. 881
Rose, circular girdle; brown-red; 4.5 carats; 12 by 4 mm................ No. 851
Rose, circular girdle; brown-red; 3.2 carats; 11 by 3 mm................. No. 852
Rose, elliptical girdle; brown-red; 3.19 carats; 12 by 9 by 3.5 mm........ No. 858
Step, rectangular girdle; brown-red; 3.07 carats; 9 by 8 by 4 mm.......... No. 865
Step-brilliant, elliptical girdle; violet-red; 3.037 carats; 10.5 by 9 by 4.5
   mm.. No. 863
Step, rectangular girdle; violet-red; 3 carats; 12 by 7 by 4 mm............ No. 860
Rose, elliptical girdle; brown-red; 2.97 carats; 11 by 9 by 3 mm.......... No. 857
Step, square girdle; violet-red; 2.727 carats; 9 by 4 mm.................. No. 862
Step, rectangular girdle; violet-red; 2.637 carats; 11 by 8.5 by 4 mm...... No. 861
Step, rectangular girdle; violet-red; 2.477 carats; 10 by 8 by 3.5 mm...... No. 866
Step, rectangular girdle; violet-red; 2.465 carats; 10 by 7 by 4 mm........ No. 867
Brilliant, rectangular girdle; violet-red; 2.3 carats; 11 by 8 by 3 mm...... No. 864
Step-brilliant, rectangular girdle; violet-red; 2.02 carats; 10 by 8 by 4 mm. No. 868
Step-brilliant, pear-shaped girdle; violet-red; 1.7 carats; 11 by 8.5 by 2.5 mm No. 892
Step-brilliant, rectangular girdle; violet-red; 1.69 carats; 9 by 7.5 by 4 mm. No. 869
Step-brilliant, pear-shaped girdle; violet-red; 1.525 carats; 10.5 by 8 by
   2 mm... No. 903
Step-brilliant, pear-shaped girdle; violet-red; 1.5 carats; 10.5 by 8 by 2 mm. No. 897
Step-brilliant, pear-shaped girdle; violet-red; 1.485 carats; 11 by 8 by 2
   mm.. No. 901
Step-brilliant, pear-shaped girdle; violet-red; 1.48 carats; 11 by 8 by 2 mm. No. 883
Step-brilliant, rectangular girdle; violet-red; 1.41 carats; 8 by 6.5 by 3 mm. No. 870
Step-brilliant, pear-shaped girdle; violet-red; 1.40 carats; 10 by 7 by 2 mm.. No. 906
Step-brilliant, rectangular girdle; violet-red; 1.37 carats; 8 by 6 by 3 mm..... No. 875
Step-brilliant, pear-shaped girdle; violet-red; 1.35 carats; 10 by 7 by 2 mm.. No. 914
Step-brilliant, pear-shaped girdle; violet-red; 1.345 carats; 10 by 7 by 2 mm. No. 898
Step-brilliant, rectangular girdle; violet-red; 1.33 carats; 8 by 7 by 3 mm.... No. 872
Step-brilliant, pear-shaped girdle; violet-red; 1.315 carats; 10 by 8 by 2 mm. No. 905
Step-brilliant, pear-shaped girdle; violet-red; 1.275 carats; 10 by 7 by 2 mm. No. 885
Step-brilliant, rectangular girdle; violet-red; 1.27 carats; 7.5 by 6.5 by 2.5 mm. No. 871
Step-brilliant, pear-shaped girdle; violet-red; 1.27 carats; 10 by 8 by 2 mm.. No. 895
Step-brilliant, pear-shaped girdle; violet-red; 1.265 carats; 9 by 9 by 2 mm.. No. 915
Step-brilliant, pear-shaped girdle; violet-red; 1.255 carats; 10 by 7 by 2 mm. No. 916
Step-brilliant, pear-shaped girdle; violet-red; 1.255 carats; 10 by 7 by 2 mm. No. 907
Step-brilliant, pear-shaped girdle; violet-red; 1.25 carats; 10 by 7 by 2 mm.. No. 889
Step-brilliant, rectangular girdle; violet-red; 1.245 carats; 8 by 6 by 3 mm.. No. 876
Step-brilliant, pear-shaped girdle; violet-red; 1.24 carats; 10 by 7.5 by 2 mm. No. 893
Step-brilliant, rectangular girdle; violet-red; 1.225 carats; 8 by 7 by 3 mm.... No. 873
Step-brilliant, rectangular girdle; violet-red; 1.214 carats; 8 by 6 by 3 mm.. No. 874
Step-brilliant, rectangular girdle; violet-red; 1.19 carats; 7.5 by 6 by 4 mm.. No. 877
Step-brilliant, pear-shaped girdle; violet-red; 1.165 carats; 9 by 7.5 by 2 mm. No. 904
Step-brilliant, pear-shaped girdle; violet-red; 1.16 carats; 10 by 8 by 2 mm.. No. 891
Step-brilliant, pear-shaped girdle; violet-red; 1.15 carats; 10 by 7 by 2 mm.. No. 899
Step-brilliant, pear-shaped girdle; violet-red; 1.145 carats; 11 by 7 by 2 mm. No. 890
Step-brilliant, pear-shaped girdle; violet-red; 1.14 carats; 9 by 7.5 by 2 mm. No. 913
Step-brilliant, pear-shaped girdle; violet-red; 1.095 carats; 10 by 8 by 2 mm. No. 887
Step-brilliant, pear-shaped girdle; violet-red; 1.09 carats; 10 by 7.5 by 2 mm. No. 886
Step-brilliant, pear-shaped girdle; violet-red; 1.085 carats; 10 by 7 by 2 mm. No. 896
Step-brilliant, pear-shaped girdle; violet-red; 1.08 carats; 9 by 8 by 2 mm... No. 911
Step-brilliant, pear-shaped girdle; violet-red; 1.07 carats; 9 by 7 by 2 mm... No. 888
Step-brilliant, pear-shaped girdle; violet-red; 1.06 carats; 9.5 by 7.5 by 2 mm. No. 894
Step-brilliant, pear-shaped girdle; violet-red; 1.00 carat; 9 by 7 by 2 mm.... No. 884

Step-brilliant, pear-shaped girdle; violet-red; 0.98 carat; 10 by 7 by 1.5 mm... No. 900
Step-brilliant, pear-shaped girdle; violet-red; 0.98 carat; 10 by 7 by 2 mm.. No. 902
Step-brilliant, pear-shaped girdle; violet-red; 0.98 carat; 9 by 7 by 2 mm.... No. 910
Step-brilliant, pear-shaped girdle; violet-red; 0.975 carat; 9 by 7 by 2 mm... No. 908
Step-brilliant, pear-shaped girdle; violet-red; 0.94 carat; 9 by 7 by 2 mm..... No. 909
Step-brilliant, pear-shaped girdle; violet-red; 0.875 carat; 9.5 by 7 by 1.5
mm.. No. 912
Madras:
Cabochon, elliptical girdle; violet-red; 20.54 carats; 19 by 11 by 9 mm.. No. 917
Cabochon, ellipsoid; violet-red; 11.02 carats; 23 by 9 by 5.5 mm........ No. 918

JAPAN.

Brilliant, elliptical girdle; violet-red; 2.385 carats; 10 by 7 by 3 mm......... No. 121 0
Brilliant, pear-shaped girdle; violet-red; 2.335 carats; 11 by 7 by 4 mm...... No. 1208
Brilliant, elliptical girdle; violet-red; 2.235 carats; 9 by 6 by 4 mm. Isaac
Lea collection... No. 1213
Brilliant, pear-shaped girdle; violet-red; 2.125 carats; 10 by 7 by 4 mm.
Isaac Lea collection.. No. 1214
Brilliant, pear-shaped girdle; violet-red; 1.955 carats; 10 by 6 by 3 mm..... No. 1209
Brilliant, pear-shaped girdle; violet-red; 1.91 carats; 8 by 7 by 4 mm.
Isaac Lea collection.. No. 1215
Brilliant, elliptical girdle; violet-red; 1.865 carats; 7.5 by 7 by 2 mm. Isaac
Lea collection... No. 1216
Cabochon, oval girdle; violet-red; 1.855 carats; 9 by 8 by 3 mm. Isaac Lea
collection... No. 1217
Brilliant, elliptical girdle; violet-red; 1.81 carats; 8 by 6.5 by 3.5 mm.
Isaac Lea collection.. No. 1218
Cabochon, oval girdle; violet-red; 1.76 carats; 8 by 7 by 3 mm. Isaac Lea
collection... No. 1219
Cabochon, irregular oval girdle; violet-red; 1.69 carats; 8 by 7 by 3 mm.
Isaac Lea collection.. No. 1220
Brilliant, pear-shaped girdle; violet-red; 1.64 carats; 8 by 6 by 4.5 mm.
Isaac Lea collection.. No. 1221
Brilliant, elliptical girdle; violet-red; 1.635 carats; 8.5 by 5 by 4 mm.
Isaac Lea collection.. No. 1222
Brilliant, elliptical girdle; violet-red; 1.555 carats; 10 by 6 by 2 mm....... No. 1211
Brilliant, pear-shaped girdle; violet-red; 1.545 carats; 7 by 6 by 4 mm.
Isaac Lea collection.. No. 1223
Rose, pear-shaped girdle; violet-red; 1.505 carats; 10 by 8 by 2 mm. Isaac
Lea collection... No. 1224
Step, elliptical girdle; violet-red; 1.5 carats; 8 by 6 by 2 mm.............. No. 1212
Cabochon, irregular oval girdle; violet-red; 1.465 carats; 8 by 7 by 3 mm.
Isaac Lea collection.. No. 1225
Cabochon, irregular oval girdle; violet-red; 1.425 carats; 9 by 7 by 2 mm.
Isaac Lea collection.. No. 1226
Step-brilliant, elliptical girdle; violet-red; 1.325 carats; 9 by 6 by 2 mm.
Isaac Lea collection.. No. 1227
Step-brilliant, elliptical girdle; brown-red; 1.27 carats; 9 by 7 by 2 mm.
Isaac Lea collection.. No. 1228
Brilliant, elliptical girdle; violet-red; 1.23 carats; 7 by 5 by 3.5 mm. Isaac
Lea collection... No. 1229
Half-brilliant; pear-shaped girdle; brown-red; 1.025 carats; 9 by 7.5 by 1.5
mm. Isaac Lea collection... No. 1230

TYROL.

Cabochon, circular girdle; brown-red; 4.48 carats; 11 by 5 mm............ No. 994
Rose, pear-shaped girdle; brown-red; 3.89 carats; 15 by 8 by 4 mm......... No. 995
Rose, circular girdle; brown-red; 1.55 carats; 8 by 3 mm................... No. 996
Rose, circular girdle; brown-red; 1.11 carats; 7 by 3 mm.................. No. 997
Rose, rectangular girdle; brown-red; 0.745 carat; 6 by 5 by 3 mm........... No. 998
Rose, square girdle; brown-red; 0.635 carat; 5 by 2 mm.................... No. 999

UNITED STATES.

Arizona.

Fort Defiance, Apache County:
  Brilliant, circular girdle; deep red; 3.386 carats; 10 by 5 mm.......... No. 1236
  Step-brilliant, circular girdle; deep red; 2.24 carats; 8 by 4.5 mm.
    Gift of Frank Springer.. No. 1241
  Brilliant, circular girdle; deep red; 2.15 carats; 8 by 5 mm. Gift of
    Frank Springer... No. 1242
  Brilliant, circular girdle; deep red; 1.97 carats; 8 by 4 mm. Gift of
    Frank Springer... No. 1243
  Step-brilliant, rectangular girdle; deep red; 1.675 carats; 8 by 7 by
    4 mm... No. 1237
  Brilliant and step-brilliant, circular girdle; three gems, two deep red,
    one violet-red; 1.31, 1.18, and 1.15 carats; 7 by 3 and 7 by 4 mm.
    Gift of Frank Springer... No. 1244
  Brilliant, rectangular girdle; deep red; 1.085 carats; 7 by 5 by 4 mm.... No. 1240
  Brilliant, circular girdle; deep red; 0.83 carat; 6 by 4 mm............. No. 1238
  Brilliant, circular girdle; deep red; 0.775 carat; 6 by 4 mm............ No. 1239

New Mexico.

Brilliant, square girdle; deep violet-red; 1.405 carats; 8 by 3 mm. Isaac
  Lea collection... No. 663
Brilliant, square girdle; red-brown; 1.315 carats; 6 by 5 mm. Isaac Lea
  collection... No. 664
Brilliant, elliptical girdle; deep violet-red; 1.16 carats; 8 by 6.5 by 3 mm.
  Isaac Lea collection... No. 665
Brilliant, square girdle; deep violet-red; 1.095 carats; 6.5 by 3 mm. Isaac
  Lea collection... No. 666
Brilliant, circular girdle; deep violet-red; 0.78 carat; 5.5 by 3 mm. Isaac
  Lea collection... No. 667
Brilliant, circular girdle; deep violet-red; 0.615 carat; 5 by 3 mm. Isaac Lea
  collection... No. 668
Step-brilliant, elliptical girdle; deep violet-red; 0.55 carat; 5.5 by 5 by 3
  mm. Isaac Lea collection... No. 669

North Carolina.

Step-brilliant, rectangular girdle; light violet-red; 1.58 carats; 7.5 by 6 by 4
  mm.. No. 1235
Macon County:
  Hollow cabochon, pear-shaped girdle; deep red; 5.67 carats; 14 by 10
    by 4 mm. Isaac Lea collection...................................... No. 1233
  Cabochon, elliptical girdle; brown-red; 2.157 carats; 8.5 by 7 by 4
    mm. (partly polished). Isaac Lea collection....................... No. 1234

Pennsylvania.

Green's Creek, Delaware County:

Cabochon, circular girdle; deep red; 4.345 carats; 9 by 5 mm.......... No. 1231

Cabochon, elliptical girdle; deep red; 3.65 carats; 12 by 8 by 4 mm.... No. 1232

LOCALITY NOT RECORDED.

Cabochon, elliptical girdle; violet-red; 13.252 carats; 18 by 13 by 6 mm.
Isaac Lea collection... No. 935

Step-brilliant, elliptical girdle; violet-red; 5.77 carats; 20 by 8 by 5 mm.
Isaac Lea collection... No. 936

Step, circular girdle (intaglio); deep violet-red; 5.6 carats; 12 by 4.5 mm... No. 670

Cabochon, elliptical girdle; brown-red; 4.47 carats; 12 by 10 by 3 mm.
Isaac Lea collection... No. 938

Step-brilliant, elliptical girdle (intaglio); violet-red; 3.67 carats; 12 by 8 by
5 mm.. No. 965

Brilliant, elliptical girdle; violet-red; 2.6 carats; 17 by 7 by 3.5 mm. Isaac
Lea collection.. No. 937

Step, octagonal girdle; brown-red; 2.089 carats; 11 by 8 by 2.5 mm. Isaac
Lea collection.. No. 939

Step-brilliant, elliptical girdle; violet-red; 1.78 carats; 9 by 7 by 3.5 mm.
Isaac Lea collection... No. 941

Cabochon, circular girdle (intaglio); violet-red; 1.68 carats; 8 by 3 mm.... No. 966

Cabochon, elliptical girdle; violet-red; 1.61 carats; 9 by 7 by 2 mm. Isaac
Lea collection.. No. 944

Step-brilliant, elliptical girdle; violet-red; 1.6 carats; 9 by 7 by 3.5 mm.
Isaac Lea collection... No. 940

Cabochon, irregular elliptical girdle; violet-red; 1.56 carats; 9 by 8 by 2 mm.
Isaac Lea collection... No. 946

Cabochon, irregular elliptical girdle; violet-red; 1.30 carats; 8 by 6 by 2
mm. Isaac Lea collection.. No. 953

Step-brilliant, elliptical girdle; violet-red; 1.257 carats; 8 by 6.5 by 3 mm.
Isaac Lea collection... No. 942

Cabochon, circular girdle (intaglio); violet-red; 1.187 carats; 7 by 2 mm... No. 967

Step, octagonal girdle; brown-red; 1.15 carats; 6.5 by 6 by 3.5 mm. Isaac
Lea collection.. No. 943

Cabochon, elliptical girdle; violet-red; 1.055 carats; 8 by 5 by 2 mm.
Isaac Lea collection... No. 960

Cabochon, irregular elliptical girdle; violet-red; 1.02 carats; 8 by 5 by 2
mm. Isaac Lea collection.. No. 950

Cabochon, irregular elliptical girdle; violet-red; 0.97 carat; 7 by 5 by 2
mm. Isaac Lea collection.. No. 949

Brilliant, pear-shaped girdle; violet-red; 0.955 carat; 11 by 5 by 2 mm.
Isaac Lea collection... No. 959

Brilliant, elliptical girdle; violet-red; 0.9 carat; 8 by 7 by 2 mm. Isaac
Lea collection.. No. 957

Step-brilliant, octagonal girdle; violet-red; 0.85 carat; 6 by 5 by 3 mm.
Isaac Lea collection... No. 952

Cabochon, elliptical girdle; violet-red; 0.785 carat; 7 by 5 by 2 mm. Isaac
Lea collection.. No. 962

Cabochon, irregular elliptical girdle; violet-red; 0.74 carat; 6 by 5 by 2 mm.
Isaac Lea collection... No. 955

Cabochon, elliptical girdle; violet-red; 0.71 carat; 8 by 6 by 1.5 mm. Isaac
Lea collection.. No. 945

Cabochon, circular girdle; violet-red; 0.55 carat; 5 by 2 mm. Isaac Lea collection... No. 956

Cabochon, irregular elliptical girdle; violet-red; 0.54 carat; 6 by 4.5 by 1.5 mm. Isaac Lea collection... No. 951

Step-brilliant, elliptical girdle; violet-red; 0.52 carat; 6 by 4 by 2 mm. Isaac Lea collection... No. 948

Cabochon, pear-shaped girdle; violet-red; 0.32 carat; 7 by 4 by 1 mm. Isaac Lea collection.. No. 961

Brilliant, elliptical girdle; brown-red; 0.235 carat; 5 by 4 by 1 mm. Isaac Lea collection.. No. 963

Step, irregular elliptical girdle; violet-red; 0.23 carat; 5 by 4 by 1.5 mm. Isaac Lea collection.. No. 947

Brilliant, elliptical girdle; brown-red; 0.185 carat; 5 by 4 by 1 mm. Isaac Lea collection.. No. 964

Brilliant, square girdle; violet-red; 0.185 carat; 4 by 1 mm. Isaac Lea collection... No. 958

Brilliant, rectangular girdle; violet-red; 0.185 carat; 4 by 3.5 by 1 mm. Isaac Lea collection... No. 954

GARNET, variety DEMANTOID.

RUSSIA (NIZHNI-TAGILSK).

Brilliant, circular girdle; brown-green; 3.1 carats; 8.5 by 6 mm........... No. 142

Brilliant, rectangular girdle; deep yellow-green; 2.26 carats; 9 by 8.5 by 4 mm... No. 141

Brilliant, circular girdle; deep yellow-green; 1.058 carats; 6.5 by 4 mm.... No. 145

Step-brilliant, rectangular girdle; deep yellow-green; 1.01 carats; 7 by 5.5 by 3.5 mm.. No. 143

Brilliant, square girdle; deep yellow-green; 1 carat; 6 by 4 mm........... No. 144

Brilliant, square girdle; light green; 0.337 carat; 5 by 2.5 mm............. No. 146

GARNET, variety ESSONITE.

CEYLON.

Step-brilliant, elliptical girdle; deep orange-brown; 64.17 carats; 30 by 24 by 12 mm. Isaac Lea collection.. No. 493

Step-brilliant, rectangular girdle; deep orange-brown; 5.7 carats; 12 by 11 by 5 mm.. No. 495

Step-brilliant, elliptical girdle; deep orange-brown; 5.68 carats; 14 by 11 by 5 mm.. No. 496

Brilliant, rectangular girdle; deep orange-brown; 3.89 carats; 11 by 10 by 5.5 mm. Isaac Lea collection.. No. 497

Step-brilliant, rectangular girdle; deep orange-brown; 3.7 carats; 10 by 8 by 5 mm. Isaac Lea collection.. No. 498

Step-brilliant, square girdle; deep orange-brown; 0.84 carat; 6 by 3 mm. Isaac Lea collection... No. 499

Two gems, step-brilliant and brilliant, elliptical girdle; deep orange-brown; 0.8 carat; 6.5 by 5 by 3 and 7 by 6 by 3 mm. Isaac Lea collection....... No. 500

Eleven gems, brilliant and step-brilliant, irregular girdles; deep orange-brown; total weight, 3.6 carats; 5 by 3 to 3 by 2 mm. Isaac Lea collection... No. 501

LOCALITY NOT RECORDED.

Step, elliptical girdle (intaglio); orange-brown; 5.02 carats; 15 by 10 by 5 mm... No. 494

GARNET, variety GROSSULARITE.

CANADA (HULL, OTTAWA COUNTY, QUEBEC).

Brilliant, square girdle; pale yellow; 1.24 carats; 7 by 4 mm.............. No. 137
Step-brilliant, rectangular girdle; pale yellow; 0.6 carat; 6 by 5 by 3 mm. No. 138

MEXICO (XALOSTOC, MORELOS).

Step-brilliant, rectangular girdle; deep rose pink; 1.2 carats; 7 by 6 by 4 mm. No. 139
Step-brilliant, circular girdle; deep rose pink; 0.88 carat; 6 by 4 mm....... No. 140

GARNET, variety PYROPE.

BOHEMIA.

Necklace of 103 rose cut and 2 cabochon; deep red. Isaac Lea collection.... No. 475
Fifty gems, rose cut, circular and elliptical girdles; deep red; total weight,
    12.275 carats; average size, 4 by 2 mm.................................. No. 474

UNION OF SOUTH AFRICA.

Six gems, brilliant, circular girdle; deep red; total weight, 2.34 carats; aver-
    age size, 5 by 3 mm... No. 464

UNITED STATES.

North Carolina.

Macon County:
    Brilliant, circular girdle; violet-red; 3.079 carats; 10 by 5 mm. Isaac
        Lea collection.. No. 476
    Brilliant, circular girdle; violet-red; 2.09 carats; 8 by 5 mm. Isaac Lea
        collection.. No. 477
    Brilliant, circular girdle; deep red; 1.476 carats; 7 by 5 mm. Isaac
        Lea collection.. No. 478
    Brilliant, circular girdle; deep red; 1.46 carats; 7 by 4.5 mm. Isaac
        Lea collection.. No. 479
    Brilliant, circular girdle; deep red; 1.45 carats; 7.5 by 4 mm. Isaac
        Lea collection.. No. 480
    Brilliant, circular girdle; brown-red; 1.35 carats; 7 by 4 mm. Isaac
        Lea collection.. No. 481
    Brilliant, circular girdle; violet-red; 1.33 carats; 6.5 by 4 mm. Isaac
        Lea collection.. No. 482
    Brilliant, circular girdle; violet-red; 1.08 carats; 7 by 4 mm. Isaac
        Lea collection.. No. 483
    Brilliant, circular girdle; violet-red; 1.07 carats; 7 by 4 mm. Isaac Lea
        collection.. No. 484
    Brilliant, circular girdle; violet-red; 1.06 carats; 7 by 4 mm. Isaac Lea
        collection.. No. 485
    Brilliant, circular girdle; brown-red; 1.05 carats; 6.5 by 4 mm. Isaac
        Lea collection.. No. 486
    Brilliant, elliptical girdle; violet-red; 0.987 carat; 7 by 6 by 4 mm.
        Isaac Lea collection.. No. 487
    Brilliant, circular girdle; violet-red; 0.915 carat; 6 by 4 mm. Isaac Lea
        collection.. No. 488
    Brilliant, circular girdle; violet-red; 0.835 carat; 6 by 3.5 mm. Isaac
        Lea collection.. No. 489
    Brilliant, circular girdle; deep violet-red; 0.74 carat; 6 by 4 mm. Isaac
        Lea collection.. No. 490

Macon County—Continued.

Brilliant, circular girdle; deep red; 0.718 carat; 6 by 3.5 mm. Isaac
Lea collection.. No. 491

Brilliant, circular girdle; brown-red; 0.567 carat; 5 by 3.5 mm. Isaac
Lea collection.. No. 492

GARNET, variety RHODOLITE.

UNITED STATES.

North Carolina.

Step-brilliant, circular girdle; deep violet-red; two stones, 2.0 and 1.97
carats; each 7 by 5 mm. Isaac Lea collection........................... No. 460

GARNET, variety SPESSARTITE.

UNITED STATES.

Virginia.

Amelia Courthouse, Amelia County:

Brilliant, circular girdle; orange-brown; 40.115 carats; 21 by 13 mm.... No. 147

Brilliant, circular girdle; orange-brown; 11.8 carats; 14 by 8 mm....... No. 152

Step-brilliant, rectangular girdle; orange-brown; 12 by 11 by 8 mm.
Gift of Ira R. Allen... No. 154

Step-brilliant, rectangular girdle; orange-brown; 9.0 carats; 12 by 10
by 7 mm. Gift of Ira R. Allen.. No. 153

Brilliant, circular girdle; orange-brown; 7.44 carats; 11.5 by 8 mm..... No. 148

Cabochon, circular girdle; orange-brown; 5.797 carats; 11 by 5.5 mm.
Isaac Lea collection .... No. 155

Brilliant, circular girdle; orange-brown; 2.67 carats; 8 by 6 mm........ No. 150

Brilliant, circular girdle; orange-brown; 2.49 carats; 8 by 5.5 mm...... No. 149

Brilliant, circular girdle; orange-brown; 1.126 carats; 6 by 4 mm....... No. 151

GOLD.

Native gold, either in the form of leaf, nugget, or embedded in
quartz, is often used in the form of scarf or breast pins and is hence
recognized here by a characteristic form. It ranks, however, more
as a curiosity or souvenir than as a commercial article.

LIST OF SPECIMENS.

Leaf gold mounted as a breastpin. California. Isaac Lea collection....... No. 1779

Graphic granite.—See under Miscellaneous on page 120.

Grossularite.—See under Garnet.

GYPSUM.

Synonyms or varieties.—Alabaster, satin spar, selenite.

Composition.—Hydrous calcium sulphate, $CaSO_4.2H_2O$.

Crystallization.—Monoclinic.

Color.—White or colorless.

Luster.—Vitreous or silky in fibrous varieties; transparent to
translucent.

Hardness.—2; entirely too soft to be used as a precious stone.

Specific gravity.—2.32 ± 0.05.

Optical properties.—Mean refractive index, 1.525; double refraction weak, 0.009; optically biaxial, positive.

Method of identification.—Can be readily recognized by its softness. Gypsum occurs in great quantities interstratified with other sedimentary rocks, and the pure white varieties are worked under the name alabaster. Only the fibrous form, satin spar, is utilized as gem material and then only in small ornaments as statuettes, beads, etc. While the luster of the fibrous variety is attractive, its softness precludes its extensive use, and it brings little more than the cost of cutting.

LIST OF SPECIMENS.

GYPSUM, variety SATIN-SPAR.

ENGLAND.

Cabochon, elliptical girdle; white; 32.03 carats; 29 by 18 by 12 mm. Gift
of Clarence S. Bement.. No. 378
Bridgeford:
    Two necklaces of 63 beads each, white, 8 mm. diameter................ No. 377

HEMATITE.

Composition.—Iron sesquioxide, Fe_2O_3.
Crystallization.—Hexagonal (trigonal), rhombohedral.
Color.—Black; when finely powdered, red.
Luster.—Metallic; practically opaque.
Hardness.—6; fairly durable.
Specific gravity.—5.20 ± 0.10.
Optical properties.—Too opaque for determination of optical properties by ordinary means.

The mineral can be best distinguished from other black minerals by the color of its powder or its red "streak," made by rubbing it on unglazed porcelain. Occurs abundantly in beds and in veins and sedimentary rocks, but is too black for use as a precious stone. Is sometimes cut into beads, intaglios, etc., which have a value little more than cost of cutting.

LIST OF SPECIMENS.

ENGLAND.

Two intaglios, tabular, rectangular; black; 17.29 and 17.23 carats; 18 by 15
    by 3 mm... No. 1245
Intaglio, tabular, rectangular; black; 11.67 carats; 16 by 11 by 3 mm...... No. 1247
Cumberland:
    Necklace of 48 beads, spherical; black; 12 to 8 mm. diameter.......... No. 1246

Hiddenite.—See under Spodumene.
Huntilite.—See under Miscellaneous on page 120.
Hyacinth.—See under Zircon.

HYPERSTHENE.

Variety.—Bronzite.
Composition.—Magnesium and iron metasilicate, $(Mg, Fe)\ SiO_3$.
Crystallization.—Orthorhombic.
Color.—Black, with bronze internal color; pleochroism distinct under the microscope.
Luster.—Submetallic.
Hardness.—5.5; not very durable.
Specific gravity.—3.50 ± 0.20.
Optical properties.—Mean refractive index, 1.70; double refraction moderate, about 0.01; biaxial, negative.

Hypersthene and bronzite are members of the pyroxene family and are common constitutents of certain types of volcanic rocks. They occasionally afford material that can be cut and are of interest but of little use as precious stones; are sometimes cut cabochon as a curiosity.

IOLITE.

Synonyms.—Cordierite, dichroite, "water-sapphire."
Composition.—Magnesium aluminum metasilicate, $Mg_4Al_8O_6(SiO_3)_{10}$.
Crystallization.—Orthorhombic.
Color.—Blue, usually somewhat smoky; strongly pleochroic, from yellow to blue.
Luster.—Vitreous; transparent.
Hardness.—7; a durable stone.
Specific gravity.—2.65 ± 0.05.
Optical properties.—Mean refractive index, 1.54; double refraction weak, 0.008; optically biaxial, negative.

The mineral occurs in pegmatite and in metamorphic rocks. When cut in such a direction that the blue color shows at the top, it is used to some extent as a precious stone. Its value is slight.

JADE.

Varieties.—Jadeite and nephrite.

Composition.—Jadeite, a mineral of the pyroxene group, is a sodium aluminum silicate $(NaAl(SiO_3)_2)$ with a granular to fibrous but compact structure. Nephrite, a member of the amphibole group, is a magnesium calcium silicate $(Mg_3CaSi_4O_{12})$ with a fibrous structure.

Crystallization.—Monoclinic.

Color.—Gray or white when pure; often green, owing to the presence of small amounts of iron silicates; usually mottled because of irregular distribution of the coloring substance.

Luster.—Vitreous; translucent.

Hardness.—6.5; can not be scratched by a knife, and fairly durable.

Specific gravity.—3.35 ± 0.10.

Optical properties.—Mean refractive index for nephrite, 1.61; for jadeite 1.67.

Distinguished from imitations by its great hardness. True jade is not produced artificially, but green glass made cloudy by stirring in some pigment is sometimes used as an imitation. Not used as a precious stone in the ordinary sense, but, because of its hardness and toughness, has been much used, particularly by the Chinese, for ornaments, carvings, etc. The hardness renders work upon it difficult, and causes genuine jade articles to bring high prices. Ignorant buyers are often imposed upon by the substitution of a green serpentine for the real article. Jadeite can usually be distinguished from nephrite by its granular structure, nephrite being more distinctly fibrous.

LIST OF SPECIMENS.

JADE, variety JADEITE.

CHINA.

Carved buckle; bright green; 68 by 18 mm. Isaac Lea collection .... No. 1813

Clasp of gold containing two pieces of green jadeite, 27 by 12 mm., at ends, and one of pink tourmaline, 42 by 25 mm., in center..................... No. 1193

Carved pendant; green to light green; 16.9 carats; 26 by 15 mm. Isaac Lea collection (fig. 9, pl. 12)... No. 1814

Carved pendant; green; 18.9 carats; 25 by 12 mm. Isaac Lea collection (fig. 11, pl. 12).. No. 1815

Two stones, irregular cabochon; bright green; 7.5 and 7.14 carats; 14 by 11 mm.. No. 1191

Charm; pale green and white; 31 by 24 mm. Isaac Lea collection....... No. 1816

JADE, variety NEPHRITE.

CHINA.

Disk with flower; gray-green; 5.5 cm. diameter. Gift of Clarence S. Bement. No. 1186

Reclining figure; light gray-green; 5.5 by 3.2 cm. Deposited by P. L. Jouy. No. 1189

Disk with slit; gray-green; 5.5 cm. diameter............................... No. 1187

Carved ornament or buckle; gray-green; 10 by 2 cm...................... No. 1188

JAPAN.

Ring; light gray-green, translucent; 7 cm. diameter........................ No. 1190

NEW ZEALAND.

Two cameos and one intaglio; rectangular girdle; dark green; 18 by 15,
15 by 12; 16 by 13 mm.. No. 1185
Carved piece, book-shaped; 28 by 19 by 6 mm.; and two pear-shaped pendants, 6.4 and 5.5 cm. long; dark green.................................. No. 1184

UNITED STATES.

Alaska.

One labret; olive-green; 9 cm. long...................................... No. 1194

LOCALITY NOT RECORDED.

Two cabochons, rectangular girdle; dark green; 14.76 and 9.5 carats; 20 by
11, and 14 by 11 mm... No. 1192
Pendant; three links carved from one piece; pale gray. Isaac Lea collection.. No. 1195

Jadeite.—See under Jade.
Jasper.—See under Chalcedony.

KYANITE.

Synonym.—Often spelled cyanite.
Composition.—Aluminum oxy-orthosilicate, Al_2O_3 (SiO_4).
Crystallization.—Triclinic; habit bladed.
Color.—Colorless when pure; often blue owing to the presence of impurities of unknown nature.
Luster.—Vitreous; translucent to transparent.
Hardness.—7 in one direction, 5 in the other; not very durable.
Specific gravity.—3.60 ± 0.05.
Optical properties.—Mean refractive index, 1.72; double refraction moderate, 0.015; optically biaxial, negative.

A great variation in hardness is highly characteristic. It is rarely found clear enough to be used as a precious stone, but is occasionally cut.

LIST OF SPECIMENS.

RUSSIA.

Step, rectangular girdle; blue; 0.579 carats; 7 by 4 by 2 mm................ No. 565

UNITED STATES.

North Carolina.

Spruce Pine, Mitchell County:
Step, rectangular girdle; deep blue; 3.728 carats; 12 by 7 by 5 mm.
Gift of D. A. Bowman... No. 564

Kunzite.—See under Spodumene.
Labradorite.—See under Feldspar.
Lapis-lazuli.—See under Lazurite.

LAZURITE.

Synonym.—Lapis-lazuli.

Composition.—The ornamental stone known as lapis-lazuli is a mixture of a number of different minerals, but the principal one, yielding the blue color, is lazurite, a sodium aluminum sulpho-ortho-silicate, $Na_5Al_3S_3(SiO_4)_3$.

Crystallization.—Isometric.

Color.—Deep blue, due to the peculiar sulphur compound present.

Luster.—Vitreous; translucent.

Hardness.—5; rather too low for the stone to be durable.

Specific gravity.—2.40 ± 0.10.

Optical properties.—Refractive index, 1.49; isotropic.

The composite nature of the rock can easily be made out by close examination, specks of pyrite in particular being almost always visible. It is decomposed by hydrochloric acid with the evolution of hydrogen sulphide. It occurs in metamorphic rocks. The artificial blue pigment known as ultramarine is essentially identical with lazurite in composition. Blue glass and blue stained chalcedony are often put on the market as imitations. Lapis-lazuli is used in the manufacture of ornaments of various kinds, and, being rather difficult to carve, brings fairly high prices. It does not occur in masses of large size. The only mineral with which it is likely to become confounded is sodalite (see p. 97).

LIST OF SPECIMENS.

CENTRAL ASIA.

Watch charm carved in imitation of a grasshopper; deep violet-blue; 19.05 carats; 40 by 11 by 6 mm... No. 356

CHILE (ANDES MOUNTAINS).

Slab; oval; deep blue; 33.7 grams (168.6 carats); 65 by 35 by 7 mm......... No. 355

PERSIA.

Cabochon, elliptical girdle; deep blue; 35.57 carats; 30 by 27 by 6 mm. (fig. 1, pl. 7)... No. 354

Leopardite.—See under Miscellaneous (Porphyry) on page 120.

Lintonite.—See under Thomsonite.

MALACHITE AND AZURITE.

Composition.—Hydrous copper carbonate, $Cu_2(OH)_2(CO_3)$.

Crystallization.—Monoclinic.

Color.—Brilliant green, characteristic of many copper compounds.

Luster.—Vitreous, or, in fibrous varieties, silky; practically opaque.

Hardness.—3.5; can be used only where not subjected to wear.

Specific gravity.—4 ± 0.05.

Optical properties.—Mean refractive index, 1.88; double refraction extremely strong, 0.2; optically biaxial, negative.

The mineral dissolves with effervescence in hydrochloric acid, yielding a yellow solution which together with its color is sufficient in most cases for identification. Occurs like azurite in weathered copper ores, and is used for ornaments, especially table tops, etc., and was formerly valued very highly. As a rule, sound pieces of only moderate size are obtainable, and on the larger objects of art small pieces are very skillfully utilized as a thin veneer. Azurite is associated with malachite in the specimen figured below (fig. 7).

LIST OF SPECIMENS.
SIBERIA.

Cabochon, circular girdle; banded green and brown; 70.8 carats; 34 by 6 mm. Isaac Lea collection (fig. 3, pl. 7). No. 1250

Tabular, elliptical girdle; banded dark and light green; 63.7 carats; 40 by 32 by 4 mm........ No. 1248

Tabular, circular girdle; dark green with light-green concentric rings; 49.79 carats; 31 by 4 mm. No. 1249

Cabochon, elliptical girdle; dark and light green, banded; 42.67 carats; 33 by 26 by 5 mm. No. 1251

FIG. 7.—MALACHITE AND AZURITE.

Microcline.—See under Feldspar, variety Amazonstone.

MOLDAVITE: TEKTITE.

Synonyms and varietal names.—Local names dependent upon sources are common, as Australites, billitonites, and obsidian bombs. Suess proposes the general name *tektite* for the entire group.

Composition.—Glass high in silica, alumina, and the alkalies.

Crystallization.—None; amorphous.

Color.—Green to black.

Luster.—Vitreous.

Hardness.—6 to 7.

Specific gravity.—2.31 to 2.5.

Optical properties.—Refractive index variable, mostly low; optically isotropic.

Resembles in many cases ordinary green bottle glass. Its lower index of refraction distinguishes it from any natural crystalline mineral. Found loose on surface or in gravels in various parts of Australia, Bohemia, and Moravia, and thought by some to be of artificial, and by others of meteoric origin. The green variety, moldavite, has sometimes been cut as a gem stone, but is of value only as a curiosity.

MORAVIA.

Two stones, step-brilliant and brilliant, elliptical and rectangular girdles; dark green; 23.11 and 4.95 carats; 24 by 17 by 11 and 13 by 10 by 7 mm... No. 681

Moonstone.—See under Feldspar.

Moss Agate.—See under Chalcedony.

Nephrite.—See under Jade.

OBSIDIAN.

Synonyms or varieties.—Rhyolite glass, volcanic glass, hyaline rhyolite.

Composition.—Glassy volcanic rocks of variable composition, chiefly silicates of aluminum, iron, calcium, and the alkalies.

Crystallization.—None.

Color.—Various shades of black, brown, or red.

Luster.—Vitreous; transparent to translucent.

Hardness.—5.5.

Specific gravity.—Varying with composition, but mostly around 2.5.

Optical properties.—Refractive index variable, but mostly about 1.6; optically isotropic.

The resemblance to ordinary glass usually distinguishes this material from other stones, but its isotropic character and low index of refraction are usually confirmatory tests. Obsidian is of common occurrence in many volcanic regions, where it is a result of the rapid cooling of a molten magma that under different conditions might have become crystalline. Artificial glasses similar in appearance to obsidian can readily be prepared. The variegated and more brilliantly colored varieties have sometimes been cut, but the color is rarely sufficiently attractive to give it any value other than as a curiosity.

LIST OF SPECIMENS.

MEXICO (AZTEC OBSIDIAN MINE, NEAR REAL DEL MONTE, HIDALGO).

Three stones, cabochon, elliptical girdle; black or dark brown with cat's-eye chatoyancy; 20.33, 13.84, 6.56 carats..................................... No. 680

UNITED STATES.

Wyoming.

Yellowstone National Park:

Two stones, cabochon, rectangular girdle; brown-black; 28 by 21 by 7 and 25 by 19 by 6 mm... No. 683

Two stones, cabochon, elliptical girdle; red-brown with black blotches; 26 by 19 by 6 mm.. No. 682

Two stones, cabochon, circular girdle; red-brown; 26 by 10 mm........ No. 684

Two stones, cabochon, rectangular girdle; red-brown mottled with black; 22 by 18 by 10 mm .... No. 686

BULLETIN 118 PL. 9

MONARCH OPAL MINE, VIRGIN VALLEY, HUMBOLDT COUNTY, NEVADA

Cabochon, elliptical girdle; dark gray; 11 carats; 22 by 17 by 6 mm.
Gift of Dr. Robert H. Lamborn .... No. 687
Two elliptical disks; black; 21 by 17 by 3 mm........................ No. 685

Oligoclase.—See under Feldspar.

Olivine.—See under Chrysolite.

Onyx.—See under Chalcedony.

OPAL.

Composition.—Silica, containing a variable amount of water ($SiO_2 + nH_2O$).

Crystallization.—None; amorphous.

Color.—Colorless when pure, but often tinted pink, blue, and even black by impurities; shows a very brilliant internal reflection color owing to the presence of innumerable minute laminae.

Luster.—Vitreous; transparent to translucent.

Hardness.—6; by reason of this moderate degree of hardness, its brittleness, and its porous nature, is not very durable under ordinary conditions of wear.

Specific gravity.—2.1 ± 0.1.

Optical properties.—Refractive index somewhat variable because of differences in water content, but chiefly about 1.40; optically isotropic except where irregular distribution of the water content causes strain phenomena, when double refraction may be observed.

No other precious stone approaches opal in the internal color, so that this property, together with the low specific gravity and index of refraction, serves to identify it.

There are many varieties to which specific names have been given. The precious opal exhibits a play of delicate colors, reflecting now one hue and then another. The harlequin opal presents a variegated play of colors on a reddish ground and resembles the fire opal. The fire opal presents red to yellow colors, with firelike reflections, somewhat irised on turning. Girasol is a blue-white translucent kind, presenting red reflections in a strong light. Lechosos opal is a name applied to those kinds showing deep green flashes of color. Hydrophane is a white or light colored opaque kind which becomes transparent when immersed in water. Cacholong is opaque porcelain-white, blue-white, pale yellow, or red. Opal agate is agatelike in structure. Jasp-opal contains several per cent of iron, and is the analogue in opal of jasper in quartz. Wood opal is wood silicified by opal; sometimes called lithoxyle when showing a woody structure. Hyalite, or Muller's glass, is either colorless and pellucid like glass, or a translucent blue-white. Moss opal contains mosslike inclusions of manganese oxide and is the analogue in opal of the moss agate in quartz.   Tabasheer is an amorphous, opal-like silica deposited within the joints of bamboo; it absorbs water and becomes transparent like hydrophane.

Opal occurs as a secondary deposit in fissures in many kinds of rocks, also in petrified wood and other fossil material, being deposited in the gelatinous form from solutions of silica, and hardening as water is gradually expelled.   Material of the composition of opal can be readily produced artificially, but it has never proved possible to reproduce the brilliant internal color phenomena shown by the natural mineral.   Opal is always cut cabochon to bring out the color to the best advantage, and, while not always of great value, it becomes at times one of the most beautiful and fascinating of gems and is correspondingly expensive.

The chief commercial sources are Australia, Hungary, and Mexico. Recently deposits in Nevada (pl. 9), have become important sources, producing black opals of extraordinary size and beauty.

LIST OF SPECIMENS.

AUSTRALIA.

Cabochon, elliptical girdle; blue and green; 31.96 carats; 33 by 16 by 10 mm.   Isaac Lea collection... No. 1830

New South Wales.

Slab, rectangular girdle; mosaic; 29 by 46 mm............................. No. 1042
Abercrombie River:
    Two cabochons, elliptical girdle; blue and pale yellow; 5.58 and 3 carats;
        20 by 10 by 4.5 and 14 by 10 by 4 mm.   Gift of H. P. Petersen...... No. 1082
Lightning Ridge:
    Six irregular fragments, polished; blue and green; greatest dimensions,
        38, 28, 25, 21, 21, and 19 mm... No. 1041
White Cliffs:
    Necklace of 50 graduated beads, separated by crystal beads; white with
        blue internal color; 9.5 to 4.5 mm. diameter.......................... No. 1083
    Cabochon, elliptical girdle; blue-green in brown matrix; 22.97 carats;
        24 by 19 by 8 mm.. No. 1044
    Cabochon, circular girdle; blue-green in matrix; 15.96 carats; 17 by 10
        mm... No. 1047
    Cabochon, elliptical girdle; blue-green and brown in matrix; 13.94
        carats; 17 by 15 by 6 mm.. No. 1049
    Cabochon, elliptical girdle; green and blue in matrix; 12.48 carats; 18
        by 15 by 7 mm.. No. 1045
    Cabochon, circular girdle; blue-green in matrix; 12.22 carats; 15 by 6.5
        mm... No. 1050
    Cabochon, elliptical girdle; green-blue and red in matrix; 11.58 carats;
        22 by 12 by 5 mm.. No. 1046
    Cabochon, elliptical girdle; violet-blue in matrix; 8.84 carats; 16 by 10
        by 7 mm.. No. 1053
    Cabochon, elliptical girdle; blue-green in brown matrix; 8.06 carats;
        18 by 15 by 4 mm... No. 1048

White Cliffs—Continued.
    Cabochon, elliptical girdle; blue-green-red in brown matrix; 7.93 carats;
        16 by 10 by 6 mm.. No. 1051
    Cabochon, elliptical girdle; blue and green, in matrix; 6.91 carats; 14.5
        by 11 by 6 mm... No. 1052
    Cabochon, elliptical girdle; blue-green; 2.84 carats; 13 by 7 by 4.5 mm.. No. 1054

Queensland.

Barcoo River:
    Carving in form of a pansy; blue-white with fine play of color; 9.26
        carats; 25 by 22 mm. Isaac Lea collection...................... No. 1817
    Six stones, cabochon, 3 circular, 3 elliptical girdles; blue and brown;
        total weight, 9.225 carats; average size, 9 by 7 by 3 mm............ No. 1077
    Two cameos representing flamingoes on limonite; green-blue.......... No. 1056
    Four polished pieces, rectangular; precious opal in limonite; total
        weight, 22.1 carats; 18 by 11 to 17 by 11 mm..................... No. 1055
Eulo Mines, Queensland border;
    Cabochon, nearly heart-shaped girdle; red-blue-green; 7.86 carats; 17
        by 15 by 7 mm. Isaac Lea collection.............................. No. 1182
    Three cabochons, one double cabochon; elliptical, circular, and pear-
        shaped girdles; red-blue-green-yellow; 2.69, 2.145, 1.9, 1.06 carats;
        12 by 9.5 by 4.5, 9 by 5, 11 by 7.5 by 4.5, and 10 by 6 by 3 mm.
        Isaac Lea collection.. No. 1183

HONDURAS.

Two cabochons, elliptical girdle; white with opalescent colors; 38.19 and
    18.22 carats; 33 by 21 by 8, 24 by 19 by 6 mm...................... No. 1079
Six small cabochons, elliptical girdle; white with play of colors; total weight,
    9.87 carats; 11 by 8 by 6 to 8 by 7 by 4.5 mm..................... No. 1080

HUNGARY.

Cabochon, rectangular girdle; white with play of colors; 2.645 carats; 10 by 9
    by 5 mm... No. 1078
Czerwenitza:
    Cabochon, elliptical girdle; blue in gray trachyte; 8.245 carats; 20
        by 15 by 6 mm.. No. 1059

MEXICO.

Cabochon, elliptical girdle; translucent with internal color; 19.99 carats; 25
    by 17 by 10 mm.. No. 461
Cabochon, elliptical girdle; red; 13.11 carats; 20 by 14 by 8 mm.............. No. 1058
Cabochon, circular girdle; transparent with internal color; 2.77 carats; 10
    by 9 by 8 mm... No. 462
Lot of 80 stones, cabochon, various colors and sizes...................... No. 826

Hidalgo.

District Zimapan:
    Five small gems, elliptical, rectangular, and circular girdles; one
        yellow; four white; total weight, 12.45 carats. Isaac Lea collection.. No. 1081

Queretaro.

Cabochon, pear-shaped girdle; white with internal color; 24.31 carats; 33 by
    20 by 7 mm... No. 1065
Cabochon, elliptical girdle; pink with play of color; 14.95 carats; 25 by 17 by
    6 mm.. No. 1060
Cabochon, elliptical girdle; white with play of color; 12.52 carats; 27 by 14
    by 6 mm... No. 1068

Cabochon, elliptical girdle; transparent, slightly cloudy, pale yellow luster; 12.46 carats; 20 by 14 by 8 mm... No. 1069

Cabochon, circular girdle; pale yellow with play of color; 10.96 carats; 20 by 6 mm.. No. 1061

Table, rectangular girdle; white with play of color; 9.32 carats; 19 by 12 by 4.5 mm.. No. 1068

Three cabochons, two elliptical, one circular girdle; white with internal color; 8.2, 5.74, 5.16 carats; 25 by 11 by 5 mm., 17 by 3 mm., 17 by 14 by 4.5 mm.. No. 1066

Cabochon, elliptical girdle; blue-white with play of colors; 7.445 carats; 20 by 13 by 5 mm.. No. 1064

Polished piece, irregularly elliptical; red; 6.57 carats; 20 by 12 by 6 mm..... No. 1071

Cabochon, elliptical girdle; white with red and green internal color; 5.96 carats; 20 by 12 by 4 mm.. No. 1063

Cabochon, pear-shaped girdle; white with play of color; 4.85 carats; 19 by 11 by 4.5 mm.. No. 1065

Five cabochons, four elliptical and one circular girdle; red; 5.73, 5.09, 4.43, 2.77, and 2.1 carats; 16 by 11 by 5.5, 15.5 by 11 by 6, 13 by 11 by 7, 12 by 9 by 5, and 9 by 5.5 mm.. No. 1067

Two cabochons, oval girdle; blue; 3.66 and 2.93 carats; 18 by 7 by 5 and 14 by 9 by 5 mm.   Gift of W. J. Knowlton...................................... No. 1057

Cabochon, elliptical girdle; transparent, deep yellow luster; 1.99 carats; 14 by 7 by 4 mm... No. 1070

Cabochon, elliptical girdle; opalescent; 1.445 carats; 12 by 6 by 4 mm....... No. 1062

Two cabochons, one square, one elliptical girdle; transparent with play of color; total weight, 3.19 carats; 8 by 5, 9 by 7 by 6 mm.................... No. 592

Cabochon, elliptical girdle; transparent with play of color; 1.17 carats; 10 by 7 by 4 mm... No. 633

Hacienda Esperanza:

Cabochon, oval girdle; transparent with harlequin colors; 14.535 carats; 25 by 16 by 7 mm.   Isaac Lea collection............................. No. 1072

Cabochon, oval girdle; yellow with gorgeous play of color; 7.207 carats; 16 by 12 by 7 mm.. No. 1073

Cabochon, elliptical girdle; red with play of colors; 6.88 carats; 15 by 12.5 by 7 mm.. No. 1074

Cabochon, oval girdle; yellow with play of colors; 4.855 carats; 15 by 11 by 6 mm... No. 1075

Cabochon, elliptical girdle, high summit; yellow with play of colors; 4.2 carats; 11 by 9 by 9 mm.. No. 1076

UNITED STATES.

Nevada.

Pendant; black with blue and green internal color; 16.62 carats; 23 by 13 by 10.   Isaac Lea collection.. No. 1084

LOCALITY NOT RECORDED.

Cabochon, elliptical girdle; smoky with play of colors; 19.28 carats; 28 by 15 by 7 mm.. No. 1085

Oriental Amethyst.—See under Corundum.

Oriental Emerald.—See under Corundum.

Oriental Topaz.—See under Corundum.

Orthoclase.—See under Feldspar, variety Adularia.

PEARL.

Calcium carbonate is most widely distributed in a number of forms, the varieties depending upon differences in origin, crystallization and structural condition, presence of impurities, etc. With the exception of pearl and coral, the many forms are used more for decorative purposes than for personal adornment.

Pearls are concretions, or, more correctly, secretions, consisting essentially of calcium carbonate, found in the shells of certain mollusks. They are the result of an abnormal secretory process caused by an irritation of the mantle of the mollusk, resulting from

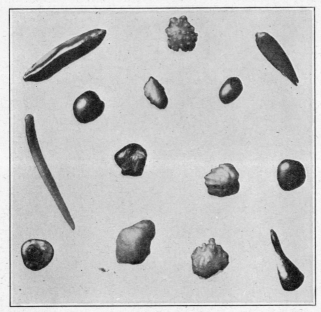

FIG. 8.—BAROQUE PEARLS.

the introduction into the shell of some foreign body, such as a grain of sand.

Pearls possess a luster peculiar to themselves, which is called pearly or nacreous. This luster may exist on the exterior surface only of the concretion, or the outer surface may be dull and dead in luster while an inner surface may be clear and lustrous. Their specific gravity is 2.5 to 2.7; their hardness 2.5 to 3.5. They may be of any shape, and in some instances of considerable size. In color they range from an opaque white, through pink, yellow, purple, red, green, brown, blue, black, in all shades; in addition they may be iridescent. In general, their color and luster will be that of the interior shell surface adjacent to which they are formed.

The beauty and value of pearls is dependent upon their color, texture or "skin," transparency or "water," luster, and form, the most valuable being those which are round or pear-shaped, slightly transparent, free from specks or blemishes, and possessing to the highest degree the characteristic luster.

Pearls are liable to deteriorate with age, contact with acids, gases, and vapors, and though various methods are in use for restoring them to their original beauty, they are by no means to be relied upon, so that care should be taken to preserve fine pearls by wiping them after use with a clean, soft cloth and keeping them wrapped and in a closed box.

Although nearly all bivalves with nacreous shells occasionally yield pearls, practically all of those of commerce are obtained from only a few families of mollusks, prominent among which are the Aviculidae, Unionidae, and Mytilidae. The pearl oyster of the Pacific and Indian oceans, which has yielded the bulk of the pearls of the world, belongs to the first of these groups. The unio, or fresh-water mussel, so abundant in the rivers and lakes of North America, belongs to the second.

The name baroque is given to irregular and sometimes almost grotesquely contorted forms, formerly considered of little value, but now when of good color highly prized. A series of these from fresh-water streams in the Mississippi Valley is shown in figure 8.

LIST OF SPECIMENS.

INDIA.

Necklace of 148 round pearls; two pear-shaped pearls; white. Gift of the
Imam of Muscat.. Nos. 1846, 1847

JAPAN (AGO BAY).

Two culture pearls, one white, one pink; 7.5 and 3.9 grains; 7 and 5 mm.
diameter. Gift of T. Kume... No. 1497
Culture pearl in shell. Showing growth of culture pearl. Gift of T. Kume.. No. 1498

PANAMA.

One lot of seed pearls. Gift of H. P. Petersen............................. No. 1500

UNITED STATES.

American fresh waters.

Five turned pearls, white; total weight, 61.7 grains; average size, 10 by
6 mm. Isaac Lea collection.. No. 1495
Fourteen wing-shaped; white, pale pink, pale brown; total weight, 117.2
grains. Isaac Lea collection.. No. 1494
Forty-nine various shapes; white, pale pink, pale brown; total weight,
321.8 grains. Isaac Lea collection.................................... No. 1493

Arkansas.

Black River:
Three white pearls, 48, 38, and 34 grains. Isaac Lea collection......... No. 1842
Two pink pearls, 38.4 and 14.6 grains. Isaac Lea collection.......... No. 1841

Indiana.

Wabash River:

One white pearl, 12.5 grains. Isaac Lea collection.................... No. 1840

Seventeen pearls, various colors and shapes, total weight, 168 grains.
Gift of B. F. Wheeler... No. 1837

White River:

One white pearl, 17.8 grains. Isaac Lea collection.................... No. 1839

Tennessee.

Holston and Clinch Rivers:

Thirty-two small pearls, various colors and shapes; total weight, 72
grains. Isaac Lea collection.. No. 1499

LOCALITY NOT RECORDED.

Bracelet and earrings of small pearls.. No. 1496

Fish carved from pearl... No. 1513

Comb carved from pearl.. No. 1514

Four pearl cat's-eyes, cabochon, circular girdle; gray-brown with pearly
internal luster; average diameter, 10 mm. Gift of Wirt Tassin.......... No. 825

Brooch of mother-of-pearl, carved in form of a feather...................... No. 1507

Brooch of mother-of-pearl, carved in form of a leaf, with red portion of shell
to represent a bunch of grapes.. No. 1508

Peridot.—See under Chrysolite.

Perthite.—See under Feldspar.

PHENACITE.

Composition.—Beryllium ortho-silicate, Be_2SiO_4.

Crystallization.—Hexagonal (trigonal), rhombohedral.

Color.—Colorless when pure; sometimes colored yellow by traces of impurities.

Luster.—Vitreous; transparent.

Hardness.—7.5; very durable.

Specific gravity.—2.95 ± 0.02.

Optical properties.—Mean refractive index, 1.66; double refraction moderate, 0.02; optically uniaxial, positive.

The mineral is best identified by its optical properties. It occurs in pegmatites and in veins, and is a rare mineral and not widely used as a precious stone, although it approaches the diamond in brilliance, especially in artificial light. The name, from φίναξ, deceiver, is said to have been applied on this account.

LIST OF SPECIMENS.

SIBERIA.

Brilliant, rectangular girdle; colorless; 5.22 carats; 12.5 by 11 by 7 mm.
Isaac Lea collection .... No. 830

Brilliant, square girdle; colorless; 2.14 carats; 8 by 5 mm............... No. 831

Plasma.—See under Chalcedony.

Porphyry.—See under Miscellaneous on page 120.

Prase.—See under Chalcedony.

PREHNITE.

Variety.—Chlorastrolite.

Composition.—Hydrogen calcium aluminum ortho-silicate, $H_2Ca_2Al_2(SiO_4)_3$.

Crystallization.—Orthorhombic.

Color.—White when pure, but usually pale green, probably owing to the presence of iron. The variety chlorastrolite is mottled green and white.

Luster.—Vitreous; in chlorastrolite somewhat silky; translucent.

Hardness.—6.5; too hard to be scratched readily by a knife; fairly durable.

Specific gravity.—2.90 ± 0.10.

Optical properties.—Mean refractive index, 1.63; double refraction strong, 0.03; optically biaxial, positive.

The mineral is distinguished by its hardness and optical properties from other minerals that resemble it. It is found in veins and cavities in basic igneous rocks, especially basalt and diabase.

Ordinary prehnite is rarely cut as a precious stone, as its color is too pale to be attractive. The variety chlorastrolite, which is mostly obtained from the beaches of Lake Superior, is cut cabochon to bring out the fibrous structure, and is used in scarfpins, etc. It brings but a moderate price, only enough to pay for handling.

LIST OF SPECIMENS.

UNITED STATES.

New Jersey.

Hoxie's Quarry, Paterson, Passaic County:

Cabochon, rectangular girdle; light green; 49.8 carats; 54 by 14 by 8 mm .... No. 361

Two gems, cabochon, circular girdle; light green; 11.98 and 11 carats; 17 by 6 and 17 by 5 mm .... No. 362

PREHNITE, variety CHLORASTROLITE.

Michigan.

Isle Royal, Lake Superior:

Cabochon, elliptical girdle; dark and light green, mottled; 12 carats; 20 by 17 by 4 mm. (fig. 2, pl. 7)... No. 364

Cabochon, elliptical girdle; dark and light green, mottled; 5.43 carats; 12 by 8.5 by 6 mm .... No. 363

Four polished stones, irregular; dark and light green, mottled; largest, 7.7 carats; total weight of three small stones, 3.29 carats; largest 16 by 11 by 7 mm .... No. 366

Three polished stones, two cabochon, one double cabochon; gray-green with dark green spots; 6.035, 4.87, and 3.67 carats; 17.5 by 12 by 3, 14 by 11 by 4, and 13 by 8 by 4.5 mm. Isaac Lea collection.......... No. 365

PYRITE.

Synonym.—Sulphur-diamond.
Composition.—Iron disulphide, FeS_2.
Crystallization.—Isometric.
Color.—Brass yellow.
Luster.—Metallic, opaque.
Hardness.—6; can not be cut by a knife; fairly durable.
Specific gravity.—5 ± 0.05.
Optical properties.—Indeterminate.
Miscellaneous properties.—Some varieties are easily decomposed by moist air, losing their luster and gradually falling to pieces. The color and luster are characteristic.

Pyrite is a very unstable mineral but occurs in a great variety of geological situations. It is used usually without cutting or polishing, as the natural luster is very brilliant. Being a very common mineral it is sold for little more than the cost of trimming and mounting.

LIST OF SPECIMENS.

UNITED STATES.

Pennsylvania.

Schuylkill County:
Two pieces, one oval, one rectangular girdle; brass yellow; 20 by 14 by
7 and 13 by 10 by 7 mm. Gift of J. W. Beath .... No. 678

Pyrope.—See under Garnet.

PYROXENE, variety DIOPSIDE.

Composition.—Calcium magnesium meta-silicate, $CaMg(SiO_3)_2$.
Crystallization.—Monoclinic.
Color.—Pale green, owing to the presence of a small amount of ferrous iron.
Luster.—Vitreous.
Hardness.—6; not very durable.
Specific gravity.—3.25 ± 0.1.
Optical properties.—Mean refractive index, 1.71; double refraction strong, 0.03; optically biaxial, positive.

The mineral occurs in metamorphosed limestones. The color, as a rule, is not attractive enough to make it of much importance as a precious stone.

LIST OF SPECIMENS.

CANADA (RENFREW COUNTY, ONTARIO).

Step-brilliant, rectangular girdle; pale green; 1.7 carats; 7.5 by 7 by 4.5 mm.
Isaac Lea collection.. No. 575

TYROL.

Step, rectangular girdle; very pale yellow; 1.65 carats; 9 by 7 by 3 mm..... No. 576
Step-brilliant, rectangular girdle; deep yellow-green; 1.33 carats; 7.5 by 6
by 4 mm.. No. 577

UNITED STATES.

New York.

De Kalb, St. Lawrence County:

Cabochon, elliptical girdle; yellow-green; 11.7 carats; 18.5 by 13 by
6 mm.. No. 571

Step-brilliant, square girdle; yellow-green; 2.2 carats; 6.5 by 5.5 mm... No. 572

Step-brilliant, rectangular girdle; pale green; 1.9 carats; 8 by 7 by 5 mm. No. 573

Brilliant, rectangular girdle; pale green; 1.56 carats; 7.5 by 6.5 by 5 mm. No. 574

LOCALITY NOT RECORDED.

Step-brilliant, rectangular girdle; yellow-green; 1.18 carats; 10.5 by 5 by
2.5 mm.. No. 578

Fig. 9.—Large amethystine quartz.

QUARTZ.

Varieties.—Silica, silicon dioxide, occurs in nature under a great
variety of forms, which are usually divided into (1) phenocrystalline
or vitreous varieties, (2) the cryptocrystalline varieties, and (3) the
amorphous or colloidal varieties. Here are included the glassy, sometimes well crystallized forms, known under the names of quartz, rock
crystal, amethyst, citrine, and smoky quartz; the massive forms
occurring mainly in veins, known as rose, or milky quartz, according to color; and a few others with local or trade names. Under
the cryptocrystalline and amorphous varieties are included those
which have, to the naked eye, no evidence of having any crystalline

structure, but which are so dense as to appear almost amorphous. (See under Chalcedony and Opal.)

Composition.—Essentially silicon dioxide, SiO_2; some varieties contain admixed iron oxides.

Crystallization.—Hexagonal (trigonal), trapezohedral; crystal habit usually prismatic, with pyramidal terminations (fig. 9); some varieties, such as chalcedony, are only known in the cryptocrystalline condition.

Color.—Colorless when pure, but many of its important varieties are based on colors due to the presence of impurities.

Luster.—Vitreous; in some varieties, waxy; transparent to opaque.

Hardness.—7; very durable.

Specific gravity.—2.66 when pure, but varying considerably in impure forms.

Crystallized quartz has a mean refractive index of 1.55 and is optically uniaxial and positive. The chief means of its ready determination are, however, its hardness, which is such that it will scratch glass, its lack of cleavage, and general glasslike appearance and fracture. It is one of the most common of minerals. Small crystals have been produced by artificial means, but never in sizes or colors to rival the natural material. Quartz and the cryptocrystalline varieties of silica are much used in the cheaper grades of jewelry, and it can be scarcely regarded as more than a semiprecious stone, although the better grades of amethyst are very beautiful. The other varieties are worth little more than the cost of cutting. (See further under Chalcedony.)

The chief commercial source of amethyst used in jewelry is the Department of Artigas in northwestern Uruguay and adjacent parts of Brazil. A great deal of the material is exported to Germany, cut, and distributed throughout the world. Cut stones of the material are to be found in all of the leading towns of the United States, and are often sold to the unwary public as a local product. The large botryoidal mass of crystals shown in a special case at the end of the mineral hall is stated to have come from a gigantic geode found in 1900 in the Province of Rio Grande do Sul, Brazil.

LIST OF SPECIMENS.

QUARTZ.

SILESIA.

Two double cabochon, circular girdle; colorless, opalescent; 11.28 and 10.30 carats; 13.5 by 10 and 13 by 9 mm... No. 1410
Brilliant, circular girdle; pale yellow, opalescent; 2.41 carats; 9.5 by 5 mm.. No. 1411

UNITED STATES.

Maine.

Paris, Oxford County:
Cabochon, rectangular girdle; white, opalescent; 103.26 carats; 44 by 23 by 12 mm... No. 1832

Virginia.

Fairfax, Fairfax County:

Cabochon, elliptical girdle; gray-green, banded; 8.25 carats; 17 by 12
by 6 mm.   Gift of Dr. Robert H. Lamborn........................... No.   421

Two pieces, tabular, keystone girdle; gray-green, banded; 22.57 and
19.75 carats; 22 by 17 by 5 and 21 by 16 by 5 mm.................... No. 1422

QUARTZ with INCLUSIONS.

BRAZIL.

Disk, elliptical girdle; colorless with brown rutile inclusions; 54.57 carats;
40 by 35 by 4 mm.   Isaac Lea collection................................. No. 1437

FIG. 10.—QUARTZ CONTAINING RUTILE NEEDLES.

Cabochon, elliptical girdle; colorless with red-brown needles of rutile; 34.73
carats; 34 by 27 by 6 mm.. No. 1438

Cabochon, elliptical girdle; colorless with planes of green chlorite; 27.03
carats; 29 by 21 by 7 mm... No. 1440

JAPAN.

Cabochon, elliptical girdle; colorless with black hornblende needles; 18.65
carats; 24 by 19 by 6 mm.   Isaac Lea collection.......................... No. 1442

Double cabochon, elliptical girdle; colorless with green actinolite needles;
17.98 carats; 20 by 15 by 9 mm.   Isaac Lea collection..................... No. 1443

SPAIN (NEAR MADRID).

Cabochon, elliptical girdle; red-brown with indistinct aventurine particles;
22.24 carats; 30 by 21 by 5 mm... No. 1412

SWITZERLAND.

Cabochon, elliptical girdle; colorless with rutile needles; 63.95 carats; 38
by 28 by 8 mm.. No. 1448

UNION OF SOUTH AFRICA (GRIQUALAND-WEST).

Step-cabochon, rectangular girdle; red-brown, mottled and banded with
white; 114.93 carats; 40 by 19 by 12 mm............................... No. 1432

UNITED STATES.

Arizona.

Clip, Yuma County:
  Cabochon, elliptical girdle; dark violet-blue, full of dumortierite;
    77.01 carats; 42 by 30 by 7 mm..................................... No. 1433
  Cabochon, elliptical girdle; mottled dark violet-blue, green-blue, and
    gray, containing dumortierite and kyanite; 69.71 carats; 45 by 25 by
    7 mm .... No. 1433

Arkansas.

Hot Springs, Garland County:
  Table, keystone girdle; colorless with red and green chlorite layer;
    40.4 carats; 27 by 22 by 9 mm..................................... No. 1434
  Step, square girdle; colorless with dull green chlorite blotches; 31.5
    carats; 22 by 9 mm.. No. 1435
  Step, elliptical girdle; colorless with dull green chlorite blotches; 21.64
    carats; 24 by 19 by 7 mm.. No. 1436

California.

Elliptical disk; white with inclusions of yellow gold; 27 by 21 by 3 mm.. No. 1650

Colorado.

Two flat pieces, heart-shaped girdle; colorless with black göthite inclusions;
  16.05 and 9.49 carats; 18 by 18 by 8 and 16 by 16 by 5 mm.............. No. 1441

North Carolina.

Alexander County:
  Flat, rectangular girdle; colorless with red-brown rutile needles; 24.12
    carats; 24 by 18 by 5 mm.. No. 1445
  Cabochon, elliptical girdle; colorless with numerous red-brown rutile
    needles; 13.5 carats; 21 by 17 by 6 mm............................ No. 1446
Iredell County:
  Flat, heart-shaped girdle; colorless with brown-red inclusions of rutile;
    15 carats; 19 by 18 by 7 mm.   Isaac Lea collection .... No. 1444
Shelby, Cleveland County:
  Six stones, four elliptical, two circular girdles; colorless with pale
    brown inclusions of actinolite needles; total weight, 18.11 carats; 21
    by 7 by 4 to 9 by 4 mm.. No. 1525

Rhode Island.

Flat, elliptical girdle; green actinolite in gray; 13.77 carats; 28 by 20 by
  3 mm .... No. 1447

Virginia.

Fairfax, Fairfax County:
  Table-cabochon, rectangular girdle; colorless with dark gray chlorite
    inclusions; 6.95 carats; 14 by 11 by 5 mm. Gift of Dr. Robert H.
    Lamborn .... No. 1449

LOCALITY NOT RECORDED.

Brilliant, circular girdle; pale smoky brown, with rutile needles; 44.615 carats; 25 by 13.5 carats.. No. 1439

Brilliant, elliptical girdle; colorless with brown and black rutile fibers; 7.27 carats; 15 by 12 by 7 mm. Isaac Lea collection........................... No. 1450

Table-cabochon, rectangular girdle; colorless, with pale red rutile needles; 6.575 carats; 16 by 12 by 4 mm. Isaac Lea collection.................... No. 1451

QUARTZ, variety AMETHYST.

BRAZIL.

Brilliant, elliptical girdle; red-violet; 21.58 carats; 21 by 16 by 11.5 mm.... No. 1274

Brilliant, circular girdle; red-violet; 18.61 carats; 16 by 10 mm.............. No. 1277

Step-brilliant, elliptical girdle; red-violet; 17.47 carats; 22 by 16 by 8 mm.. No. 1273

Brilliant, circular girdle; red-violet; 16.36 carats; 17 by 10 mm............. No. 1275

Step-brilliant, elliptical girdle; red-violet, smoky; 10.69 carats; 16 by 15 by 8 mm.. No. 1276

Step-brilliant, circular girdle; pale red-violet; 8.025 carats; 13 by 8 mm..... No. 1278

Necklace of 61 beads, separated by rock crystal beads; pale to dark red-violet; 11 to 5 mm. diameter... No. 1279

Minas Geraes:

Step-brilliant, elliptical girdle; deep red-violet; 182.57 carats; 48 by 33 by 21 mm. Isaac Lea collection...................................... No. 1272

GERMANY (HARZ MOUNTAINS).

Step-brilliant, irregular elliptical girdle; very pale red-violet; 2.71 carats; 10 by 9 by 6 mm. Gift of Dr. Henry A. Fischer .... No. 1280

JAPAN.

Step-brilliant, irregular oval girdle; pale red-violet; 24.175 carats; 21 by 19 by 11 mm .... No. 1281

Step-brilliant, irregular triangular girdle; mottled very pale to deep violet; 17.09 carats; 24 by 15 by 9 mm. Isaac Lea collection .... No. 1387

Step-brilliant, elliptical girdle; very pale violet; 12.76 carats; 19 by 14 by 9 mm. Isaac Lea collection .... No. 1388

SIBERIA.

Brilliant, square girdle; deep red-violet; eleven stones, total weight, 3.925 carats; average size 5 by 3 mm.. No. 1282

UNITED STATES.

Maine.

Stow, Oxford County:

Step-brilliant, circular girdle; deep red-violet; 22.9 carats; 19 by 12 mm. No. 1271

Rose, elliptical girdle; red-violet; 13.05 carats; 17 by 14 by 10 mm...... No. 1270

North Carolina.

Amity Hill, Alexander County:

Double-brilliant, circular girdle; red-violet; 44.5 carats; 24 by 15 mm. Isaac Lea collection... No. 1298

Franklin, Macon County:

Step-rose, briolette, heart-shaped girdle; red-violet; 15.32 carats; 17 by 17 by 11 mm .... No. 1297

Step-brilliant, rectangular girdle; deep red-violet; 21.03 carats; 21 by 16 by 10 mm. Isaac Lea collection............................... No. 1300

Macon County:

Brilliant, elliptical girdle; red-violet; 10.185 carats; 17 by 13 by 8 mm.. No. 1285

Statesville, Alexander County:

Step-brilliant, elliptical girdle; pale red-violet; 202.47 carats; 46 by 34
by 22 mm. Isaac Lea collection.................................... No. 1286

Double-brilliant, circular girdle; deep red-violet; 122.067 carats; 32 by
23 mm. Isaac Lea collection...................................... No. 1287

Step-brilliant, circular girdle; red-violet; 33.2 carats; 21 by 14 mm.
Isaac Lea collection .... No. 1288

Step-brilliant, circular girdle; red-violet; 27.48 carats; 20 by 14 mm.
Isaac Lea collection . . .. No. 1289

Step-brilliant, circular girdle; red-violet; 12.88 carats; 15 by 11 mm.
Isaac Lea collection.. No. 1290

Step-brilliant, circular girdle; pale red-violet; 9.99 carats; 14 by 10
mm. Isaac Lea collection .... No. 1291

Step-brilliant, circular girdle; pale red-violet; 9.95 carats; 14 by 10
mm. Isaac Lea collection .... No. 1292

Step-brilliant, circular girdle; red-violet; 9.32 carats; 14 by 10 mm.
Isaac Lea collection.. No. 1293

Step-brilliant, circular girdle; pale red-violet; 6.55 carats; 12 by 8 mm.
Isaac Lea collection.. No. 1294

Step-brilliant, circular girdle; very pale red-violet; 6.22 carats; 12 by 8
mm. Isaac Lea collection .... No. 1295

Step-brilliant, circular girdle; very pale red-violet; 2.42 carats; 8 by 6
mm. Isaac Lea collection .... No. 1296

Warlick, Burke County:

Step-brilliant, elliptical girdle; pale red-violet; 14.98 carats; 18 by 16
by 9 mm. Isaac Lea collection .... No. 1284

Pennsylvania.

Upper Providence, Delaware County:

Double brilliant, circular girdle; red-violet; 53.65 carats; 24 by 18 mm.
Isaac Lea collection .... No. 1299

Step-brilliant, octagonal girdle; red-violet; 36.157 carats; 21 by 15 mm.
Isaac Lea collection .... No. 1283

Virginia.

Nelson County:

Brilliant, circular girdle; deep red-violet; 18.7 carats; 17 by 12 mm.
Isaac Lea collection .... No. 1301

LOCALITY NOT RECORDED.

Step-brilliant, elliptical girdle; deep red-violet; 33.47 carats; 25 by 21 by
10 mm.. No. 1302

Step-brilliant, rectangular girdle; pale red-violet; 21.28 carats; 23 by 18 by
9 mm.. No. 1303

Step, rectangular girdle, intaglio; pale red-violet; 15.05 carats; 18 by 16 by
9 mm.. No. 1309

Step-brilliant, elliptical girdle; red-violet; 9.725 carats; 17 by 13 by 9 mm.. No. 1304

Brilliant, elliptical girdle; red-violet; 6.34 carats; 14 by 12 by 8 mm...... No. 1305

Step-brilliant, oval girdle; pale red-violet; 5.9 carats; 16 by 13 by 6 mm.
Isaac Lea collection... No. 1308

Step-brilliant, elliptical girdle; red-violet; 5.11 carats; 14 by 11 by 6 mm.. No. 1306

Step-brilliant, octagonal girdle; red-violet; 4.66 carats; 11 by 10 by 7 mm.. No. 1307

Step-brilliant, elliptical girdle; pale violet and violet; two gems, 17.37 and
8.9 carats; 20 by 16 by 9 and 15 by 12 by 8 mm. Bequest, Miss Harriet
Jekyll.. No. 1389

Step-brilliant, elliptical girdle; very pale violet; three gems, 5.38, 3.87, and 2.47 carats; 17 by 12 by 8, 12 by 9 by 6, and 11 by 8 by 5 mm. Bequest, Homer N. Lockwood... No. 1390
Eleven gems, step-brilliant, 10 elliptical, 1 square girdle; deep to very pale violet; total weight, 34.85 carats; 15 by 12 by 7 to 8 by 7 by 5 mm.. No. 1386
Twenty-one gems, step-brilliant and brilliant, various girdles; deep to very pale violet; total weight, 89.55 carats; 18 by 14 by 8 to 7 by 7 by 4 mm. Isaac Lea collection.. No. 1385

QUARTZ, variety CATALINITE.

SANTA CATALINA ISLAND.

Cabochon, elliptical girdle; green, red, and brown, mottled; three stones, 77.1, 37.48, and 16.82 carats; 51 by 28 by 7, 40 by 19 by 6, 34 by 13 by 5 mm. .... No. 1538

QUARTZ, variety CAT'S-EYE.

BAVARIA.

Two gems, cabochon, circular girdle; gray-green; 2.86 carats; 7 by 4 mm.. No. 1417
Cabochon, elliptical girdle; brown-green; 14.69 carats; 22 by 13 by 7 mm.. No. 1418

CEYLON.

Cabochon, elliptical girdle; pale green; 11.61 carats; 18 by 14 by 7 mm.... No. 1416
Cabochon, elliptical girdle; pale green; 9.06 carats; 15 by 12 by 8 mm...... No. 1415
Four gems, cabochon, elliptical girdle; pale green; 36.78, 11.55, 8.7, and 2.375 carats; 29 by 17 by 10, 20 by 9 by 9, 14 by 12 by 8, and 10 by 6 by 5 mm. Isaac Lea collection... No. 1414

HUNGARY.

Two gems, cabochon, elliptical girdle; dark gray-green; 5.57 and 2.28 carats; 14 by 10 by 6 and 12 by 8 by 4 mm....................................... No. 1419

INDIA (MADRAS).

String of 22 beads, pale green, 52.68 carats, 10 by 6 to 6 by 4 mm.......... No. 1420

UNITED STATES.

Rhode Island.

Cumberland, Providence County:
    Cabochon, elliptical girdle; dark green; 7.57 carats; 19 by 13 by 5 mm. No. 1413

LOCALITY NOT RECORDED.

Cabochon, circular girdle; dark gray-green; 1.71 carats; 9 by 4 mm....... No. 1421

QUARTZ, variety CITRINE.

AUSTRALIA.

Step-brilliant, elliptical girdle; deep yellow-brown; 169 carats; 45 by 34 by 18 mm... No. 1373

BRAZIL.

Step-brilliant, elliptical girdle; pale yellow; 159.85 carats; 44 by 33 by 20 mm.. No. 1310
Step-brilliant, elliptical girdle; yellow-brown; 155.72 carats; 43 by 35 by 18 mm.. No. 1311
Step-brilliant, elliptical girdle; pale brown-yellow; 59.33 carats; 32 by 25 by 13 mm.. No. 1312
Step-brilliant, elliptical girdle; very pale yellow; 54.57 carats; 30 by 23 by 13 mm.. No. 1313

Step-brilliant, rectangular girdle; pale yellow; 35 carats; 23 by 20 by
11 mm.. No. 1314
Step-brilliant, elliptical girdle; very pale yellow; 33.3 carats; 27 by 20 by
11 mm.. No. 1315
Step-brilliant, elongated octagonal girdle; brown-yellow; 25.18 carats; 24
by 18 by 9 mm... No. 1318
Step-brilliant, rectangular girdle; pale yellow; 25 carats; 22 by 16 by 11
mm. Isaac Lea collection... No. 1316
Step-brilliant, elliptical girdle; brown-yellow; 24.25 carats; 24 by 18 by
10 mm.. No. 1317
Step-brilliant, rectangular girdle; pale yellow; 22.18 carats; 20 by 17 by
10 mm.. No. 1319
Step-brilliant, elliptical girdle; pale green-yellow; 14.1 carats; 19 by 14 by
7 mm... No. 1320
Step-brilliant, elongated octagonal girdle; pale green yellow; 11.92 carats;
16 by 12 by 9 mm.. No. 1321
Step-brilliant, elliptical girdle; pale green-yellow; 9.5 carats; 17 by 13 by
7 mm... No. 1323
Step-brilliant, elliptical girdle; pale yellow, cloudy; 9.15 carats; 17 by 13
by 8 mm.. No. 1322
Brilliant, rectangular girdle; very pale yellow, almost colorless; 8.48 carats;
15 by 13 by 8 mm.. No. 1324
Step-brilliant, elliptical girdle; pale yellow, cloudy; 7.25 carats; 16 by
11.5 by 7 mm.. No. 1327
Brilliant, elliptical girdle; pale green-yellow; 7.185 carats; 15 by 11.5 by
8 mm... No. 1325
Brilliant, elliptical girdle; pale green-yellow; 6.75 carats; 15 by 11 by 7 mm. No. 1326
Step, octagonal girdle; pale yellow; 4.51 carats; 12 by 5 mm. Isaac Lea
collection.. No. 1329
Step-brilliant, elliptical girdle; very pale yellow; 4.425 carats; 12 by 10 by
7 mm. Isaac Lea collection.. No. 1330
Three gems, step-brilliant, elliptical girdle; yellow-brown; 6.62, 5.25, and
3.97 carats; 17 by 11 by 6, 14 by 11 by 6, and 12 by 9 by 5.5 mm........ No. 1328

ITALY.

Step-brilliant, elliptical girdle; very pale yellow; 51.14 carats; 29 by 22 by
12 mm. Isaac Lea collection... No. 1332

SCOTLAND.

Step-brilliant, octagonal girdle; brown-yellow; 35.2 carats; 22 by 13 mm... No. 1374
Step-brilliant, elliptical girdle; brown-yellow; 8.12 carats; 17 by 13 by 10 mm. No. 1375

SWITZERLAND.

Step, rectangular girdle; pale yellow; 91.88 carats; 34 by 27 by 15 mm.... No. 1331

UNITED STATES.

Colorado.

Florissant, Teller County:
    Step-brilliant, elliptical girdle; pale yellow; 143.32 carats; 40 by 28
    by 20 mm. Isaac Lea collection.................................. No. 456

North Carolina.

White Plains, Surry County:
    Brilliant, square girdle; very pale yellow; 136.34 carats; 34 by 23 mm.
    Isaac Lea collection.. No. 1333

LOCALITY NOT RECORDED.

Step-brilliant, elliptical girdle; very pale yellow; 99.65 carats; 37 by 30 by 15 mm. Isaac Lea collection.. No. 1372
Step-brilliant, elliptical girdle; yellow; 58.24 carats; 33 by 23 by 12 mm... No. 1360
Step-brilliant, elliptical girdle; pale yellow; 34.31 carats; 28 by 21 by 9 mm. No. 1361
Step, elongated octagonal girdle; yellow; 33.89 carats; 26 by 17.5 by 11 mm.. No. 1362
Step-brilliant, square girdle; pale yellow; 29.29 carats; 20 by 12 mm...... No. 1363
Step-brilliant, rectangular girdle; yellow; 21.35 carats; 20 by 17 by 9 mm.. No. 1364
Step-brilliant, elliptical girdle; pale yellow; 18.5 carats; 20 by 16 by 9 mm.. No. 1366
Step-brilliant, elliptical girdle; deep yellow; 17.16 carats; 21 by 17 by 10 mm. No. 1365
Brilliant, elliptical girdle; deep yellow-brown; 12.81 carats; 18 by 14 by 9 mm. Isaac Lea collection... No. 1382
Step, elongated octagonal girdle; pale yellow; 11.225 carats; 17 by 14 by 7 mm.. No. 1367
Step-brilliant, rectangular girdle, intaglio; red-brown; 10.74 carats; 18 by 14 by 7 mm. Isaac Lea collection.. No. 1381
Step-brilliant, elliptical girdle; pale yellow; 6.3 carats; 15 by 11 by 6.5 mm. No. 1368
Brilliant, elliptical girdle; pale yellow; 6.17 carats; 14 by 12 by 7 mm.... No. 1369
Brilliant, circular girdle; yellow-brown; 1.215 carats; 7 by 5 mm.......... No. 1384
Two gems, step-brilliant, rectangular girdle; pale yellow and very pale yellow; 13.32 and 8.37 carats; 18 by 15 by 8 and 17 by 14 by 5 mm. Isaac Lea collection... No. 1380
Two gems, step-brilliant, square and elliptical girdles; very pale yellow, almost colorless; 4.74 and 2.32 carats; 12 by 5 and 10 by 8 by 5 mm.... No. 1371
Two gems, step-brilliant, elliptical girdle, brilliant, irregular oval girdle; pale yellow; 3.5 and 3.45 carats; 13 by 10 by 5 and 12.5 by 11 by 5 mm.. No. 1370
Three gems, step-brilliant, elliptical girdle; yellow; 30.135, 19.52, and 12.33 carats; 25 by 18 by 12, 22 by 17 by 8, and 18 by 15 by 7 mm. Isaac Lea collection... No. 1376
Five gems, step-brilliant, elliptical girdle; very pale and pale yellow; total weight, 18.6 carats; 14 by 9 by 6 to 11 by 9 by 6 mm. Isaac Lea collection.. No. 1377
Six gems, step-brilliant, pear-shaped girdle; pale yellow; total weight, 13.135 carats; 14 by 8 by 5 to 12 by 6 by 4 mm........................... No. 1383
Nine gems, step-brilliant, elliptical girdle; pale yellow; 7.125 to 1.45 carats; average size, 14 by 10 by 6 mm. Isaac Lea collection.................... No. 1378
Eleven gems, brilliant, circular girdle; pale yellow; total weight, 8.12 carats; 10 by 5 and 8 by 4 mm.; 6 by 4 mm., average size of nine. Isaac Lea collection.. No. 1379

QUARTZ, variety ROCK CRYSTAL.

BRAZIL.

Cabochon, circular girdle; colorless; 92.73 carats; 32 by 16 mm............ No. 1391
Step-brilliant, rectangular girdle; colorless; 3.21 carats; 13 by 10.5 by 4 mm. Isaac Lea collection... No. 1392

GERMANY.

Two lenses, cabochon, circular girdle; colorless, 23.25 and 18.63 carats; 21 by 9 and 19 by 9 mm. Isaac Lea collection.............................. No. 1393

ITALY.

Step, octagonal girdle; colorless; 10.84 carats; 13 by 10 mm. Isaac Lea collection.. No. 1394

JAPAN.

Two spheres; colorless; 38.11 and 23.86 carats; 18 and 15 mm. diameter.
Isaac Lea collection.. No. 1396
Thirteen gems; various cuts; colorless; total weight, 50.88 carats; 17 by 13
by 5.5 to 7 by 7 by 5.5 mm. Isaac Lea collection...................... No. 1395

UNITED STATES.

North Carolina.

Chestnut Hill Township, Ashe County:
    Brilliant, circular girdle; colorless; 353.62 carats; 47 by 26 mm. Isaac
        Lea collection.. No. 1397
    Brilliant, circular girdle; colorless; 350 carats; 50 by 23 mm. Isaac
        Lea collection.. No. 1398
    Brilliant, circular girdle; colorless; 19.58 carats; 17 by 12 mm. Isaac
        Lea collection .... No. 1399

LOCALITY NOT RECORDED.

Step-brilliant, elliptical girdle; colorless; 47.035 carats; 39 by 21 by 13 mm. No. 1400
Tetrahexahedron; colorless; 32.66 carats; 16 mm. diameter................. No. 1409
Brilliant, pear-shaped girdle; colorless; 23.01 carats; 26 by 18 by 9 mm.... No. 1401
Step-brilliant, rectangular girdle; colorless; 24.5 carats; 23 by 19 by 8 mm.. No. 1403
Four gems, step-brilliant, elliptical girdle; colorless; 18.58, 11.15, 9.52, and
    8.34 carats; 18.5 by 16 by 11, 16 by 13.5 by 9, 15 by 13 by 9, and 13 by 12
    by 9 mm.. No. 1402
Step, rectangular girdle; colorless; 15.92 carats; 20 by 18 by 7 mm. Isaac
    Lea collection.. No. 1406
Two gems, brilliant, one oval, one elongated octagonal girdle; 13.96 and
    13.41 carats; 24 by 18 by 4 and 19.5 by 15 by 6 mm...................... No. 1404
Two gems, step-brilliant, elliptical girdle; colorless; 5.95 and 4.98 carats; 15
    by 13 by 9 and 14 by 13 by 9 mm. Isaac Lea collection................. No. 1407
Eight gems, various cuts; colorless; total weight, 33.23 carats; average size,
    9 by 5 mm... No. 1405
Thirteen gems, variously cut; colorless; total weight, 62.4 carats; 13 by 7.5
    to 10 by 5 mm. Isaac Lea collection..................................... No. 1408

QUARTZ, variety ROSE.

BAVARIA (ZWIESEL).

Step-brilliant, rectangular girdle; very pale pink, opalescent; 16 carats; 20
    by 15 by 18.5 mm.. No. 1269
Mixed-cabochon, elliptical girdle; pale pink; 13.2 carats; 22 by 13 by
    7 mm.. No. 1268

BRAZIL.

Necklace of 34 spherical beads; pink to pale pink; 15 to 9 mm. diameter.... No. 1831

CEYLON.

Brilliant, rectangular girdle; pale pink, opalescent; 43.49 carats; 25 by 20
    by 15 mm.. No. 1267

FRANCE.

Brilliant, elliptical girdle; pale pink, opalescent; 18.43 carats; 19 by 15 by
    11 mm... No. 1266

UNITED STATES.

Maine.

Paris, Oxford County:
    Cabochon, elliptical girdle; pale pink, opalescent; 66.18 carats; 35 by
        26 by 11 mm.. No. 1263
Stoneham, Oxford County:
    Cabochon, elliptical girdle; pale pink; opalescent; 19.83 carats; 23 by
        17 by 7 mm... No. 1264

North Carolina.

McDowell County:
    Four rose cut beads; very pale pink, opalescent; total weight, 38.4
        carats; two 12 mm. diameter, two 10 mm........................... No. 1265

QUARTZ, variety SMOKY.

CEYLON.

Brilliant, elliptical girdle; smoky yellow-brown; 128.1 carats; 39 by 30 by 16
    mm.   Isaac Lea collection.. No. 1343
Step-brilliant, rectangular girdle; pale smoky yellow; 97.02 carats; 31 by 26
    by 18 mm.   Isaac Lea collection... No. 1344
Step, square girdle; pale smoky yellow; 62.95 carats; 27 by 12 mm.   Isaac
    Lea collection... No. 1345
Step-brilliant, circular and rectangular girdles; very pale brown; 20.69 and
    6.79 carats; 17 by 11 mm. and 15 by 10 by 6 mm.   Isaac Lea collection. No. 1347
Step-brilliant, rectangular girdle; smoky brown; 6.96 carats; 18 by 13 by 4
    mm.   Isaac Lea collection... No. 1346

SCOTLAND (ABERDEENSHIRE).

Two gems, step-brilliant, rectangular girdle; pale smoky brown; 15 and 6.73
    carats; 19 by 16 by 7 and 14 by 12 by 6 mm.   Isaac Lea collection...... No. 1342

SWITZERLAND.

Step-brilliant, elliptical girdle; pale smoky brown; 268.5 carats; 51 by 40 by
    21 mm.. No. 1348

UNITED STATES.

Arkansas.

Magnet Cove, Hot Springs County:
    Brilliant, elliptical girdle; deep smoky brown; 80 carats; 36 by 27 by 15
        mm.. No. 1334

Colorado.

Florissant, Teller County:
    Brilliant, elliptical girdle; pale smoky brown; 785.20 carats; 73 by 54
        by 33 mm.   Isaac Lea collection.................................... No. 1335
Pikes Peak, El Paso County:
    Brilliant, circular girdle; smoky brown; 163.44 carats; 35 by 27 mm... No. 1336

Maine.

Mount Mica, Paris, Oxford County:
    Step-brilliant, elliptical girdle; smoky yellow-brown; 17.58 carats; 18
        by 15 by 11 mm... No. 1337

Stoneham, Oxford County:
  Step-brilliant, square girdle; deep smoky brown; 62.977 carats; 27 by 14
  mm .... No. 1338

North Carolina.

Mount Pisgah, Alexander County:
  Brilliant, elliptical girdle; very pale smoky brown, almost colorless;
  543.38 carats; 68 by 51 by 25 mm.   Isaac Lea collection .... No. 1339
Spring Mountain, Iredell County:
  Brilliant, elliptical girdle; pale smoky brown; 284.09 carats; 55 by 42
  by 20 mm.   Isaac Lea collection .... No. 1340

Virginia.

Fairfax, Fairfax County:
  Three gems, brilliant, elliptical and rectangular girdles; smoky brown;
  8.16, 5.58, and 2.87 carats; 16 by 13 by 7, 15 by 10 by 6, and 11 by
  8 by 5 mm .... No. 1341

LOCALITY NOT RECORDED.

Brilliant, rectangular girdle; smoky brown; 241.73 carats; 49 by 35 by 22
  mm.   Isaac Lea collection .... No. 1351
Step-brilliant, elliptical girdle; smoky brown; 83.22 carats; 35 by 28 by 14
  mm .... No. 1353
Step-brilliant, square girdle; pale brown; 53.58 carats; 25 by 14 mm.   Isaac
  Lea collection .... No. 1352
Step-brilliant, elliptical girdle; smoky brown; 41.8 carats; 28 by 19 by 12
  mm .... No. 1354
Tetragonal prism; smoky brown; 24.68 carats; 24 by 11 mm .... No. 1349
Two cuff buttons, circular girdle; smoky brown; 20 carats each; 19 mm.
  diameter .... No. 1350
Step-brilliant, rectangular girdle; smoky brown; 13.1 carats; 19 by 16 by
  6 mm.   Isaac Lea collection .... No. 1357
Two gems, step-brilliant, elongated octagonal girdle; very pale smoky
  brown; 5.57 and 3.25 carats; 12 by 10 by 7 and 12.5 by 9 by 4 mm.   Isaac
  Lea collection .... No. 1358
Step-brilliant, elliptical girdle; pale smoky brown; 4.95 carats; 14 by 11 by
  5 mm.   Isaac Lea collection .... No. 1359
Step-brilliant, rectangular girdle; pale smoky brown; 3.57 carats; 12 by
  9.5 by 5 mm .... No. 1356
Three gems, step-brilliant, elliptical girdle; smoky yellow-brown; 11.25,
  6.61, and 3.81 carats; 17 by 14 by 9, 14 by 11.5 by 7, and 12 by 10 by 6 mm.   No. 1355

Rhodolite.   See under Garnet.

RHODONITE.

Composition.—Manganese metasilicate, $MnSiO_3$.
Crystallization.—Triclinic.
Color.—Pink, characteristic of manganese compounds.
Luster.—Vitreous; translucent.
Hardness.—6; not very durable.
Specific gravity.—3.50 ± 0.10.
Optical properties.—Mean refractive index, 1.73; double refraction
moderate, 0.01; optically biaxial, negative.

Alters to black manganese oxides in moist air. The mineral is distinguished by its color, rather high specific gravity, and optical properties. It is sometimes cut cabochon and used for scarfpins, buttons, etc., but more often carved into ornaments. Worth little more than the cost of cutting.

LIST OF SPECIMENS.

RUSSIA (URAL MOUNTAINS, EKATERINBURG DISTRICT).

Necklace of 47 beads; rose cut; dull red; 10 mm. diameter................. No. 381
Two sleeve buttons, circular; dull red; 35 mm. diameter.................. No. 383

UNITED STATES.

California.

Happy Camp, Siskiyou County:
    Cabochon, circular girdle; light red and gray; 10.715 carats; 18 by 4 mm.. No. 370

Massachusetts.

Cummington, Hampshire County:
    Flat ellipsoid; dull pink; 36 by 26 by 12 mm.......................... No. 384

New Jersey.

Trotter Mine, Franklin, Sussex County:
    Cabochon, elliptical girdle; pink; 53 by 40 by 9 mm.................... No. 382

Rock crystal.—See under Quartz.

Ruby.—See under Corundum.

RUTILE.

Variety.—Nigrine.

Composition.—Titanium dioxide, TiO_2; may also contain small amounts of iron, vanadium, chromium, and other metal oxides.

Crystallization.—Tetragonal; habit usually prismatic, and at times acicular (needlelike).

Color.—Usually red, varying to black in the variety nigrine, these colors being largely due to the impurities, especially vanadium oxide; pleochroism distinct.

Luster.—Adamantine to submetallic; transparent to opaque.

Hardness.—6.5; fairly durable.

Specific gravity.—4.20 ± 0.10.

Optical properties.—Mean refractive index 2.75; double refraction extremely high, 0.3; optically uniaxial, positive.

The mineral may as a rule be identified by the high specific gravity, refractive index, and double refraction. Occurs in metamorphic rocks of various kinds and often in acicular crystals penetrating quartz, giving rise to the forms known as sagenitic quartz, Venus's hair stone, fleche d'amour, etc. Rutile is sometimes cut facetted, but the color is too dark and not very attractive, hence it is not widely used as a precious stone. Sagenitic quartz often yields ornamental stones. Rutile is worth little more than the cost of cutting.

Hiddenite, Alexander County:
  Five gems, brilliant, circular girdle; dark red, nearly opaque; total
  weight, 2.93 carats; average size, 5 by 3 mm .... No. 457

SAMARSKITE.

Composition.—Complex iron, yttrium, and uranium columbate.
Crystallization.—Orthorhombic.
Color.—Black.
Luster.—Submetallic; practically opaque.
Hardness.—5.5; not durable.
Specific gravity.—5.70 ± 0.50.
Optical properties.—Indeterminate.
Methods of identification.—Can be recognized more or less definitely
by the luster and specific gravity, but can be distinguished from
closely related minerals only by analysis.
Occurrence.—Occurs in pegmatite rocks and is sometimes cut bril-
liant, and is used in place of jet, but is of no greater value than
cost of cutting.

Mitchell County:
  Brilliant, circular girdle; black, opaque; 6.55 carats; 12 by 6 mm.   Isaac
  Lea collection .... No. 588

Sapphire.—See under Corundum.
Sardonyx.—See under Chalcedony.
Satelite.—See under Serpentine.
Satin spar.—See under Gypsum.
Selenite.—See under Gypsum.

SERPENTINE.

Varieties.—Williamsite, satelite, precious serpentine, verde-antique.
Composition.—Hydrous magnesium silicate, $H_2Mg_3Si_2O_9$.
Crystallization.—Probably monoclinic, but never found in good
crystals.
Color.—Normally green, owing to a small amount of ferrous iron
replacing the magnesium.
Luster.—Vitreous or somewhat greasy; translucent.
Hardness.—4; does not wear well.
Specific gravity.—2.5 ± 0.2.
Optical properties.—Mean refractive index 1.53; double refraction
very weak.

The mineral may be distinguished by its softness, color, and by chemical tests. It occurs as a secondary product in rocks of many kinds, both igneous and metamorphic. It is used mainly as an ornamental stone and is too soft to be of great value as a gem. The variety williamsite is sometimes cut cabochon and used in scarf pins, as are also the fibrous forms. A beautiful variety from the Yu-Yen district of South Manchuria, China, is often carved into various forms and sold to the unwary for jade. According to Dr. J. Morgan Clements it is known locally as Yu Yen Shi (Stone of Yu Yen), or Yu Yen Yue (Jade of Yu Yen).

LIST OF SPECIMENS.

SERPENTINE, common.

UNITED STATES.

California.

San Francisco, San Francisco County:
  Flower ornament; gray-green; 27 by 20 mm. Gift of Dr. R. E. C. Stearns. No. 371

Massachusetts.

Newburyport, Essex County:
  Necklace of 51 beads; light and dark green; average, 12 mm. diameter. No. 1644

SERPENTINE, variety BOWENITE.

Rhode Island.

Smithfield, Providence County:
  Flat cabochon, elliptical girdle; dark olive green; 29.26 carats; 28 by 22 by 7 mm. Gift of George F. Kunz............................ No. 373
  Cabochon, circular girdle; pale yellow; 3.11 carats; 9.5 by 6 mm. Gift of George F. Kunz.. No. 374

SERPENTINE, variety SATELITE.

California.

Visalia, Tulare County:
  Cabochon, rectangular girdle; gray-green with silky luster; 152.35 carats; 39 by 35 by 15 mm... No. 376
  Cabochon, pear-shaped girdle; gray-green with silky luster; 9.01 carats; 23 by 12 by 7 mm.. No. 375

SERPEPENTINE, variety WILLIAMSITE.

Pennsylvania.

Wood's Mine, Lancaster County:
  Cabochon, circular girdle; bright green; 5.13 carats; 10 by 7 mm. Gift of Dr. Robert H. Lamborn... No. 372

Silicified Wood.—See under Chalcedony.

SMITHSONITE.

Composition.—Zinc carbonate, $ZnCO_3$.
Crystallization.—Hexagonal (trigonal), rhombohedral.
Color.—White when pure, but often yellow, green, or blue, owing to the presence of impurities, especially copper carbonates.

Luster.—Vitreous; translucent.

Hardness.—5; not durable.

Specific gravity.—4.40 ± 0.05.

Optical properties.—Mean refractive index, 1.7; double refraction very strong, 0.2; optically uniaxial, negative.

The mineral dissolves with effervescence in hydrochloric acid, as does calcite and several other carbonates, from which it can be distinguished only by reacting for zinc. It is found as a secondary product associated with sulphide zinc ores above the permanent water level. Bright colored specimens are sometimes cut cabochon and used for scarfpins, etc. The value, however, is little greater than the cost of cutting.

LIST OF SPECIMENS.

GREECE (LARIUM).

Cabochon, elliptical girdle; pale green; 79.73 carats; 25 by 22 by 13 mm.... No. 595

UNITED STATES.

Arkansas.

Marion County:

Cabochon, elliptical girdle; pale yellow; two gems, 49.26 and 11.04 carats; 26 by 22 by 8 and 18 by 12 by 5 mm.................................. No. 594

SODALITE.

Composition.—Sodium aluminum chloro-orthosilicate, Na_4Al_3 $Cl(SiO_4)_3$.

Crystallization.—Isometric.

Color.—Intense blue.

Luster.—Vitreous; translucent.

Hardness.—5.5; not durable.

Specific gravity.—2.20 ± 0.05.

Optical properties.—Refractive index, 1.48; optically isotropic.

The mineral may be distinguished from lazurite, the mineral with which it is most likely to be confounded, by failure to evolve hydrogen sulphide when treated with acids. It is occasionally cut cabochon, but not widely used and of no great value. By artificial light nearly black in color.

LIST OF SPECIMENS.

UNITED STATES.

Maine.

Litchfield, Kennebec County:

Cabochon, elliptical girdle; deep blue; 4.44 carats; 14 by 12 by 5 mm.. No. 367

Spessartite.—See under Garnet.

SPHALERITE.

Synonym.—Zinc-blende.

Composition.—Zinc sulphide, ZnS, with some iron replacing zinc, to which the color is probably due.

Crystallization.—Isometric;   tetrahedral;   showing   prominent dodecahedral cleavage.

Color.—Colorless when pure, but usually pale yellow or brown because of the presence of traces of iron and possibly other elements.

Luster.—Adamantine to resinous; transparent to translucent.

Hardness.—4; too soft to be of much use as a precious stone.

Specific gravity.—4 ± 0.10.

Optical properties.—Refractive index, 2.37.   Isotropic.

The mineral dissolves in hot hydrochloric acid with evolution of hydrogen sulphide. This and its optical properties will usually suffice for its determination. It occurs in veins, beds, and pockets, and is used chiefly as an ore of zinc. Clear material suitable for cutting as a precious stone is exceptional and its use limited.

LIST OF SPECIMENS.

SPAIN (PICOS DE EUROPA, SANTANDER).

Step-brilliant, square girdle; deep yellow; 12.45 carats; 12 by 9 mm........ No. 589
Step-rose, circular girdle; yellow; 6.02 carats; 11 by 6.5 mm .... No. 590

SPINEL.

Varieties.—Balas ruby or spinel ruby.

Composition.—Magnesium aluminate, $MgAl_2O_4$, with some iron or other elements replacing magnesium and aluminum.

Crystallization.—Isometric.

Color.—Usually red, owing to the presence of small amounts of chromium; also colored green by iron or blue by cobalt.

Luster.—Vitreous; transparent.

Hardness.—8; an extremely durable stone.

Specific gravity.—3.7 ± 0.2.

Optical properties.—Refractive index, 1.72; in ordinary varieties, optically isotropic.

With the microspectroscope red and green varieties show no well-defined absorption bands, but blue varieties show a strong band in the green and one in the blue, characteristic of the metal cobalt. The mineral may be distinguished from true ruby and sapphire by the isotropic character, and from other stones by the properties above listed.

Following the order of the prismatic hues there are red, orange, yellow, green, blue, indigo, and violet colored spinels; and also there are those showing a whole series of intermediate hues, such as pink, heliotrope, lavender, lilac, purple, fawn, corn color, etc.   The transparent, lively, red-colored spinel is called *spinel ruby*, and may readily be taken for the true ruby, though its small refractive and dispersive power, together with the absence of pleochroism, render it less brilliant than and lacking the fire of the red corundums.   The rose-red to pink-colored kinds are called *balas ruby;* the yellow or orange-red spinels are known as *rubicelle;* the violet and purple ones as *almandine;* the pale to sapphire-blue kinds as *sapphirine;* the blacks as *pleonast.*

Spinel occurs embedded in granular limestone, and with calcite in serpentine, gneiss, and allied rocks; occurring also in cavities in the ejected masses from certain volcanoes. Found also as rolled pebbles in certain alluvials, such as those of Ceylon and Burma, where it occurs in water-worn masses of fine colors in the channels of streams, along with quartz, garnet, tourmaline, sapphire, zircon, and other gem minerals. Spinel ruby is frequently found along with the ruby corundum in the crystalline limestone of the ruby mines of Burma. Most of the gem spinel comes from Ceylon, Burma, Siam, India, and other eastern countries. Small crystals of good color are found in the gem-bearing gravel of Expailly, France. The old lavas of Monte Somma, Italy, afford small black crystals of great brilliancy. A pale blue to pearl gray kind is found in the limestone near Aker, Sweden. From Amity, New York, to Andover, New Jersey, a distance of about 30 miles, is a region of granular limestone and serpentine in which localities of spinel abound, the crystals sometimes being fine enough to afford green, black, brown, and, less commonly, red gems. The localities near Franklin, New Jersey, yield crystals of various shades of black, blue, green, and red, which will occasionally afford small gems. While in some demand as a precious stone it is not as generally sought as the ruby varieties of corundum.

LIST OF SPECIMENS.

CEYLON.

Step, rectangular girdle; red-violet; 3.15 carats; 10 by 8 by 5 mm. Isaac Lea collection... No. 606

Brilliant, square girdle; deep green; 2.40 carats; 9 by 4 mm.................. No. 599

Step, rectangular girdle; dark blue-green; 2.1 carats; 9 by 7 by 4 mm. Isaac Lea collection... No. 608

Step-brilliant, elliptical girdle; deep red; 1.88 carats; 9 by 8 by 4 mm. Isaac Lea collection... No. 609

Brilliant, square girdle; violet; 1.86 carats; 8 by 5 mm...................... No. 596

Step-brilliant, elliptical girdle; blue-green; 1.85 carats; 8 by 7 by 5 mm. Isaac Lea collection... No. 611

Step-brilliant, rectangular girdle; violet; 1.82 carats; 9 by 7 by 5 mm. Isaac Lea collection... No. 607

Step-brilliant, elliptical girdle; bright red; 1.645 carats; 7.5 by 7 by 4 mm. Isaac Lea collection... No. 610

Step-brilliant, square girdle; violet-red; 1.48 carats; 7 by 4 mm. Isaac Lea collection... No. 613

Step-brilliant, rectangular girdle; yellow-green; 1.466 carats; 7 by 6 by 5 mm. Isaac Lea collection... No. 614

Step-brilliant, circular girdle; dark smoky violet; 1.46 carats; 7.5 by 4 mm. Isaac Lea collection... No. 612

Table, rectangular girdle; violet; 1.355 carats; 7 by 6 by 4 mm............. No. 601
Table, square girdle; deep blue-green; 1.35 carats; 7 by 4 mm............... No. 600
Step-brilliant, elliptical girdle; violet; 1.178 carats; 7 by 6 by 4 mm........ No. 597
Step-brilliant, square girdle; dark violet; 1.036 carats; 6 by 4 mm.......... No. 598
Cabochon, circular girdle; deep red; 1.01 carats; 6 by 3 mm................ No. 603
Step-brilliant, rectangular girdle; dark green; 0.955 carat; 7 by 5.5 by 3.5 mm. No. 615
Step-brilliant, circular girdle; red-violet-brown; 0.92 carat; 6 by 3 mm..... No. 620
Table, rectangular girdle; light violet; 0.918 carat; 7 by 5 by 3 mm......... No. 602
Step-brilliant, rectangular girdle; orange-red; 0.83 carat; 6 by 5 by 4 mm... No. 616
Step-brilliant, square girdle; deep rose-red; 0.7 carat; 5 by 3 mm........... No. 617
Step-brilliant, elliptical girdle; dark red-violet; 0.635 carat; 6 by 5 by 3 mm. No. 618
Brilliant, circular girdle; blue-violet; 0.575 carat; 5 by 3 mm.............. No. 619
Cabochon, circular girdle; bright red; 0.467 carat; 5 by 3 mm.............. No. 604
Step-brilliant, square girdle; deep red; 0.435 carat; 5 by 3 mm. Isaac Lea
  collection. .... No. 605

EAST INDIES.

Polished pebble; deep red; 9.1 carats; 13 by 11 by 7 mm................... No. 622
Polished pebble; deep red; 5.3 carats; 10 by 8 by 7 mm................... No. 623
Polished pebble, pear-shaped; deep red; 4.66 carats; 12 by 8 by 5 mm...... No. 625
Polished pebble; deep red; 4.58 carats; 10 by 9 by 5 mm.................. No. 624
Polished pebble; deep red; 3.79 carats; 10 by 7 by 5 mm.................. No. 627
Polished pebble; deep red; 2.9 carats; 10 by 7 by 4 mm................... No. 626
Table, rectangular girdle; deep red; 2.815 carats; 8.5 by 7 by 4 mm........ No. 621
Polished pebble; deep red; 1.88 carats; 9.5 by 8 by 2.5 mm................ No. 628
Polished pebble; deep red; 1.72 carats; 8.5 by 5.5 by 3.5 mm.............. No. 629

SPODUMENE.

Varieties.—Hiddenite and kunzite.

Composition.—Lithium aluminum metasilicate, $Li, Al (SiO_3)_2$. The variety hiddenite carries a little chromium, to which it is thought its color may be due.

Crystallization.—Monoclinic; prismatic.

Color.—White to yellow, rarely amethystine. Hiddenite, yellow green to emerald green; kunzite, pale pink.

Luster.—Vitreous, transparent to translucent.

Hardness.—6.5 to 7.

Specific gravity.—3.13 to 3.20.

Optical properties.—Refractive index, 1.66; pleochroism strong.

Hiddenite, or lithia emerald, is a variety of spodumene varying in color from a yellow-green to a deep emerald-green tinged with yellow, the colors of the crystal usually being yellow at one extremity and a more or less deep green at the other. The deeper colored kinds afford a gem resembling the emerald, but having a greater variety of color because of its strong pleochroism. The mineral occurs in slender prismatic crystals one-half inch to 2 inches in length, affording small gems only, the largest being under 3 carats in weight. Hiddenite is at present known from but one locality, Stony Point, Alexander County, North Carolina, where it is found in metamorphic rocks, generally gneiss or mica schist, in veins of kaolin. The associated minerals are quartz, mica, rutile, beryl, and feldspar.

Kunzite is a pale pink to amethystine variety discovered within the past few years in the pegmatite dikes near Pala, San Diego County, California. It affords very handsome, delicately tinted stones. (See pegmatite collection in the geological hall.)

Most of the gem spodumene other than that mentioned above comes from the province of Minas Geraes, Brazil, where it occurs rather abundantly in crystals closely resembling chrysoberyl in color.

LIST OF SPECIMENS.

SPODUMENE, common.

BRAZIL.

Brilliant, circular girdle; pale yellow; 0.97 carat; 6.5 by 4 mm............. No. 252
Brilliant, rectangular girdle; pale yellow; 0.735 carat; 6.5 by 5.5 by 3 mm.. No. 253
Brilliant, circular girdle; green-yellow; 0.315 carat; 4.5 by 3 mm.......... No. 254

SPODUMENE, variety HIDDENITE.

UNITED STATES.

North Carolina.

Stony Point, Alexander County:
  Brilliant, circular girdle; streaked deep and pale green; 0.7 carat; 6 by
    3.5 mm. Isaac Lea collection....................................... No. 255
  Step, rectangular girdle; pale yellow-green; 0.678 carat; 5.5 by 5 by 3.5
    mm .... No. 258
  Step, rectangular girdle; pale yellow-green; 0.585 carat; 7 by 4 by 3 mm. No. 260
  Step, rectangular girdle; pale green-yellow; 0.535 carat; 5.5 by 5 by 3 mm. No. 259
  Brilliant, square girdle; pale yellow-green; 0.466 carat; 5 by 3 mm .... No. 261
  Brilliant, rectangular girdle; green; 0.373 carat; 5.5 by 4 by 2.5 mm.
    Isaac Lea collection .... No. 256
  Step, rectangular girdle; green; 0.224 carat; 4 by 3.5 by 2 mm. Isaac
    Lea collection.. No. 257

SPODUMENE, variety KUNZITE.

California.

Pala, San Diego County:
  Step, elongated octagon girdle; very pale pink; 7.19 carats; 12 by 10 by
    8 mm... No. 1566
  Step-brilliant, circular girdle; pale pink; 7.137 carats; 12 by 7.5 mm.
    Isaac Lea collection .... No. 1030

STAUROLITE.

Synonyms.—Cross-stone, fairy-stone.

Composition.—Iron aluminum hydroxy silicate, $FeAl_5(OH)(SiO_6)_2$.

Crystallization.—Orthorhombic, habit prismatic; frequently twinned in cross or star-like forms.

Color.—Brown, due to the iron present; slightly pleochroic.

Luster.—Vitreous; translucent to opaque.

Hardness.—7 when unaltered, but sometimes less because of decomposition.

Specific gravity.—3.70 ± 0.05.

Optical properties.—Mean refractive index, 1.75; double refraction weak, 0.01; optically biaxial, positive.

The mineral occurs in metamorphic rocks, especially mica schist and is usually recognized from the cruciform character of its crystals.

This peculiar cross or star shape of the crystal renders well-developed specimens somewhat prized for ornaments. The crystal faces are usually coated with mica when found, but this can be readily scraped off with a knife and the surfaces can be improved by polishing slightly, and the mineral is usually put on the market in this form. The natural crystals are often ground on the edges to "improve" the cross-like effect. The values are purely nominal.

LIST OF SPECIMENS.

FIG. 11.— STAUROLITES OR "FAIRY STONES."

LOCALITY NOT RECORDED.

Five crosses of various sizes.   Gift of H. P. Petersen (fig. 11) .... No. 1029

Sunstone.—See under Feldspar.

THOMSONITE.

Variety.—Lintonite.

Composition.—Aluminum, calcium, and sodium hydrous silicate.

Crystallization.—Orthorhombic, commonly columnar radiated.

Color.—Variable flesh-red, yellow, green, and white.

Luster.—Vitreous, inclined to pearly.

Hardness.—5.5.

Specific gravity.—2.4.

Optical properties.—Doubly refracting, mean refractive index 1.503.

The mineral occurs as a secondary product in radiating and concretionary forms, filling amygdaloidal cavities in basic lavas. On exposure these lavas sometimes break down and the amygdules are liberated, and in the Lake Superior region often accumulate as pebbles in considerable quantities along the beaches, whence they are gathered to be cut for local souvenirs.   The value is little more than cost of cutting.

LIST OF SPECIMENS.

UNITED STATES.

Minnesota.

Grand Marais, Cook County:
   Cabochon, elliptical girdle; mottled, white, red-brown, etc.; 50.92
      carats; 37 by 24 by 9 mm.   Isaac Lea collection..................... No. 1261

Grand Marais, Cook County—Continued.

    Three stones, one cabochon, rectangular girdle; two double cabochon, elliptical girdle; mottled white to red brown, dark green and blue; 27.52, 13.83, and 7.73 carats; 22 by 18 by 9, 19 by 14 by 10, and 16 by 12 by 7 mm. Isaac Lea collection (fig. 6, pl. 7)................... No. 436

    Four stones, cabochon, elliptical girdle; mottled various colors; 5.97, 5.95, 5.76, and 4.49 carats; 14 by 11 by 6, 15 by 11.5 by 5, 13 by 11 by 7, and 18 by 8 by 5 mm. Isaac Lea collection........................ No. 1261

Thulite.—See under Zoisite.

Tiger Eye.—See under Crocidolite.

TITANITE.

Synonym.—Sphene.

Composition.—Calcium titanium oxy-orthosilicate, $Ca(TiO)(SiO_4)$.

Crystallization.—Monoclinic; usually wedge shaped.

Color.—Gray when pure, but usually colored yellow, green, or brown by iron, manganese, or other metals not as yet recognized.

Luster.—Adamantine; transparent.

Hardness.—5.5; not very durable.

Specific gravity.—3.50 ± 0.05.

Optical properties.—Mean refractive index, 1.95; double refraction very strong, 0.15; optically biaxial, positive. Slightly pleochroic.

The high index of refraction renders titanite very brilliant, the play of colors, in fact, approaching that of the diamond. It is best distinguished by the optical properties.

Titanite occurs in metamorphic rocks, both limestone and schist, as well as in veins, from which the best quality stones are obtained. It is usually cut facetted; the inferior hardness renders it somewhat unsatisfactory as a precious stone.

LIST OF SPECIMENS.

TYROL (ZILLERTHAL).

Brilliant, rectangular girdle; brown-green; 6.177 carats; 12 by 10.5 by 7.5 mm. No. 548

Step-brilliant, rectangular girdle; green-yellow; 2.68 carats; 10 by 7 by 4 mm.. No. 549

UNITED STATES.

New York.

Brewster, Putnam County:

    Step-brilliant, circular girdle; yellow-brown; 8.5 carats; 13 by 12 by 8 mm .... No. 550

    Brilliant, circular girdle; yellow; 2.55 carats; 9.5 by 5.5 mm. Isaac Lea collection... No. 551

Pennsylvania.

Bridgewater, Delaware County:

    Step-brilliant, rectangular girdle; dark green-brown; 4.33 carats; 11 by 8.5 by 6 mm. Gift of Dr. W. H. Forwood........................... No. 552

TOPAZ.

Composition.—Aluminum fluo-orthosilicate, $Al_2(F,OH)_2(SiO_4)$.

Crystallization.—Orthorhombic; habit prismatic; cleavage basal.

Color.—Colorless when pure, but often showing disperse colors due to constituents of unknown nature; may be pale blue, pale yellow, or pink; pleochroism weak.

Luster.—Vitreous; transparent.

Hardness.—8; a very durable stone.

Specific gravity.—3.50 ± 0.05.

Optical properties.—Mean refractive index, 1.62; double refraction weak, 0.008; optically biaxial, positive.

The best colorless topazes have considerable fire, and, when properly cut, exhibit brilliant reflections of white light, approximating that of the diamond. The pink topaz is probably not known in

FIG. 12.—TOPAZ CRYSTAL IN MATRIX.

nature, the delicate tint being commonly obtained by heating the yellow or brown colored stones. The process of "pinking" is quite simple. The selected stone is packed in magnesia, asbestos, or lime, and carefully heated to a low red heat, care being taken that the temperature is raised gradually; the stone is then allowed to cool slowly. If the temperature reached has been sufficiently high, the desired pink tint is obtained; if not high enough, a salmon tint; if too high or too long continued, the color is lost completely.

There are several distinct minerals which are commonly called topaz—the topaz proper; the yellow sapphire known as the "oriental topaz;" and certain colored quartzes, known as "Saxon," "Scotch,"

"Spanish," "smoky," and "false topaz." These stones vary rather widely in hardness and specific gravity, which, together with the power of developing frictional electricity possessed by the true topaz, furnishes a ready means for their discrimination. Thus:

Name.	Hardness.	Specific gravity.
Oriental topaz	9	4.01
True topaz	8	3.53
Scotch topaz, etc	7	2.65

Topaz occurs in gneiss or granite, associated with tourmaline, mica, beryl, etc., and occasionally with apatite, fluorite, and cassiterite; occurs also in certain talcose rocks, in mica slate, in rhyolite, and in alluvial deposits and drift (fig. 12). It is cut facetted and the better grades are highly valued as a precious stone.

LIST OF SPECIMENS.

BRAZIL (MINAS GERAES).

Rose, elliptical girdle; pale pink; 14.705 carats; 25 by 17 by 3.5 mm .... No. 280

Step-brilliant, rectangular girdle; pale violet-red; 6.54 carats; 13 by 11.5 by 5 mm ... No. 281

Step-brilliant, elliptical girdle; pale yellow; 5.94 carats; 13 by 10 by 5.5 mm ... No. 270

Step-brilliant, elliptical girdle; pale pink; 5.77 carats; 14 by 8 by 6.5 mm. No. 314

Step-brilliant, elliptical girdle; pale violet-red; 5.65 carats; 14 by 10 by 5 mm ... No. 282

Rose, pear-shaped girdle; pale pink; 5.57 carats; 14 by 10 by 6 mm .... No. 283

Step-brilliant, elliptical girdle; pale pink; 4.569 carats; 15 by 9 by 4 mm .. No. 315

Step-brilliant, irregular elliptical girdle; pale violet-red; 4.035 carats; 11 by 10 by 4 mm ... No. 284

Step-brilliant, square girdle; pale yellow; 3.89 carats; 10 by 5.5 mm .... No. 271

Step-brilliant, elliptical girdle; pale red-orange; 3.605 carats; 12 by 9 by 5.5 mm ... No. 288

Step-brilliant, square girdle; pale pink; 3.398 carats; 10 by 4.5 mm .... No. 285

Step-brilliant, elliptical girdle; pale orange-yellow; 3.24 carats; 11 by 8 by 5 mm ... No. 272

Step-brilliant, rectangular girdle; pale violet-red; 3.06 carats; 10 by 8 by 5 mm ... No. 287

Step-brilliant, elliptical girdle; pale red-violet; 2.96 carats; 12 by 8 by 4 mm ... No. 292

Step-brilliant, pear-shaped girdle; pale red-violet; 2.918 carats; 16 by 6.5 by 4 mm ... No. 286

Step-brilliant, rectangular girdle; pale pink; 2.89 carats; 10 by 8 by 4 mm. No. 316

Step-brilliant, elliptical girdle; pale pink; 2.85 carats; 12 by 7.5 by 4 mm. No. 289

Step-brilliant, rectangular girdle; very pale violet-red; 10 by 8 by 5 mm... No. 297

Step-brilliant, rectangular girdle; pale violet-red; 2.79 carats; 9 by 8 by 5 mm ... No. 294

Double-rose, elliptical girdle; pale violet-red; 2.7 carats; 7 by 6 by 6 mm .. No. 303

Step-brilliant, pear-shaped girdle; very pale red-violet; 2.59 carats; 15 by 6 by 4 mm ... No. 293

Step-brilliant, elliptical girdle; pale violet-red; 2.59 carats; 11 by 7 by 4 mm.. No. 302
Step-brilliant, elliptical girdle; pale violet-red; 2.43 carats; 10 by 7.5 by 4.5 mm.. No. 298
Step-brilliant, rectangular girdle; pale violet-red; 2.3 carats; 9 by 8 by 4 mm.. No. 290
Step-brilliant, elliptical girdle; pale violet-red; 2.28 carats; 10 by 7.5 by 4 mm.. No. 299
Step-brilliant; rectangular girdle; pale orange; 2.255 carats; 8 by 6.5 by 5 mm.. No. 317
Step-brilliant, square girdle; yellow; 2.255 carats; 9 by 4 mm............. No. 274
Step-brilliant, elliptical girdle; pale orange-red; 2.2 carats; 11.5 by 7 by 4 mm.. No. 296
Step-brilliant, rectangular girdle; pale orange-red; 2.15 carats; 9 by 7.5 by 4 mm.. No. 295
Step, irregular rectangular girdle; pale orange-yellow; 2.07 carats; 11 by 6 by 3.5 mm.. No. 273
Step, rectangular girdle; pale violet-red; 1.99 carats; 11 by 5.5 by 4 mm... No. 301
Step, rectangular girdle; pale violet-red; 1.92 carats; 10 by 8 by 2.5 mm... No. 291
Step-brilliant, rectangular girdle; pale violet-red; 1.87 carats; 9 by 8 by 3 mm... No. 300
Step, rectangular girdle; pale yellow; 1.8 carats; 10 by 6 by 3 mm......... No. 275
Brilliant, square girdle; pale violet-red; 1.77 carats; 7 by 5 mm.......... No. 308
Step-brilliant, square girdle; pale orange-red; 1.74 carats; 7 by 4 mm...... No. 305
Step-brilliant, circular girdle; deep yellow; 1.7 carats; 7.5 by 4.5 mm...... No. 277
Step-brilliant, rectangular girdle; pale violet-red; 1.67 carats; 8.5 by 7 by 4 mm.. No. 304
Step-brilliant, pear-shaped girdle; pale yellow; 1.66 carats; 9 by 8 by 4 mm. No. 276
Step-brilliant, elliptical girdle; pale violet-red; 1.528 carats; 9 by 6 by 4 mm. No. 307
Step-brilliant, rectangular girdle; pale violet-red; 1.48 carats; 8 by 6.5 by 4 mm.. No. 306
Step-brilliant, elliptical girdle; pale violet-red; 1.467 carats; 8.5 by 6 by 4 mm.. No. 309
Step-brilliant, rectangular girdle; pale yellow; 1.375 carats; 8 by 5 by 4 mm. No. 278
Step-brilliant, rectangular girdle; pale violet-red; 1.309 carats; 7 by 5.5 by 4 mm.. No. 312
Step-brilliant, elliptical girdle; pale violet-red; 1.28 carats; 10 by 5 by 3 mm No. 310
Step-brilliant, elliptical girdle; pale violet-red; 1.078 carats; 9 by 5.5 by 3 mm.. No. 311
Step-brilliant, rectangular girdle; pink; 1.01 carats; 7.5 by 5 by 3 mm..... No. 313
Rose, elliptical girdle; pale yellow; 0.93 carat; 7 by 5 by 4 mm........... No. 279

JAPAN.

Brilliant, circular girdle; colorless; 18.12 carats; 15 by 10.5 mm........... No. 1178
Takayama:
    Brilliant, circular girdle; colorless; 50.787 carats; 22 by 16.5 mm........ No. 268

RUSSIA.

Alabashka, Ekaterinburg District.

Step, rectangular girdle; pale blue; 155.46 carats; 31 by 28 by 20 mm....... No. 262

Siberia.

Step-brilliant, elliptical girdle; pale blue; 7.27 carats; 13 by 9 by 7.5 mm... No. 266
Brilliant, circular girdle; colorless; 2.638 carats; 8 by 6 mm.............. No. 267

TOURMALINE AND FELDSPAR MINE, AUBURN, MAINE

Ural Mountains.

Step, rectangular girdle; colorless; 12.816 carats; 19 by 11 by 7 mm......... No. 263
Brilliant, elliptical girdle; colorless; 4.165 carats; 12 by 9 by 6 mm......... No. 264
Step-brilliant, elliptical girdle; pale blue; 2.05 carats; 10 by 8 by 3 mm.... No. 265

SCOTLAND.

Step, square girdle; pale blue; 3.525 carats; 10 by 5 mm.   Isaac Lea collection... No. 269

UNITED STATES.

Colorado.

Brilliant, rectangular girdle; colorless; 17.77 carats; 17 by 12 by 10 mm..... No. 319
Step-brilliant, rectangular girdle; red-brown; 14.626 carats; 19 by 14 by 6 mm.
   Isaac Lea collection... No. 318

Maine.

Stoneham, Oxford County:
   Brilliant, square girdle; colorless; 2.875 carats; 9 by 6 mm.............. No. 324

New Hampshire.

Baldface Mountain, Chatham, Carroll County:
   Brilliant, circular girdle; colorless; 12.357 carats; 15 by 9 mm......... No. 323

Utah.

30 miles southwest of Salt Lake City, Salt Lake County:
   Brilliant, circular girdle; colorless; 1.46 carats; 7 by 5 mm........... No. 320
   Brilliant, circular girdle; colorless; 1.369 carats; 7 by 5 mm.......... No. 321
   Brilliant, circular girdle; colorless; 0.89 carat; 5.5 by 4 mm.   Isaac
   Lea collection.. No. 322

TOURMALINE.

Varieties.—Achroite, colorless; indicolite, blue; rubellite, pink.

Composition.—A complicated boro-silicate of magnesium, iron, aluminum, and alkali metals.

Crystallization.—Hexagonal (trigonal), hemimorphic; habit usually prismatic with strong vertical striation and different terminal faces at the opposite ends of the crystal.

Color.—Colorless when containing but traces of iron, but usually colored intensely blue, green, brown, pink, to dense black, etc., by iron, manganese, chromium, or possibly other elements; strongly pleochroic.

Luster.—Vitreous; transparent to translucent and opaque.

Hardness.—7; a durable stone.

Specific gravity.—Varying considerably with composition, but averaging 3.1.

Optical properties.—Mean refractive index varying with the composition, but usually about 1.65; double refraction moderately strong, 0.02; optically uniaxial, negative.

The matter of color is of interest. Some specimens are of one color only; others are green at one extremity and red at the other; some are green, then yellow, red, and finally green; others are crimson, tipped with black, or dark green passing into blue. A crystal may be white at the termination, then green of varying shades, pink and colorless, and in cross section dark blue or red at the center, surrounded by concentric layers of white, pink, and green. Another specimen may be red internally, passing into a lighter hue and finally green, or it may be blue or black internally, then red, and then green externally. In some specimens the different colors pass imperceptibly into one another; in others the line of demarcation is well defined.

The optical structure of the tourmaline is unique. When a crystal is viewed along the direction of its vertical axis it is less transparent and of different color than when viewed across that axis. For instance, a crystal viewed through the side is a transparent green, but when viewed through the end of the prism it may be either opaque or yellow green.

The marked pleochroism of the colored tourmalines influences to a great degree the appearance of the fashioned stone. For example, if a green-colored specimen is cut so that the table is parallel with the vertical axis of the crystal, the gem will exhibit a play and interchange of colors of two shades of green; if, however, the specimen is so cut that the table of the fashioned stone is perpendicular to the vertical axis, the gem will appear more or less opaque and dark colored, and will exhibit its transparency and green coloring only when viewed across the girdle. Care should be taken, therefore, in fashioning the tourmaline that the table is parallel with the vertical axis of the crystal; further, the facets of the crown should be large and well developed in order to exhibit to the utmost the differences of color for light transmitted in different directions as the gem is viewed from different positions.

The geological occurrence of the four types of tourmaline is of interest. The lithia group—which is often beautifully colored and affords the best gem material—is associated with soda and potash feldspar in pegmatite veins along with lepidolite and muscovite. The iron and the magnesia-iron groups, which are commonly black or brownish black, occur in granites, gneisses, schists, and also to a certain extent in pegmatites along with the lithia group. The magnesia group—commonly brown in color—occurs chiefly in crystalline magnesian limestones associated with mica, pyroxene, scapolite, etc.

In the United States magnificent colored tourmalines have been found in Maine at Auburn, Hebron, Norway, Andover, Rumford, Standish, and Paris. (See pl. 10.) The famous locality at Mount Mica, near Paris, was discovered in 1820, and for many years yielded fine specimens of green and parti-colored tourmalines. Some crystals were over an inch in diameter, transparent ruby red within, surrounded by green, or red at one extremity and green at the other. One blue crystal found was 9 inches long. The locality affords all of the colored varieties, achroite, indicolite, and rubellite. Red and green tourmalines are found at Chesterfield, Massachusetts, in a granite vein with albite, uraninite, and pyrochlore, the crystals small and curved, nearly opaque, and fragile; green crystals, often with distinct prisms of red color inside, are found at this locality. At Goshen, Massachusetts, similar varieties occur, and the blue is met with in great perfection. At Haddam, Connecticut, in crystals in mica-slate with anthophyllite, also in granite with iolite, and also at the gneiss quarries, on the east side of the river. At Haddam Neck, in fine green, and parti-colored crystals affording magnificent gems. Near Gouverneur, New York, light and dark brown crystals, often highly modified. Good crystals are found in Chester County, Pennsylvania.

The most noted American locality for the pink and variegated tourmaline is the Mesa Grande region in San Diego County, southern California. The mineral occurs here also in pegmatitic rocks associated with the variety of spodumene commercially known as kunzite, and occasional gem minerals of other varieties. A very complete and systematic series of these pegmatites from both the Appalachian regions and California, with their associated minerals, is to be found among the rock collections in the geological hall on the first floor of the Museum. (See also pp. 136–139.)

In Canada magnificent green-yellow crystals occur in the limestone at Great Calumet Island; amber-colored ones at Fitzroy, Ontario; transparent brown at Hunterstown, Quebec; black at Bathurst and Elmsley, Ontario, and St. Jerome, Quebec. Small brilliant crystals of the black variety are found in decomposed feldspar, at Andreasberg in the Hartz. Rubellite and green tourmaline occur near Ekaterinburg in Russia. The Island of Elba yields pink, red, white, green, black, and parti-colored crystals. Brazil affords a large proportion of the specimens used for gems, and has been one of the great sources of supply for more than 200 years. Ceylon, India, and Burma produce good gem material, the latter locality affording some magnificent rubellites, rivaling the ruby in color.

LIST OF SPECIMENS.

BRAZIL.

Cabochon, triangular girdle; red and green; 59.99 carats; 28 by 10 mm.... No. 225
Step-brilliant, elliptical girdle; blue-green; 36.78 carats; 24 by 21 by 12 mm.. No. 1118
Brilliant, rectangular girdle; green-yellow; 9.19 carats; 15 by 13 by 8 mm.. No. 1114
Step, rectangular girdle; deep green; 8.59 carats; 14.5 by 13 by 6 mm..... No. 1115

Brilliant, rectangular girdle; pale violet-red; 5.192 carats; 11.5 by 9 by 7.5 mm.. No. 221
Brilliant, elliptical girdle; violet-red; 5.155 carats; 14 by 9.5 by 6 mm.... No. 226
Step-brilliant, elliptical girdle; deep blue-green; 4.912 carats; 14.5 by 11 by 4 mm.. No. 220
Step-brilliant, rectangular girdle; dull green-brown; 3.827 carats; 10 by 9 by 6 mm.. No. 1116
Step-brilliant, rectangular girdle; deep blue-green; 2.79 carats; 10 by 8 by 4.5 mm.. No. 223
Step-brilliant, square girdle; deep blue-green; 2.378 carats; 9 by 5 mm.... No. 222
Step-brilliant, elliptical girdle; pale yellow; 2.276 carats; 8 by 7.5 by 6 mm. No. 1117
Step, rectangular girdle; dark green; 1.725 carats; 15 by 3.5 by 3 mm...... No. 230
Step-brilliant, rectangular girdle; dark green; 1.5 carats; 9 by 7.5 by 3 mm. No. 224
Step, rectangular girdle; yellow-green; 1.4 carats; 9 by 6 by 3 mm......... No. 227
Step, rectangular girdle; yellow-green; 1.36 carats; 9 by 6 by 3 mm........ No. 228
Step, rectangular girdle; dark green; 1.285 carats; 14 by 4 by 3 mm........ No. 231
Step, rectangular girdle; dark green; 1.13 carats; 7.5 by 6.5 by 3 mm...... No. 229
Step, rectangular girdle; dark green; 0.885 carats; 14 by 3 by 2.5 mm..... No. 232
Step, rectangular girdle; dark green; 0.76 carat; 12 by 3 by 2 mm........ No. 233
Step-brilliant; rectangular girdle; violet-red; 0.515 carat; 5 by 4 by 3.5 mm... No. 235
Step-brilliant, square girdle; dark blue; 0.425 carat; 5 by 2.5 mm......... No. 234
Brilliant, circular girdle; light green; 0.425 carat; 4.5 by 3.5 mm.......... No. 236

CEYLON.

Cabochon, elliptical girdle; pale green; 12.53 carats; 15 by 12 by 6.5 mm. Isaac Lea collection.. No. 237
Step-brilliant, elliptical girdle; brown; 3.14 carats; 10 by 9 by 6 mm.   Isaac Lea collection... No. 238
Step-brilliant, square girdle; brown; 2.749 carats; 9 by 5 mm.   Isaac Lea collection.. No. 239
Step-brilliant, elliptical girdle; brown-yellow; 2.66 carats; 8.5 by 6 by 5 mm.   Isaac Lea collection... No. 241
Step-brilliant, rectangular girdle; brown; 1.9 carats; 7.5 by 7 by 5 mm. Isaac Lea collection.. No. 240
Step-brilliant, rectangular girdle; red-brown; 1.06 carats; 8 by 6 by 4 mm. Isaac Lea collection.. No. 242
Step-brilliant, elliptical girdle; orange-yellow; 0.829 carat; 6 by 5 by 5 mm. Isaac Lea collection.. No. 243
Three gems, step-brilliant, elliptical girdle; pale orange-yellow; total weight, 1.454 carats; average size, 4 by 3 by 2 mm.   Isaac Lea collection........ No. 244

ISLAND OF ELBA.

Step-brilliant, rectangular girdle; pale red and yellow-green; 9.844 carats; 16.5 by 9.5 by 8 mm... No. 251

SIBERIA.

Step-brilliant, elliptical girdle; pale red-violet; 2.5 carats; 9 by 7.5 by 6 mm... No. 247
Step-brilliant, elliptical girdle; pale red-violet; 2.445 carats; 9 by 7 by 6 mm... No. 248
Step-brilliant, circular girdle; red-violet; 1.598 carats; 7 by 6 mm......... No. 249
Step-brilliant, square girdle; red; 0.557 carat; 5 by 3.5 mm............... No. 250

UNITED STATES.

California.

Step-brilliant, circular girdle; violet-red; 3.75 carats; 9.5 by 7 mm. (Rubellite)... No. 1175

Brilliant, circular girdle; yellow-green; 2.73 carats; 9 by 6 mm............ No. 1176

Mesa Grande, San Diego County:

Cabochon, elliptical girdle; violet-red; 76.65 carats; 33 by 25 by 13 mm. Isaac Lea collection.. No. 1790

Cabochon, elliptical girdle; violet-red; 19.115 carats; 21 by 14 by 8 mm. Isaac Lea collection.. No. 1792

Cabochon, elliptical girdle; violet-red; 12.68 carats; 17 by 13 by 8 mm. Isaac Lea collection.. No. 1791

Trap, octagon girdle; violet-red; 10.75 carats; 14 by 12 by 7 mm. Isaac Lea collection... No. 1172

Trap, octagon girdle; pale brown-yellow; 5.79 carats; 11 by 10 by 7 mm. Isaac Lea collection.. No. 1173

Cabochon, elliptical girdle; violet-red; 5.48 carats; 12 by 9 by 6 mm. Isaac Lea collection .... No. 1793

Brilliant, elliptical girdle; violet-red; 4.54 carats; 12 by 10 by 6 mm. Isaac Lea collection.. No. 1780

Trap, octagon girdle; pale orange-red; 3.96 carats; 10 by 9.5 by 6 mm. Isaac Lea collection.. No. 1174

Cabochon, circular girdle; violet-red; 3.84 carats; 10 by 5 mm. Isaac Lea collection .... No. 1794

Brilliant, elliptical girdle; very pale violet-red; 2.69 carats; 9 by 8 by 5 mm. Isaac Lea collection.. No. 1781

Brilliant, circular girdle; violet-red; 2.525 carats; 9 by 5 mm. Isaac Lea collection .... No. 1782

Brilliant, elliptical girdle; yellow-green; 2.35 carats; 9.5 by 7 by 5 mm. Isaac Lea collection... No. 1783

Brilliant, circular girdle; pale violet-red; 2.29 carats; 8.5 by 5 mm. Isaac Lea collection .... No. 1784

Cabochon, elliptical girdle; pale violet-red; 2.25 carats; 10 by 7 by 4.5 mm. Isaac Lea collection .... No. 1795

Brilliant, elliptical girdle; pale yellow-green; 1.92 carats; 9 by 7 by 5 mm. Isaac Lea collection .... No. 1785

Brilliant, elliptical girdle; pale orange-yellow; 1.76 carats; 9 by 7 by 4.5 mm. Isaac Lea collection... No. 1786

Brilliant, elliptical girdle; very pale blue, almost colorless; 1.68 carats; 9 by 7 by 4 mm. Isaac Lea collection............................... No. 1787

Brilliant, elliptical girdle; violet-red; 1.6 carats; 9 by 7 by 4 mm. Isaac Lea collection .... No. 1788

Two stones, cabochon, circular girdle; violet-red; 1.6 and 1.5 carats; 7 by 4 and 6.5 by 4 mm. Isaac Lea collection .... No. 1796

Brilliant, circular girdle; violet-red; 0.95 carats; 7 by 4 mm. Isaac Lea collection.. No. 1789

Cross section, triangular; violet-red edge, yellow-green interior with opalescent colors; 32 by 33 by 7 mm. Isaac Lea collection......... No. 1797

Six cross sections; violet-red and yellow; 15 by 13 by 6 to 9 by 8 by 3 mm. Isaac Lea collection .... No. 1798

Thirty-one crystals; violet-red and green, various sizes................. No. 1799

Connecticut.

Rock Landing, Middlesex County:

Brilliant, circular girdle; blue-green; 0.995 carat; 6.5 by 5 mm ...... No. 1111

Brilliant, circular girdle; blue-green; 0.857 carat; 6.5 by 4 mm ...... No. 1112

Brilliant, circular girdle; blue-green; 0.772 carat; 6 by 4 mm .... No. 1113

Maine.

Auburn, Androscoggin County:

Step-brilliant, rectangular girdle; pale violet-blue; 2.779 carats; 12 by
6.5 by 5 mm .... No. 1119

Step-brilliant, rectangular girdle; pale blue-green; 1.797 carats; 8 by 7
by 4 mm.. No. 1120

Brilliant, rectangular girdle; blue-green; 1.737 carats; 8 by 6 by 5 mm. No. 1121

Step, rectangular girdle; deep green; 1.625 carats; 7 by 6 by 5 mm .... No. 1122

Brilliant, rectangular girdle; colorless; 1.54 carats; 8 by 7 by 5 mm..... No. 1123

Step-brilliant, square girdle; blue-green; 1.35 carats; 6.5 by 5 mm..... No. 1124

Step-brilliant, rectangular girdle; very pale green; 1.22 carats; 7 by 5
by 5 mm .... No. 1125

Step-brilliant, rectangular girdle; very pale blue-green; 1.12 carats; 6.5
by 5.5 by 5 mm.. No. 1126

Step-brilliant, elliptical girdle; very pale blue; 1.08 carats; 7 by 6 by 4
mm .... No. 1127

Step, rectangular girdle; deep green; 0.73 carat; 6 by 5 by 4 mm ...... No. 1128

Paris, Oxford County:

Brilliant, square girdle; deep green; 58.459 carats; 23 by 17 mm.   Isaac
Lea collection... No. 1108

Brilliant, circular girdle; pale red; 18.39 carats; 18 by 12 mm.   Isaac
Lea collection... No. 1109

Brilliant, circular girdle; orange-brown; 16.72 carats; 17 by 11 mm.
Isaac Lea collection .... No. 1110

Step-brilliant, rectangular girdle; parti-colored, pale red and pale
green; 11.967 carats; 19 by 11 by 7 mm............................. No. 1134

Brilliant, circular girdle; white, smoky; 8.79 carats; 13 by 10 mm.
Isaac Lea collection .... No. 1131

Step, square girdle; pale green; 7.936 carats; 12 by 8 mm............... No. 1135

Step, rectangular girdle; pale green; 7.68 carats; 16 by 10 by 6 mm.... No. 1145

Brilliant, circular girdle; blue-green; 5.549 carats; 12 by 6 mm......... No. 1146

Step, rectangular girdle; blue-green; 4.9 carats; 11 by 9 by 6 mm ...... No. 1138

Brilliant, rectangular girdle; violet-red; 4.47 carats; 12 by 10 by 6 mm. No. 1136

Brilliant, circular girdle; very dark blue; 4.41 carats; 11.5 by 6.5 mm... No. 1133

Step, rectangular girdle; pale blue-green; 4.16 carats; 11 by 9 by 6 mm. No. 1147

Step, square girdle; violet-red; 4.117 carats; 10 by 6 mm............... No. 1137

Step-brilliant, rectangular girdle; parti-colored, green, colorless; 3.4
carats; 13 by 9 by 4.5 mm.   Isaac Lea collection..................... No. 1129

Step, rectangular girdle; pale green; 3.367 carats; 10.5 by 8 by 5 mm... No. 1148

Step, rectangular girdle; pale green; 3.088 carats; 11 by 7 by 5 mm.... No. 1149

Step, square girdle; deep violet-red; 2.73 carats; 9.5 by 4 mm......... No. 1150

Step, rectangular girdle; pale green; 2.428 carats; 10.5 by 7 by 4.5 mm. No. 1139

Step, square girdle; very pale pink; 2.286 carats; 9 by 4 mm........... No. 1151

Step, square girdle; parti-colored, pale red, very pale red, orange; 2.277
carats; 9 by 8.5 by 4 mm.   Isaac Lea collection...................... No. 1130

Brilliant, square girdle; pale pink; 2.08 carats; 8 by 6 mm............. No. 1158

Step-brilliant, rectangular girdle; pale violet-red; 1.497 carats; 8.5 by
6.5 by 4 mm .... No. 1141

Paris, Oxford County—Continued.

Brilliant, square girdle; pale violet-blue; 1.23 carats; 6 by 5 mm....... No. 1142
Brilliant, circular girdle; pale pink; 1.104 carats; 6.5 by 4 mm......... No. 1159
Step-brilliant, rectangular girdle; very pale blue; 1.095 carats; 6.5 by
  5.5 by 5 mm .... No. 1143
Step-brilliant, rectangular girdle; colorless; 1.06 carats; 8 by 5.5 by 3
  mm .... No. 1160
Step, rectangular girdle; deep blue; 1.014 carats; 8 by 6 by 3 mm...... No. 1140
Step, square girdle; deep green; 0.952 carat; 6 by 3 mm................. No. 1161
Step-brilliant, rectangular girdle; colorless; 0.84 carat; 6 by 5 by 4 mm. No. 1162
Step-brilliant, rectangular girdle; colorless; 0.839 carat; 8 by 5 by 3 mm. No. 1163
Step-brilliant, triangular girdle; green-yellow; 0.745 carat; 5 by 3.5 mm. No. 1156
Step-brilliant, rectangular girdle; colorless; 0.726 carat; 7 by 5 by 3 mm. No. 1164
Brilliant, circular girdle; deep green-blue; 0.672 carat; 6 by 4 mm..... No. 1153
Step, square girdle; deep green; 0.657 carat; 5.5 by 3 mm.............. No. 1165
Step, rectangular girdle; deep blue; 0.65 carat; 6.5 by 5 by 2.5 mm.... No. 1152
Step-brilliant, rectangular girdle; very pale pink, almost colorless; 0.636
  carat; 6.5 by 4.5 by 3 mm... No. 1166
Brilliant, rectangular girdle; pale green; 0.627 carat; 5.5 by 5 by 4 mm. No. 1154
Step, rectangular girdle; deep green; 0.607 carat; 6 by 5 by 3 mm...... No. 1155
Step-brilliant, elliptical girdle; yellow-green; 0.555 carat; 6 by 5 by 3
  mm... No. 1167
Brilliant, rectangular girdle; black, opaque; 0.55 carat; 6 by 4 by 3 mm. No 1144
Brilliant, circular girdle; pale yellow-green; 0.54 carat; 5 by 4 mm.
  Isaac Lea collection .... No. 1132
Brilliant, circular girdle; pale green; 0.5333 carat; 6 by 3.5 mm........ No. 1168
Step, square girdle; deep green; 0.515 carat; 5 by 3 mm................ No. 1157
Step, rectangular girdle; pale green; 0.5 carat; 6 by 4 by 2.5 mm...... No. 1169
Brilliant, circular girdle; colorless; 0.41 carat; 4.5 by 4 mm........... No. 1170
Step, rectangular girdle; pale blue-green; 0.388 carat; 7 by 3 by 2 mm. No. 1171

New York.

De Kalb, St. Lawrence County:

Step-brilliant, rectangular girdle; pale yellow; 5.68 carats; 11.5 by 8 by
  6 mm.. No. 1106

Macomb, Essex County:

Two gems, brilliant, circular girdle; brown; 1.21 and 0.87 carats; 7 by
  5 mm. and 6 by 4 mm.. No. 1107

LOCALITY NOT RECORDED.

Trap, rectangular girdle; dull violet-red; 2.72 carats; 10 by 8 by 4 mm.... No. 1177

TURQUOISE.

Composition.—Copper aluminum hydrous phosphate, $CuAl_6(PO_4)_4 + 9H_2O$.

Crystallization.—Triclinic; distinct crystals rare, the mineral being almost always crypto-crystalline.

Color.—Blue, owing to the copper present.

Luster.—Vitreous; translucent to opaque.

Hardness.—6; not very durable.

Specific gravity.—2.70 ± 0.10.

Because of its crypto-crystalline character, turquoise will absorb grease and oils readily, and it is not, therefore, absolutely satisfactory as a precious stone, particularly when worn as a necklace and next to the skin. Its opaque nature and robin's-egg blue color are its most pronounced characteristics, but it can be determined absolutely only by chemical tests. The only natural stone with which it is likely to become confused is variscite, likewise an aluminum phosphate. From this last it can, as a rule, be distinguished by its blue cast, variscite being green, inclined to yellowish. The mineral occurs

as a secondary product in veins and pockets in aluminous rocks, both igneous and sedimentary. It is easily and abundantly imitated artificially, and on this and other accounts the so-called "matrix" turquoise—that is, stones including portions of the matrix—are most desirable. Turquoise is usually cut cabochon because of its opaque nature, and has been for centuries much admired as a gem, both by civilized and barbarous people. In the United States it is found only in Arizona, Nevada, and New Mexico.

FIG. 13.—CHINESE CARVING
IN TURQUOISE.

LIST OF SPECIMENS.

CHINA.

Carving, representing man and dragon; blue-green; 71.075 carats; 34 by 33 mm. (fig. 13)... No. 1093

FRANCE.

Five fossil bone turquoise, cabochon, elliptical girdle; three green-blue, two blue-green; total weight, 5.8 carats; 17 by 11 by 3 to 9 by 7 by 2 mm.. No. 591

PERSIA.

Two stones, cabochon, circular girdle; blue with brown matrix; 13.67 and 12.55 carats; 19 by 5.5 and 18 by 6 mm. Isaac Lea collection (fig. 13, pl. 12). No. 1812

UNITED STATES.

Arizona.

Mineral Park, Mohave County:
　Rectangular fragment polished; veinlet of blue in light brown matrix; 9.045 carats; 15 by 12 by 5 mm. Isaac Lea collection............... No. 1097
　Cabochon, circular girdle; cobweb matrix, pale blue, green, and brown; 5.99 carats; 15 by 4 mm... No. 1088

Nevada.

Belmont, Nye County:
　Cabochon, elliptical girdle; blue in dark brown matrix; 9.315 carats; 24 by 10 by 6 mm... No. 1098
Near Millers, Nye County:
　Polished piece; dark and light blue and green in brown matrix; 14.465 carats; 25 by 15 by 5 mm. Isaac Lea collection (fig. 14, pl. 12)..... No. 1096
　Tabular, keystone girdle; mottled pale and dark blue with white matrix; 10.93 carats; 19 by 21 by 3 mm.................................. No. 1092
　Cabochon, elliptical girdle; pale blue with brown and green matrix; 10.89 carats; 23 by 17 by 4 mm. (fig. 10, pl. 12).................. No. 1090
　Cabochon, elliptical girdle; blue with matrix of green and brown; 9.6 carats; 30 by 10 by 4 mm....................................... No. 1091
　Cabochon, elliptical girdle; dark and light blue and brown matrix; 5.39 carats; 14 by 10 by 6 mm...................................... No. 1089

VARISCITE, TURQUOISE, CHRYSOPRASE, AND JADE

FOR DESCRIPTION OF PLATE, SEE PAGE VIII

New Mexico.

Cerrillos, Santa Fe County:

Cabochon, elliptical girdle; blue-green; 26.90 carats; 28 by 18 by 7 mm. (fig. 12, pl. 12)... No. 650

Cabochon, elliptical girdle; blue-green; 18.54 carats; 23 by 18 by 6 mm. Gift of Dr. Robert H. Lamborn.. No. 652

Cabochon, elliptical girdle; pale blue-green; 13.99 carats; 24 by 16 by 6 mm. Gift of Dr. Robert Lamborn..................................... No. 653

Cabochon, circular girdle; green-blue; 9.355 carats; 14 by 7 mm. Gift of American Turquoise Company..................................... No. 655

Cabochon, elliptical girdle; green-blue; 7.69 carats; 16 by 10 by 6 mm. Gift of American Turquoise Company.................................. No. 657

Cabochon, elliptical girdle; green-blue; 5.38 carats; 14 by 9 by 6 mm. Gift of American Turquoise Company.................................. No. 658

Cabochon, circular girdle; green: 4.95 carats; 16.5 by 3 mm. Gift of American Turquoise Company... No. 659

Cabochon, elliptical girdle; green-blue; 4.7 carats; 20 by 9 by 4 mm. Gift of American Turquoise Company.................................. No. 656

Cabochon, elliptical girdle; green-blue; 4.16 carats; 12 by 10 by 5.5 mm. Gift of American Turquoise Company................................ No. 660

Cabochon, elliptical girdle; blue-green; 3.79 carats; 16 by 8 by 4 mm. Gift of American Turquoise Company.................................. No. 661

Nine matrix stones, eight elliptical, one circular girdle; one pale blue; eight blue-green; total weight, 55.48 carats; 20 by 13 by 6 to 11 by 5 by 3.5 mm. Gift of H. P. Petersen.................................... No. 651

Carved arrowhead mounted as a scarfpin; blue-green; 22 by 9 mm.... No. 654

LOCALITY NOT RECORDED.

Carving in imitation of a frog; green-blue; 0.635 carat; 6 by 5 by 3 mm. Gift of O. T. Jonassohn.. No. 1087

Unakite.—See under Miscellaneous (Granite) on page 120.

VARISCITE.

Synonym.—Utahlite.

Composition.—Hydrous aluminum phosphate, $Al(PO_4) + 2H_2O$.

Crystallization.—Orthorhombic; distinct crystals rare, the material being usually crypto-crystalline.

Color.—Green to blue-green, owing to the presence of chromium or vanadium, or both.

Luster.—Vitreous; translucent to opaque.

Hardness.—4; not a durable stone under ordinary conditions of wear.

Specific gravity.—2.40 ± 0.05.

Optical properties.—Mean refractive index, 1.55; double refraction moderate, 0.02; optically biaxial.

The mineral may be distinguished from turquois, which it sometimes closely resembles, by its more greenish color and less hardness, and from other gems which resemble it, by chemical tests. It occurs filling fissures and cavities in rocks high in aluminum, mostly in shale or slate (pl. 13). In use it is usually cut cabochon because of its practically opaque character. Of less value than turquoise.

Nevada.

Cabochon, circular girdle; green and black, mottled; 31.425 carats; 18 by 7 mm. Gift of Pacific Gem Company..................................... No. 1100
Candelaria, Esmeralda County:
    Table; elliptical girdle; bright green with dark spots; 5.24 carats; 21 by 10 by 3 mm. Gift of Mack Weber............................. No. 1099

Utah.

Lucin, Boxelder County:
    Seventy-one stones, cabochon, elliptical and pear-shaped girdles; showing variation from pale green to deep green, mottled with gray and black; 25.19 to 1.6 carats; 29 by 20 by 7 to 9 by 7 by 4 mm. (figs. 1–3, 4, 6, pl. 12)... No. 1104
    Six stones, cabochon, elliptical girdles; green mottled with gray and white; 113.15 to 56.42 carats; 45 by 35 by 12 to 35 by 25 by 10 mm. (figs. 7, 8, pl. 12)... No. 1101

VESUVIANITE.

Variety.—Californite.

Composition.—A complex silicate.

Crystallization.—Tetragonal; habit prismatic to columnar.

Color.—May be yellow, brown, or yellow-green, depending on the state of oxidation of the iron present; pleochroism faint.

Luster.—Vitreous; translucent.

Hardness.—6.5; a fairly durable stone.

Specific gravity.—3.40 ± 0.10.

Optical properties.—Mean refractive index, 1.72; double refraction weak, 0.006; optically uniaxial, negative.

Vesuvianite in general is distinguished by its optical properties; californite, a deep green variety, resembles some forms of serpentine and jade; from the former it is distinguished by its much greater hardness, from the latter by the fact that it is softer, more crystalline, and has a distinctly higher index of refraction. It occurs in metamorphic rocks, chiefly in limestone. Is rarely cut as a precious stone, but the variety californite is sometimes carved or cut into slabs for ornamental purposes.

Brilliant, circular girdle; green-yellow; 0.51 carats; 5 by 4 mm............. No. 570

VESUVIANITE, variety CALIFORNITE.

California.

Happy Camp, Siskiyou County:
    Thirty stones, cabochon, various girdles; green and cloudy white; total weight, 174.825 carats; 28 by 10 to 8 by 4 mm........................ No. 1542

WERNERITE.

Synonym.—Scapolite.

Composition.—A complex calcium aluminum sodium chloro-silicate.

Crystallization.—Tetragonal; pyramidal; habit prismatic.

Color.—White when pure; may be colored pale violet or pale yellow by impurities of unknown composition.

Luster.—Vitreous.

Hardness.—5.5; not very durable.

Specific gravity.—2.70 ± 0.10.

Optical properties.—Mean refractive index 1.55; double refraction moderate, 0.01. Optically uniaxial, negative.

The mineral is distinguished by color and optical properties. Occurs chiefly in metamorphosed limestone. Because of its peculiar color it is occasionally cut cabochon, but is worth little more than the cost of cutting.

LIST OF SPECIMENS.

CANADA (TEMPLETON, QUEBEC).

Cabochon, elliptical girdle; yellow; 46.68 carats; 30 by 22 by 11 mm. Isaac Lea collection... No. 593

MADAGASCAR.

Tsarasaotra Province.

Brilliant, square girdle; pale yellow; 8.2 carats; 12 by 9 mm. Isaac Lea collection .... No. 1818

Step-brilliant; elongated octagonal girdle; pale yellow; 5.77 carats; 12 by 10 by 7 mm. Isaac Lea collection .... No. 1819

WILLEMITE.

Composition.—Zinc orthosilicate, $Zn_2(SiO_4)$, with some manganese replacing the zinc.

Crystallization.—Hexagonal (trigonal), tri-rhombohedral.

Color.—Colorless when pure, but usually pale green-yellow.

Luster.—Vitreous; translucent.

Hardness.—5.5; not very durable.

Specific gravity.—4.10 ± 0.10.

Optical properties.—Mean refractive index, 1.70; double refraction moderate, 0.02; optically uniaxial, positive.

The high specific gravity of the mineral is a rather characteristic feature, and in color and general appearance it differs from practically every other precious stone. The only willemite thus far found suitable for cutting occurs in the zinc-ore deposit at Franklin Furnace, New Jersey. Most of the material is opaque, or only translucent, and is used as an ore of zinc; but occasional specimens are found which are clear and yield small stones, which are usually cut brilliant.

4555—22——10

New Jersey.

Franklin Furnace, Sussex County:
Brilliant, circular girdle; deep yellow; 11.045 carats; 12 by 11 mm.
Gift of Clarence S. Bement... No. 1086
Three small gems, brilliant, circular girdle; pale green-yellow; total
weight, 0.79 carat; 5 by 3 and 3 by 2 mm.......................... No. 547

ZIRCON.

Variety.—Hyacinth.

Composition.—Zirconium orthosilicate, $Zr(SiO_4)$.

Crystallization.—Tetragonal, habit prismatic.

Color.—Colorless when pure, but usually showing disperse colors, especially pale green, yellow, or brown, owing to iron and perhaps other constituents; rarely blue.

Luster.—Adamantine; transparent.

Hardness.—7.5; a very durable stone.

Specific gravity.—Averaging about 4.7.

Optical properties.—Mean refractive index 1.95; double refraction strong, 0.06; optically uniaxial, positive.

Some varieties of zircon yield with the microspectroscope a brilliant and characteristic absorption spectrum, due to the presence of small amounts of uranium in the lower state of oxidation. This spectrum consists of eight narrow bands, the strongest of which lies in the orange, the others being somewhat uniformly distributed through the whole spectrum. Specimens free from uranium, however, show no spectrum whatever, so that this is not a certain test for the mineral. The high specific gravity and refractive index are sufficiently characteristic for identification. In this last respect, indeed, the zircon resembles diamond in luster and play of colors, or "fire." It is cut facetted and rather widely used as a precious stone, although its colors are, as a rule, not particularly attractive.

Queensland.

Policeman Knob:
Brilliant, circular girdle; pale green-blue; 2.55 carats; 7.5 by 5 mm.
Isaac Lea collection.. No. 1809
Brilliant, circular girdle; pale green-blue; 2.55 carats; 7.5 by 5 mm.
Isaac Lea collection.. No. 1827
Brilliant, circular girdle; pale green-blue; 2 carats; 7 by 5 mm. Isaac
Lea collection... No. 1828
Brilliant, circular girdle; pale green-blue; 1.59 carats; 6.5 by 4 mm.
Isaac Lea collection.. No. 1810
Brilliant, circular girdle; pale green-blue; 1.49 carats; 6 by 5 mm.
Isaac Lea collection.. No. 1829
Brilliant, circular girdle; pale green-blue; 0.96 carat; 5 by 4 mm.
Isaac Lea collection.. No. 1811

CEYLON.

Step-brilliant, rectangular girdle; dull green-brown; 21.22 carats; 18 by 17 by 7 mm... No. 325

Rose, elliptical girdle; pale green-brown; 6.866 carats; 15 by 10 by 5.5 mm. Isaac Lea collection.. No. 449

Step-brilliant, elliptical girdle; brown-yellow; 5.09 carats; 9 by 8 by 7 mm. No. 337

Rose, circular girdle; green-brown; 4.98 carats; 12 by 4 mm............... No. 333

Rose, circular girdle; pale green-yellow; 4.85 carats; 11 by 5 mm.......... No. 334

Rose, circular girdle; pale green-yellow; 4.614 carats; 11 by 4 mm......... No. 335

Step-brilliant, rectangular girdle; yellow-brown; 4.377 carats; 11 by 8 by 5.5 mm... No. 330

Rose, circular girdle; pale green-yellow; 4.335 carats; 11 by 4 mm......... No. 336

Brilliant, square girdle; pale smoky brown; 4.31 carats; 10 by 6 mm....... No. 328

Step-brilliant, rectangular girdle; yellow-green; 3.777 carats; 10 by 8 by 7 mm.. No. 331

Step-brilliant, elliptical girdle; brown; 3.24 carats; 8.5 by 8 by 5.5 mm.... No. 339

Step-brilliant, elliptical girdle; brown-green; 3.058 carats; 11 by 7.5 by 5 mm.. No. 338

Brilliant, elliptical girdle; pale blue; 2.406 carats; 9 by 7 by 5 mm.   Gift of Clarence S. Bement... No. 329

Brilliant, elliptical girdle; smoky red-brown; 2.335 carats; 11 by 7.5 by 3 mm... No. 340

Rose, elliptical girdle; nearly colorless; 1.94 carats; 8 by 7 by 5 mm...... No. 342

Rose, oval girdle; nearly colorless; 1.926 carats; 9 by 6.5 by 4 mm........ No. 341

Step-brilliant, rectangular girdle; brown-green; 1.88 carats; 9 by 7.5 by 5 mm... No. 326

Step-brilliant, rectangular girdle; pale green-blue; 1.46 carats; 7 by 6 by 4 mm.. No. 345

Step-brilliant, rectangular girdle; pale green-blue; 1.436 carats; 7 by 5.5 by 4 mm.. No. 346

Step-brilliant, elliptical girdle; brown-yellow; 1.415 carats; 7 by 6 by 3 mm... No. 332

Brilliant, elliptical girdle; yellow-green; 1.38 carats; 7.5 by 7 by 4 mm.... No. 344

Brilliant, elliptical girdle; violet-brown; 1.32 carats; 9 by 5.5 by 3 mm.... No. 347

Brilliant, rectangular girdle; green-yellow; 1.27 carats; 6.5 by 5 by 4 mm.. No. 348

Brilliant, rectangular girdle; orange-yellow; 1.2 carats; 7 by 6 by 4 mm.... No. 349

Step-brilliant, circular girdle; red-brown; 1.12 carats; 7 by 4.5 mm........ No. 350

Brilliant, square girdle; dull yellow-green; 1 carat; 7 by 5 mm............. No. 327

Step-brilliant, square girdle; pale yellow; 0.98 carat; 6 by 5 by 3 mm...... No. 351

Step, elliptical girdle; green-yellow; 0.707 carat; 7 by 4 by 2 mm......... No. 352

Ninety-one small gems, rose, circular girdle; blue and pale yellow; total weight, 17.94 carats; 5 by 3 to 3 by 2 mm............................. No. 353

Ninety-eight very small gems, brilliant, circular girdle; colorless; total weight, 3.325 carats; Isaac Lea collection............................. No. 450

LOCALITY NOT RECORDED.

Brilliant, elliptical girdle; brown; 51.29 carats; 25 by 19 by 12 mm. Isaac Lea collection... No. 1179

ZOISITE: THULITE.

This is a massive form of a calcium aluminum silicate which is gray when pure, but often colored pink or red by traces of manganese. It is hard and quite durable and occurs in metamorphic rocks like mica schists.   Being compact and opaque, it is cut only cabochon or carved into small ornaments.

LIST OF SPECIMENS.

NORWAY.

Cabochon, elliptical girdle; violet-red; 44.25 carats; 22 by 19 by 13 mm.... No. 582
Cabochon, elliptical girdle; violet-red; 8.465 carats; 17 by 13 by 5 mm...... No. 583

MISCELLANEOUS.

GRANITE.

NORWAY (HITTERÖ).

Cabochon, elliptical girdle, *graphic granite;* dark and light brown; mounted in silver as a breastpin.   Gift of Mrs. Spencer F. Baird.................... No. 380

UNITED STATES.

Virginia (Milan's Gap, Madison County).

Cabochon, circular girdle, *unakite,* epidotic granite; mottled green and pink; 53.31 carats; 29 by 7 mm.   Isaac Lea collection........................... No. 1258

HUNTILITE.

CANADA (SILVER ISLET, LAKE SUPERIOR).

Two rectangular disks; 16.66 and 14.46 carats; 20 by 15 by 4 mm.......... No. 379

PORPHYRY.

SWEDEN.

Tabular, rectangular girdle; black matrix with red feldspar; 41 by 36 by 4 mm... No. 359

UNITED STATES.

North Carolina (Charlotte, Mecklenberg County)

Cabochon, elliptical girdle, *leopardite;* white with black spots; 43.11 carats; 40 by 30 by 5 mm... No. 360

VARISCITE IN MATRIX, VARISCITE MINE, NEAR LUCIN, UTAH

4. SUPPLEMENTAL COLLECTIONS.

1. ROUGH AND CUT STONES.

It was Dr. Leander T. Chamberlain's expressed desire that the Lea collection should consist, for the most part, of cut stones. For educational purposes, however, it seemed desirable to show in many cases the rough materials as well, since there is often a marked difference in appearance of the material in the two conditions. A

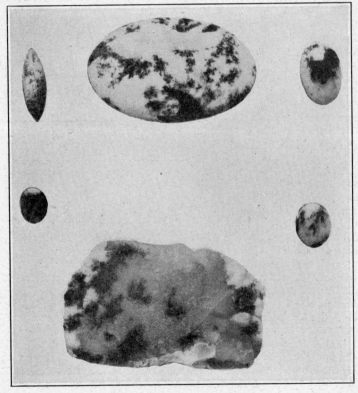

FIG. 14.—MOSS AGATES IN ROUGH AND CUT FORMS.

supplemental collection has, therefore, been established, duplicating the first in part. As at present installed this is limited to a single case, comprising the minerals listed below, the rough material and the stones cut from it being placed side by side, usually on the same block or pad.

BENITOITE, San Benito County, California. Brilliant, circular girdle; blue; two gems, total weight, 1.24 carats; 6 by 4 and 4 by 3 mm. Cut from specimen 86539... No. 1568

BERYL, San Diego County, California. Brilliant, circular girdle; very pale pink; 4.315 carats; 11 by 7 mm... No. 1569

BERYL (AQUAMARINE), Sekinotsu, Omi, Japan. Brilliant, circular girdle; very pale blue-green; 5.695 carats; 11 by 9 mm. Cut from crystal 61774... No. 1040

CALAMINE, Ysabelita, Mexico. Cabochon, elliptical girdle; blue and white; two gems, 9.43 and 7.89 carats; 15 by 12 by 6.5 and 17 by 10 by 6 mm. Cut from specimen 87466... No. 1558

CALCITE (SATIN SPAR), Cumberland, England. Cabochon, elliptical girdle; white, satin luster; 31.97 carats; 33 by 19 by 7 mm. Cut from specimen 81675... No. 1572

CHALCEDONY, Mohave Desert, California. Five gems, cabochon, four elliptical, one circular girdles; very pale opalescent; total weight, 17.12 carats; 18 by 7 by 5 to 11 by 8 by 4 mm. Cut from specimen 87415..... No. 1527

CHALCEDONY, 35 miles east of Johannesburg, California. Twenty-two gems, cabochon, various girdles; cloudy blue; total weight, 103.035 carats: 22 by 13 by 5 to 11 by 8 by 4 mm. Cut from specimen 87407..... No. 1528

CHALCEDONY in JASPER, Death Valley, California. Twelve gems, cabochon, elliptical girdle; mottled gray and red; total weight, 45.615 carats; 15 by 12 by 5 to 11 by 9 by 4 mm. Cut from specimen 87401.... No. 1532

CHALCEDONY, Amelia, Virginia. Seven gems, cabochon, various girdles; yellow mottled with red and brown; total weight, 21.635 carats; 15 by 7 to 12 by 7 mm. Cut from specimen 87412.............................. No. 1529

CHALCEDONY, Ellensburg, Washington. Cabochon, elliptical girdle; cloudy blue; 6.85 carats; 20 by 10 by 6 mm. Cut from specimen 87414.. No. 1526

CHALCEDONY (JASPER), Death Valley, California. Twenty gems, cabochon, various girdles; mottled red, green, and brown; total weight, 145 carats; 31 by 13 by 8 to 10 by 5 mm. Cut from specimen 87405......... No. 1533

CHALCEDONY (JASPER var. KINRADITE), San Francisco, California. Twelve gems, cabochon, elliptical and circular girdles; mottled red, gray, and green; total weight, 47.6 carats; 21 by 9 by 5 to 8 by 4 mm. Cut from specimen 87422.. No. 1534

CHALCEDONY (JASPER var. KINRADITE), San Francisco, California. Cabochon, elliptical girdle; red and light brown; 13.7 carats; 25 by 14 by 6mm . Cut from specimen 87422....................................... No. 1535

CHALCEDONY (MOSS AGATE), Glendive, Montana. One cabochon, elliptical girdle, two table, elliptical and square girdles; gray with dark brown inclusions; 35.67, 25.43, and 15.69 carats; 53 by 32 by 3, 23 by 4, 32 by 20 by 4 mm. Cut from specimen 87400.......................... No. 1549

CHALCEDONY (MOSS AGATE), Fremont County, Wyoming. Two gems, cabochon, elliptical girdle; cloudy with black inclusions; 26.04 and 11.69 carats; 24 by 16 by 10 and 19 by 14 by 7 mm........................ No. 1531

CHALCEDONY (MOSS AGATE), Guernsey County, Wyoming. Two stones, white with black inclusions; total weight, 58.73 carats; 48 by 30 by 7 mm., 10 by 7 by 2 mm. Cut from specimen 8740 (fig. 14).............. No. 1550

CHALCEDONY (MYRICKITE), near Johannesburg, California. Nine stones, one cabochon, eight elliptical girdles; mottled red-brown and white; total weight, 34.5 carats; 15 by 12 by 5.5 to 9 by 7 by 4 mm. Cut from specimen 87411... No. 1530

CHALCEDONY (SILICIFIED WOOD), Adamana, Arizona. Cabochon, elliptical girdle; mottled red, brown, and yellow; 64.25 carats; 42 by 28 by 8 mm. Cut from specimen 34059.. No. 1548

CHALCEDONY (SILICIFIED WOOD), Adamana, Arizona. Twelve stones, cabochon, ten elliptical, two circular girdles; total weight, 41.55 carats; yellow, brown, red, mottled; 23 by 7 by 4 to 9 by 4 mm. Cut from specimen 87406... No. 1537

CHLORASTROLITE, Grand Marais, Cook County, Minnesota. Cabochon, three elliptical, one rectangular girdle; mottled green and black; total weight, 19.57 carats; 18 by 11.5 by 5 to 10 by 8.5 by 3 mm. Cut from specimen 93426... No. 1262

CHRYSOLITE, Navajo Indian Reservation, Arizona. Two gems, brilliant, circular and elliptical girdles; yellow-green; 1.78 and 1.43 carats; 8 by 5 and 9 by 6 by 4 mm. Gift of Frank Springer........................... No. 1571

CROCIDOLITE, Griqualand, South Africa. Pair of cuff buttons, circular girdle; brown; 19 mm. diameter; with specimens 92892................. No. 1546

EPIDOTE, Canon City, Colorado. Six stones, cabochon, elliptical and circular girdles; yellow-brown; total weight, 27.67 carats; 19 by 8 by 5 to 10 by 5 mm. Cut from specimens 87417 .... No. 1556

FELDSPAR (AMAZONSTONE), Florissant, Colorado. Eighteen stones, cabochon, various girdles; blue-green; total weight, 61.7 carats; 21 by 15 by 4.5 to 8 by 4 mm. Cut from specimen 87418......................... No. 1554

FELDSPAR (AMAZONSTONE), Amelia Courthouse, Virginia. Three stones, cabochon, elliptical girdle; green; 42.30, 36.67, and 31.38 carats; 36 by 24 by 7, 39 by 21.5 by 6, and 35.5 by 22 by 5.5 mm. Cut from specimen 49164... No. 1259

FOSSIL CORAL, Alpena, Michigan. Cabochon, elliptical girdle; 134.87 carats; 45 by 38 by 9 mm. Polished specimen of 37475................... No. 1551

GARNET (ALMANDITE), Navajo Indian Reservation, Arizona. Brilliant, circular girdle; deep red; two gems, 2.12 and 1.12 carats; 8.5 by 5 and 7 by 4 mm. Gift of Frank Springer...................................... No. 1570

GYPSUM (SATINSPAR), Sicily. Two stones, cabochon, elliptical girdle; white, with satin luster; 22.6 and 20 carats; 25 by 17 by 9 and 25 by 17 by 7 mm. Cut from specimen 82367... No. 1573

LABRADORITE, Modoc County, California. Six gems, cabochon, elliptical girdle, and brilliant, circular girdle; pale yellow to red-brown; total weight, 8.2 carats; 13 by 7 by 3 to 7 by 5 mm. Cut from specimen 87269.. No. 1567

LAPIS-LAZULI, Chile, South America. Cabochon, elliptical girdle; mottled blue; 16.96 carats; 22 by 16 by 6 mm. Cut from specimen 62802...... No. 1260

OBSIDIAN, Glass Buttes, Oregon. Cabochon, elliptical girdle; dark and light brown, banded; 71.9 carats; 43 by 31 by 9 mm. Cut from specimen 35268.. No. 1552

QUARTZ (AMETHYST), Warren County, North Carolina. Two gems, brilliant, elliptical and circular girdles; deep red-violet; 9.47 and 4.49 carats; 17 by 14 by 7 and 11 by 7 mm. Cut from specimen 87184........ No. 1522

QUARTZ (BRECCIATED CHERT), New Mexico. Cabochon, elliptical girdle; gray, 20.95 carats; 32 by 12 by 8 mm. Cut from specimen 87467.... No. 1545

QUARTZ (CATALINITE), Santa Catalina Island. Six stones, cabochon, 5 elliptical, one pendant; green, red, and brown, mottled; total weight, 69.5 carats; 31 by 13 by 7 to 12.5 by 10 by 4.5 mm. Cut from specimen 87461.. No. 1536

QUARTZ (CITRINE), Brazil. Step-brilliant, rectangular girdle; deep yellow; 10.94 carats; 17 by 11 by 8. Exhibited with specimen 44678...... No. 1521

QUARTZ (CREOLITE), Hart, San Bernardino County, California. Tabular, rectangular girdle; brown, light and dark banded; 10.56 carats; 18 by 15 by 4 mm. With specimen 86943................................... No. 1544

QUARTZ (CREOLITE), Hart, San Bernardino County, California. Cabochon, elliptical girdle; mottled white and brown; 8.34 carats; 25 by 9 by 5 mm. With specimen 86943... No. 1543

QUARTZ (ROSE), twelve miles southeast of California Hot Springs, California. Nine stones, cabochon, seven elliptical, two circular girdles; pink; total weight, 30 carats; 19 by 8 by 5 to 8 by 4 mm. Cut from specimen 87420.. No. 1524

QUARTZ (ROSE), Scott Mine, Custer, South Dakota. Fifteen gems, cabochon, various girdles; pale pink; total weight, 62.57 carats; 20 by 8 by 4 to 10 by 5 mm. Cut from specimen 87419.................................... No. 1523

QUARTZ (SMOKY), Alexander County, North Carolina. Step-brilliant, elliptical girdle; smoky brown; 7.4 carats; 15 by 10 by 7 mm. With specimen 92878.. No. 1520

RHODONITE, Lemoncove, California. Ten stones, cabochon, elliptical and circular girdles; dull red and black, mottled; total weight, 46.5 carats; 18 by 8 by 4 to 9 by 4 mm. Cut from specimen 87408.................... No. 1555

RHYOLITE (WABANITE), Wellesley, Massachusetts. Cabochon, elliptical girdle; gray and white banded; 10.42 carats; 19 by 14 by 4.5 mm. Cut from specimen 87468... No. 1553

SERPENTINE (SATELITE), Venice Hill, Tulare County, California. Three stones, cabochon, elliptical girdle; gray-green; 13.94, 7.61, 2.81 carats; 26 by 13 by 7, 18 by 13 by 6, and 15 by 8 by 4 mm. Cut from specimen 87462... No. 1559

SMITHSONITE, Kelly, New Mexico. Two stones, cabochon, elliptical girdle; green; 13.04 and 1.82 carats; 19 by 11 by 6 and 9 by 6 by 3 mm. Cut from specimen 87465.. No. 1557

SPODUMENE (KUNZITE), Pala, San Diego County, California. Brilliant, circular girdle; pale pink; 2.035 carats; 8 by 5 mm. Cut from specimen 86882... No. 1565

STAUROLITE, Henry County, Virginia. Two specimens; 24 by 13, 18 by 15 mm... No. 1560

THOMSONITE, Grand Marais, Minnesota. Six specimens, cabochon, elliptical, and square girdles; mottled white, red-brown, etc.; total weight, 40.315 carats; 15 by 8 to 11 by 5 mm. Cut from specimen 93426.......... No. 1261

TOURMALINE, Auburn, Maine. Brilliant, circular girdle; blue-green; 1.02 carats; 7 by 5 mm. Cut from specimen 87204........................... No. 1561

TOURMALINE, Pala, San Diego County, California. Cabochon, elliptical girdle; pink and green; 6.95 carats; 19 by 9 by 5 mm. Cut from specimen 93104... No. 1562

TOURMALINE, Mesa Grande, California. Cabochon, circular girdle; violet-red; 3.55 carats; 9 by 5 mm.. No. 1563

TOURMALINE, Mesa Grande, California. Brilliant, circular girdle; violet-red; 0.86 carat; 6 by 4 mm.. No. 1564

UNAKITE, Milan's Gap, Madison County, Virginia. Cabochon, ellipitical girdle; mottled green and pink; 55.175 carats; 36 by 29 by 7 mm. (fig. 11, pl. 7). Cut from specimen 36784.................................... No. 1258

VARISCITE, Columbus, Nevada. Fifteen stones, cabochon, mostly elliptical girdles; varying from greenish-white to green, brown, and black, mottled; 23.24 carats to 3.06 carats; 35 by 18 by 5 to 13 by 9 by 4 mm. Cut from specimen 87403.. No. 1103

VARISCITE, Lucin, Utah. Nine gems, cabochon, elliptical and pear-shaped girdles; green and gray, mottled; total weight, 56.79 carats; 27 by 20 by 5 to 10 by 8 by 4 mm. Cut from specimen 87416.................. No. 1102

VARISCITE (AMATRICE), Tooele County, Utah. Twelve stones, cabochon, elliptical girdle; varying from pale to dark green, mottled with brown and white; 13.67 carats to 1.94 carats; 22 by 15 by 6 to 11 by 7 by 4 mm. Cut from specimen 87402.. No. 1105

VESUVIANITE (CALIFORNITE), Big Bar, California. Thirty-seven stones, cabochon, various girdles; green, some with matrix; total weight, 206.65 carats; 30 by 13 by 8 to 9 by 5 mm. Cut from specimen 87409........... No. 1539

VESUVIANITE (CALIFORNITE), Fresno County, California. Cabochon, elliptical girdle; green; 5.88 carats; 16 by 8 by 10 mm. Cut from specimen 86945... No. 1541

VESUVIANITE (CALIFORNITE), Lindsay, California. Eleven stones, cabochon, mostly elliptical girdles; green; total weight, 56.4 carats; 23 by 9 by 5 to 10 by 5 mm. Cut from specimen 87410.......................... No. 1540

2. IMITATION STONES.

The basis of most imitation gems is a very brilliant lead glass known as "paste" or "strass." Imitation gems may consist of paste alone, or of part paste and part stone, as in the "doublet" and "triplet." The one is made up of a table of a genuine stone, usually off-color, cemented to a pavilion made of a paste having the approved color. The other consists of a crown, table, and pavilion made of a pale or inferior stone, with a thin layer of colored glass at the girdle.

Imitation pearls are made by coating the inner surfaces of glass beads with a preparation made from the scales of certain fishes.

LIST OF SPECIMENS.

AMETHYST; eight stones, various cuts; red-violet; 25 by 13 to 10 by 7 mm.. No. 1603

AQUAMARINE; seven stones, various cuts; green-blue; 16 by 9 by 5 to 8 by 5 mm... No. 1596

CARNELIAN (artificially colored chalcedony); two stones, one table, rectangular, one cabochon, circular girdle; red-brown; 20 by 15 by 3 and 16 by 7 mm... No. 1588

CAT'S-EYE; cabochon, four stones, circular and elliptical girdles; various colors; 19 by 8 to 13 by 7 mm... No. 1581

CHRYSOPRASE (artificially colored chalcedony); three stones, cabochon, elliptical girdle; green; 14 by 10 by 4, 12 by 8 by 4, and 13 by 5 by 3 mm.. No. 1580

DIAMOND ("Jagersfontein"); brilliant, circular girdle; colorless; 9 by 6 mm... No. 1590

DIAMOND ("Light canary"); brilliant, circular girdle; pale yellow; 13 by 9 mm... No. 1591

DIAMOND; 25 stones, brilliant, circular girdle; 15 by 10 to 7 by 5 mm..... No. 1592

EMERALD (doublet); step-brilliant, rectangular girdle; green; 5.5 by 4 by 3 mm. Mounted in a ring. Isaac Lea collection...................... No. 827

EMERALD (triplet); two stones, step, octagon girdle; green; 8 by 5 mm.. No. 1607

EMERALD; eight stones, step and step brilliant, circular, octagonal, and square girdles; 20 by 12 to 8 by 4 mm.................................. No. 1595

GARNET; two stones, cabochon, circular girdle; deep red; 10 by 7 and 8 by 6 mm... No. 1602

GEM STONE colored with uranium oxides; brilliant, circular girdle; 8 by 5 mm. Gift of Capt. Harry Bryan....................................... No. 1610

HARLEQUIN STONE (artificially colored crocidolite); three stones, cabochon, circular and elliptical girdles; red, brown, and blue-gray; 16 by 7 to 10 by 5 by 4 mm.. No. 1587

JADE; cabochon, elliptical girdle; green; 40 by 30 by 6 mm.................... No. 1579

JADE; cabochon, circular girdle; dark green; 16 by 7 mm....................... No. 1578

MOONSTONE; four stones, cabochon, pendant; colorless; 26 by 16 to 22 by 10 mm.. No. 1582

MOSS AGATE; cabochon, rectangular girdle; light brown with dark inclusions; 19 by 12 mm... No. 1575

OLIVINE; three stones, brilliant and step, circular, square, and rectangular girdles; deep green; 12 by 8, 9 by 6, and 11 by 8 by 5 mm............. No. 1601

OPAL; two, one round, one bulb-shaped; iridescent colors................... No. 1586

PEARL; four round beads, white, 12 to 8 mm. diameter....................... No. 1583

PEARL; four round beads; steel-gray; 12 to 8 mm. diameter................. No. 1585

PEARL; four round beads; very pale pink; 12 to 6 mm. diameter.......... No. 1584

ROSE QUARTZ; five stones, cabochon, various girdles; pale pink; 15 by 15 by 6 to 15 by 10 by 5 mm.. No. 1589

RUBY (doublet); step-brilliant, circular girdle; deep red; 10 by 5.5 mm... No. 1608

RUBY; four stones, brilliant and step-brilliant; circular and square girdles; deep red; 13 by 7 to 8 by 4 mm................................. No. 1593

SAPPHIRE (doublet); two stones, brilliant, circular girdle; deep blue; 5 by 3 mm.. No 1609

SAPPHIRE; four stones, step-brilliant, circular and square girdles; deep blue; 12 by 6 to 4 by 3 mm .... No. 1594

TOPAZ; three stones, step, rectangular and square girdles; pale pink; 34 by 9 by 5, 11 by 8 by 5, and 8 by 6 mm.................................... No. 1599

TOPAZ; cabochon, brilliant, and step-brilliant; various girdles; deep yellow; 27 by 16 by 10 to 9 by 7 mm.. No. 1597

TOPAZ; step-brilliant, elliptical girdle; very pale red-orange; 26 by 15 by 10 mm.. No. 1598

TOURMALINE; three stones; step-brilliant and brilliant, rectangular and elliptical girdles; deep pink; 12 by 10 by 5 to 6 by 5 by 3 mm............. No. 1600

TURQUOISE; 30 stones, cabochon, circular girdle; average size, 4 by 2 mm.. No. 1577

TURQUOISE (artificially colored chalcedony); two stones, cabochon, circular and elliptical girdles; blue; 16 by 6 and 20 by 6 by 3 mm.......... No. 1576

MODELS OF FAMOUS DIAMONDS.

CULLINAN, rough, and largest stone cut from it.

EMPRESS EUGENIE.

EXCELSIOR.

FLORENTINE.

GREAT MOGUL.

HOPE.

KOHINOOR, before and after recutting.

NASSAK.

ORLOFF.

PASHA OF EGYPT.

PIGGOTT.

POLAR STAR.

REGENT or PITT.

SANCY.

SHAH OF PERSIA

STAR OF THE SOUTH.

3. ARTIFICIAL OR SYNTHETIC STONES.

A sharp distinction is to be drawn between the imitation of a gem stone and its formation by artificial methods. The imitation gem only simulates the natural substance; the artificial gem is identical with it. Examples of the latter class are to be found in the diamond

as produced by heat and pressure in cast iron; the ruby as produced
by the fusion of alumina with traces of chrome oxide; and the sapphire as made in a similar way.

RUBY; step-brilliant, square girdle; deep red; 1.015 carats; 5.5 by 4 mm.... No. 1605
RUBY; step-brilliant, elliptical girdle; deep red; 2.08 carats; 8 by 7.5 by
   4.5 mm... No. 1604
SAPPHIRE; brilliant, circular girdle; pale blue; 8.98 carats; 13 by 9 mm.... No. 1606

4. MODELS SHOWING FORMS INTO WHICH GEMS ARE CUT.

The cutting of many gem stones is necessary for the complete
development of those properties upon which their beauty largely
depends. In order that the inherent properties of a gem may be
developed to the maximum it should be cut and polished in that
form best suited to the exhibition of its beauties. The various
styles of cut represented are:

Brilliant.

Old square cut brilliant.

English square cut brilliant.

Split brilliant.

Double brilliant.

Single brilliant.

Star.

Portuguese.

Rose.

Step.

Step brilliant.

Table.

5. SMALL ORNAMENTAL OBJECTS NOT USED FOR PERSONAL ADORNMENT.

The materials listed and described below, while in some cases of
the same mineralogical nature as the gems described above, are not
utilized for the most part for personal adornment, but as small ornaments and works of art. Their beauty is dependent in some cases
on that of the material, in others the art of the lapidary is largely
responsible for their attractiveness.

AGALMATOLITE—PAGODITE.

The material known by this name is a soft stone of compact texture
which may consist of pyrophyllite, an aluminum hydrous silicate, or
talc, a magnesium hydrous silicate. The color is gray when pure,
but often bluish, greenish, brownish, or yellowish, or mottled with
different colors due to the presence of iron in various forms. The
luster is dull, waxy. The material occurs usually in metamorphic
rocks, chiefly crystalline schists. The commercial sources are China
and Japan, where it is used extensively for carving grotesque images
and objects of art which are frequently sold to the unwary under the
name of jade, from which it can readily be distinguished by its
softness.

Vase, carved with figures of birds and flowers; green-gray with pale red tint-
   ing; 22.5 cm. high, 12.5 cm. greatest width. China..................... No. 1651
Vase, carved with figure of deer, birds, and flowers; red and black mottled
   on dark base; 26 cm. high, 18 cm. wide. China.......................... No. 1655

Vase, carving of vine; very pale green-gray on brown base; 25 cm. high. China.. No. 1657

Vase, carving of leaves; red-brown and gray on brown base; 24 cm. high. China.. No. 1658

Vase, carved human figure in branches of tree; red-brown on brown base. China.. No. 1662

Vase, gray-green and dark brown, on brown base; 12 cm. high, 4.5 cm. wide. China.. No. 1668

Urn with carved handles and cover; mottled red, gray, and light brown; 18 by 21 cm. China.. No. 1659

Ornamental carved piece, deer with flowers; yellow on dark brown base; 20.5 by 90 cm. China.. No. 1652

Carved piece, rectangular, lattice-work sides; light green-gray; 9 by 4.5 by 4 cm. China.. No. 1667

Group of five baboons; light gray-green; 17 cm. high. China.............. No. 1653

Two Chinese priests on dark pedestals, one red mottled with gray-green; one gray-green; 22.5 cm. high. China.. No. 1654

Three Chinese figures on end of pedestal; gray-green faintly mottled with red. China... No. 1656

Carving of a bird in a tree; yellow-brown. China.......................... No. 1660

Small Chinese figure on a pedestal; brown-red. China...................... No. 1666

Ash tray, carved with leaves; gray; 10 by 6.5 cm. China.................. No. 1663

Ash tray, carved with small trees; red-brown and gray; 12 by 7 cm. China.. No. 1664

Ash tray; carved with leaves and fruit; red-brown and gray, 11 by 5.5 cm. China.. No. 1665

Carved tray; red-brown and gray; 22 by 16 cm. Japan..................... No. 1661

AMAZONSTONE.

LIST OF SPECIMENS.

Two spheres; green; 40 and 37 mm. diameter; Amelia Courthouse, Virginia. Isaac Lea collection... No. 451

Tray; light green; 8.8 by 6.2 cm. Amelia Courthouse, Virginia............. No. 246

CATLINITE—PIPESTONE.

This material is an indurated clay or argillite. The prevailing colors are dull reddish, often more or less mottled with white. It occurs in Minnesota and South Dakota intercalated with other sedimentary rocks and was formerly used by the Sioux Indians for the making of pipes, and more recently has been used for small ornaments and paper weights. It is soft and readily carved.

LIST OF SPECIMENS.

Indian head carved on rectangular block; dull red; Minnesota............. No. 1760

Indian pipe. Minnesota.. No. 1759

CHALCEDONY.

LIST OF SPECIMENS.

Paper weight, pentagonal dodecahedron; blue (artificially colored); 6.5 cm. Isaac Lea collection.. No, 1761

Snuff box; blue (artificially colored); 42 by 30 mm...................... No. 1773

Carved handle; very pale pink; 5.8 cm. long............................... No. 1777

CHALCEDONY, variety AGATE.

Thin polished slab gray with green inclusions; 14.5 by 9.5 cm. Brazil...... No. 1733

Cube with truncated edges; red and gray; 5 cm. Brazil.................... No. 1716

Penholder; brown and white banded; 16.9 cm. long. Germany. Isaac
Lea collection... No. 1717

Seal handle; brown; 5.7 cm. long. Germany. Isaac Lea collection...... No. 1736

Cane head; red, banded; 5.2 cm. long. Germany. Isaac Lea collection... No. 1737

Seven snuff boxes; various colors and sizes. Oberstein, Prussia. Isaac
Lea collection .... No. 1772

Dish; brown, banded with white; 10.7 by 9 cm. Oberstein, Prussia.
Isaac Lea collection.. No. 1731

Dish; red, banded; 8 by 6.2 cm. Oberstein, Prussia. Isaac Lea collection.. No. 1718

Seal handle, carved; black, banded with white; 8.3 cm. long. Oberstein,
Prussia... No. 1734

Cube; brown; 4 cm. Oberstein, Prussia............................. No. 1757

Cube with truncated edges; black, banded with white; 4.5 cm. Isaac Lea
collection... No. 1758

Two spheres; brown and white banded; 7.7 and 5.4 cm. diameter.......... No. 1763

Seal handle; brown, banded; 8.6 cm. long. Gift of Dr. Robert Fletcher... No. 1738

Paperweight, with round knob engraved with human face; dark brown;
12.3 by 8.3 cm... No. 1726

Dental tools (four) and mixing slab; gray and brown. Gift of Alexander A.
Anzell.. No. 1700

Book; brown and black with white banding; 10 by 5.5 cm................. No. 1721

Card case; agate covers mounted on leather; colorless, red and yellow
banded; 8.5 by 5.5 cm. Bequest of William H. Forwood............... No. 1774

Paper knife; red banded; 15 cm. long. Bequest of William H. Forwood... No. 1775

CHALCEDONY, variety BLOODSTONE.

Two snuff boxes; green mottled with red; 40 by 25 mm. India............ No. 1461

CHALCEDONY, variety CARNELIAN.

Elliptical slab; red and yellow; 12 by 10 cm............................. No. 505

Paper cutter; red; 14.8 cm. long. Brazil............................. No. 504

CHALCEDONY, variety JASPER.

Paper weight; red and yellow; 16.5 by 10 by 1.9 cm. Orenburg, Ural
Mountains, Russia... No. 1713

Paper weight; green and red; 9 by 6.3 cm. Siberia...................... No. 1714

Small carved piece, monument-shaped; green, red, and dark gray; 9.7 cm.
high... No. 1739

CHALCEDONY, variety MOSS AGATE.

Paper cutter; green and gray; 35 cm. long. Germany. Isaac Lea collection.. No. 1720

CHALCEDONY, variety SILICIFIED WOOD.

Sphere; violet red and red, banded; 11 cm. diameter. Chalcedony Park,
Arizona.. No. 1767

Dish; brown mottled; 12.5 by 8.5 cm. Chalcedony Park, Arizona......... No. 1732

Four polished slabs; red predominates; 21 by 15.5, 21 by 12, 17 by 16.5,
16.5 by 9.4 cm. Chalcedony Park, Arizona. Gift of The Drake Company. No. 1682

Polished slab; gray; 17 by 17 cm. Chalcedony Park, Arizona............. No. 1688
Mosaic slab; 25 by 25 cm. Chalcedony Park, Arizona........................ No. 1683
Rectangular paper weight; brown; 6 by 5 by 2.5 cm. Humboldt County,
Nevada.. No. 1684
Paper weight; yellow and red-brown, and gray; 10.2 by 7 by 2 cm........... No. 1685
Cube; gray and white streakea; 5 cm...................................... No. 1686
Carved dog's head; pink and yellow. Chalcedony Park, Arizona. Gift of
Maj. J. W. Powell.. No. 1687

COAL.

Rectangular slab carved with a bunch of flowers; 15 by 10.5 cm.............. No. 1735

CROCIDOLITE.

LIST OF SPECIMENS.

Paper weight; aark blue-black; 11 by 8 cm. Griqualand, South Africa.... No. 1744
Dish; brown in white quartz; 13 by 9 cm. Griqualand, South Africa...... No. 1745
Half sphere; brown; 5.5 cm. diameter; Griqualand, South Africa. Isaac
Lea collection... No. 1746
Sphere; brown; 3.8 cm. diameter. Griqualand, South Africa............. No. 1747

FLUORITE.

LIST OF SPECIMENS.

Cup on black marble base; dark purple; 10 cm. diameter. England...... No. 1754
Two ash trays; mottled; 8.7 and 8.5 cm: England........................ No. 1755

GRAPHIC GRANITE—PEGMATITE.

This is a variety of pegmatite in which the quartz and feldspars
have crystallized in long, parallel prisms which on cutting at right
angles to the axis of elongation give rise to peculiar figures suggestive
of letters of the Phoenician alphabet, hence the name *Graphic*. The
light color and slight contrast of the two principal minerals render
the material of little interest from a gem standpoint, but of considerable interest when cut into ornaments.

LIST OF SPECIMENS.

Ash tray; light brown; 14 by 8.2 cm. Siberia............................ No. 1727
Sphere; gray and white; 7 cm. Auburn, Maine........................... No. 1769

GYPSUM, variety SATINSPAR.

LIST OF SPECIMENS.

Goose egg; white; 9.5 cm. long. Bridgeford, England..................... No. 1669
Sphere; white; 6.5 cm. diameter... No. 1722

JADE.

LIST OF SPECIMENS.

Paper weight in form of a lotus leaf; dark green; 15 by 6 cm. China...... No. 1701
Carving in the form of a vase; gray-green; 14 cm. long. China............ No. 1702
Inkstand on a base of teak; light green. China......................... No. 1705
Vase on a base of teak; gray-green; 11.5 cm. high. China................ No. 1704
Small bird mounted on gold stand; light green. China................... No. 1703

LABRADORITE.

LIST OF SPECIMENS.

Medallion of a knight's head; gray, blue, green, etc., in play of colors; 10.5
  by 7.5 cm. Labrador .... No. 1750
Small monumental shaped object; gray; 10 cm. high. Labrador........... No. 1749

LEPIDOLITE.

A lithia mica of a pink color and sometimes sufficiently compact
to be carved into small ornaments. It occurs associated with gem
minerals (tourmaline) in the pegmatite quarries of Maine, California,
and elsewhere.

LIST OF SPECIMENS.

Ash tray; rectangular; violet-red; 9 by 4.7 by 1.3 cm. Rozena, Moravia.
  Gift of C. S. Bement... No. 1748

MALACHITE.

LIST OF SPECIMENS.

Cube with truncated edges; green; 5 cm. Morenci, Arizona............... No. 1696
Composite slab; green; 11 by 8.5 cm. Ural Mountains..................... No. 1697

MARBLE, CALCITE, and ARAGONITE.

Calcium carbonate occurs in nature under a great variety of forms,
usually included under the mineralogical names of calcite and aragonite, or occurring in large rock-like masses as limestone and marble.
The last named forms are used extensively in building and the finer
grades (marble) for decorative work, statuary, and ornaments.
Travertine, cave marble, and onyx marble are the names given to
deposits on the surface or in caves and crevices in limestone, from
water solutions. These are sometimes of exceptional beauty. The
so-called oriental alabaster used by the ancient Egyptians was a
travertine found in caves and fissures in the Eocene limestone of
Egypt. Lumachelle is a name given to a variety in which the
included shell fragments still retain their original nacreous or pearly
luster. Other varietal names are given according to origin, color, and
structure. These are to be found in the collection of building and
ornamental stones. (See also under coral and pearl, pp. 31 and 77.)

LIST OF SPECIMENS.

Sphere of onyx marble; green-yellow; 9 cm. diameter. Big Buck Creek,
  Arizona... No. 1766
Sphere of travertine; pale yellow; 7.8 cm. diameter. Yavapai County,
  Arizona... No. 1765
Carving of a dragon on black limestone. Japan.......................... No. 1689
Sphere of marble; brown and gray; 8 cm. diameter. Japan................ No. 1770
Paper knife of onyx; 19.2 cm. long. Puebla, Mexico..................... No. 1715

Paper weight of onyx with irregular oval handle; base white, handle red-brown, mottled; 8 by 5.5 cm.   Puebla, Mexico............................ No. 1835
Carved ornament in imitation of fruit; banded onyx; 6.7 cm. diameter.
Mexico.. No. 1751
Model of mounted cannon of stalagmite. Rock of Gibraltar............... No. 1692
Paper weight of onyx; pale green; triangular; 6.5 cm. Near Upper Soda
Spring, Siskiyou County, California...................................... No. 1691
Paper weight of fossil coral; gray; 8.5 by 7.5 by 4.5 cm. Iowa.............. No. 1699
Paper weight of fossil coral; gray-brown; 7.9 by 6.5 by 3.4 cm. Iowa..... No. 1834
Paper weight of fossil coral; dark gray brown; 5.7 by 3.9 by 2 cm. Gift of
E. F. Boss.. No. 1693
Paper weight; brown, mottled; 11 by 6.5 cm. Colusa County, California.. No. 1724
Conch shell with cameo engraved on one side; white and brown. West
Indies.. No. 1752

MOSAIC.

Jewel box of rhodonite, aventurine quartz, agate, and jasper mosaic; square
and diamond shaped pieces.   Material obtained in the Urals.............. No. 1708

FIG. 15.—LIZARD CARVED IN OPAL ON LIMONITE.

Mosaic slab of the 17th century, made of agate and lapis-lazuli. Russia... No. 1707
Mosaic paper weight made of agate, quartz, jasper, etc. Russia.......... No. 1706

OPAL.

LIST OF SPECIMENS.

Carving of a lizard on a base of limonite; blue. Queensland, Australia (fig. 15)................. No. 1043
Paper weight; pale yellow; 5.7 by 2.3 cm. Noto, Japan.................... No. 1743

QUARTZ.

LIST OF SPECIMENS.

Polished elliptical slab inclosing rutile needles; 12.2 by 9.5 by 1.5 cm.
Madagascar... No. 1753
Two small prisms inclosing hairlike tremolite needles; 50 by 10 and 45 by
23 mm. Isaac Lea collection. Japan.................................... No. 1672
Carved seal handle of pale yellow quartz, inclosing rutile needles; 64 by
40 mm... No. 1681
Seal handle of amethyst; red-violet. Germany. Isaac Lea collection..... No. 1694
Small basin of beekite carved in a mass of fossil coral; yellow. Devon,
England.. No. 1756
Knife handle of citrine quartz; yellow; 7.5 cm. long. Switzerland........ No. 1680
Carved turtle of rock crystal; colorless. Japan. Isaac Lea collection...... No. 1677
Carved seal of rock crystal; colorless; 7 cm. long. Mursinsk, Russia........ No. 1671
Carved eagle; colorless; 58 mm. Siberia.................................. No. 1670
Drawer knob of rock crystal; colorless; 61 by 18 mm. Siberia............. No. 1678
Knob of rock crystal; colorless; 57 by 6 mm. Switzerland................. No. 1679

Arrow heads of rock crystal; colorless; 15 specimens, average size 40 mm. long. Red Hill, near Bakersville, North Carolina. Isaac Lea collection.. No. 245

Sphere of rock crystal; colorless; 11 cm. diameter. Chestnut Hill Township, Ashe County, North Carolina. Isaac Lea collection................ No. 1673

Sphere of rock crystal; colorless; 7.3 cm. diameter.......................... No. 1674

Sphere of rock crystal; colorless; 48 mm. diameter.......................... No. 167

Three small spheres of rock crystal; colorless; 25 mm. diameter............ No. 1676

Seal handle of rock crystal; colorless; 4.4 cm. long. Bequest of William H. Forwood.. No. 1778

Sphere of rose quartz; pale pink; 42 mm. diameter. Albany, Oxford County, Maine. Isaac Lea collection...................................... No. 1728

Seal handle of smoky quartz; dark brown; 5.5 cm. long. Australia....... No. 1695

RHODONITE.

LIST OF SPECIMENS.

Ash tray; red with black inclusions; 14.5 by 8.2 cm. Ural Mountains..... No. 1729

Polished slab; red; 11 by 7.7 cm. Ural Mountains........................ No. 1730

SERPENTINE.

LIST OF SPECIMENS.

Carving of an antique lamp; dark and light green. Newburyport, Massachusetts. Isaac Lea collection... No. 1776

Sphere; green; 5.9 cm. diameter. Montville, New Jersey.................. No. 1771

Diamond-shaped slab; green; 10.8 by 7.1 by 3.5 cm. Near Montville, New Jersey... No. 1762

Cylindrical paper weight; dark green; 6.5 by 2.7 cm. Lizard Point, Cornwall, England... No. 1742

Vase; green-gray with black veins; 20 cm. high. Gift of W. H. Abbott.... No. 1698

Monument-shaped piece of bowenite; light green; 6.5 by 4 by 2.2 cm. Smithfield, Rhode Island... No. 1690

Sphere; green and white banded; 7.2 cm. diameter. Gila Bend, New Mexico.. No. 1768

SOAPSTONE.

LIST OF SPECIMENS.

Paper weight; mottled green and brown; 8.2 by 8.2 cm. Santa Catalina Island... No. 1725

Circular box with cover; mottled green and brown; 8.8 cm. diameter. Santa Catalina Island.. No. 1740

Three turned cups; dark green. Santa Catalina Island.................... No. 1741

TALC.

LIST OF SPECIMENS.

Carving of a turtle; green-gray. India.................................. No. 1711

Box, carved; green-gray; 12.5 by 8.5 cm. India.......................... No. 1710

Small bottle; green-gray; 6 by 3.7 cm. China............................ No. 1712

UNCLASSIFIED.

Carvings of fruits mounted on a tablet: Red currants, carnelian; white currants, rock crystal; blackberries, black chalcedony and serpentine; raspberries, rhodonite and amethyst; red cherries, carnelian; black cherries, black chalcedony; leaves, serpentine; base, jasper and black chalcedony. Ekaterinburg, Russia.. No. 1709

6. OCCURRENCE AND ASSOCIATION OF PRECIOUS STONES.

Under this heading are included exhibits designed to illustrate the occurrence and association in nature of the various stones described in the preceding pages. These are (1) a comparatively small miscellaneous collection of specimens from various sources showing the rough gem material embedded in or associated with other minerals as found; (2) a larger collection arranged in what is known as an American case, and comprising the Gardner F. Williams collection illustrating the occurrence of the diamond in South Africa; (3) the granite pegmatites and their associated minerals from the eastern United States and southern California, the last named exhibited in the Geological Hall on the first floor.

1. MISCELLANEOUS SERIES.

This comprises two cases in one of which is shown a variety of gem minerals, including both precious and semiprecious stones, either in the matrix or in the rough state as found in nature. The other contains precious opal in the matrix and includes examples from Australia and Mexico, as well as from the more recently discovered field in Humboldt County, Nevada, which furnishes a great variety of colors, ranging from the so-called "black opal" to the pale, iridescent shades.

2. DIAMOND-BEARING ROCKS OF SOUTH AFRICA.

The South African collection comprises about 100 specimens of rocks and mineral concentrates typical of the mines, together with illustrations in the form of photographs and engravings. Below is given a transcript of the label accompanying the collection.

SOUTH AFRICAN DIAMOND MINES.

[Collections illustrating the occurrence of diamonds in the De Beers Consolidated Mines (Ltd.), Kimberley, South Africa. Gift of Mr. Gardner F. Williams.]

The country rock immediately below the surface soil is an olivine diabase, locally called basalt (specimen no. 75898). Below this is a dark shale (specimen no. 75902) which is succeeded by a melaphyr (specimen no. 75910), and this by quartzite (specimen no. 75920). Through all of these have been extruded the diamond-bearing peridotite-breccia, shown in its fresh condition in specimen no. 75,933, and in the decomposed condition known as "blue ground" in specimen no. 75,932. The diamonds are now regarded as having originated through the condensation of metallic carbides in the peridotite while at a great depth below the surface, and to have been brought up in the magma to their present position at the time of its intrusion. In specimen 87701 is shown a cavity from which was removed a large crystal. There are also shown a cast of a diamond crystal weighing 363 carats and several small very perfect crystals and rounded bits (bortz) of genuine diamonds.

SOUTH AFRICAN DIAMOND MINE.

LIST OF ROCKS FROM THE SOUTH AFRICAN DIAMOND MINES IN THE GARDNER F. WILLIAMS COLLECTION.

[From De Beers Consolidated Mines (Ltd.), Kimberley.]

Below is given a complete list of the rocks from the various shafts together with the depths below the surface at which they were found to occur:

DU-TOITS-PAN SHAFT.

Museum number.	Kind of rock.	Position in shaft.
		Feet.
75897	Decomposed basalt	19– 52
75898	Hard basalt	52– 94
75899	Coarse grained basalt	94–121
75900	Fine grained basalt	121–125
75901	Gray shale	125–132
75902	Black shale	132–161
75903	Sandy shale	161–162
75904	Black shale	162–364
75905	Glacial conglomerate	364–370
75906	Glacial conglomerate at contact with quartzite	370
75907	Glacial conglomerate with embedded boulder	370
75908	Quartzite	370–452
75909	Diorite—(*a*) light color; (*b*) dark color	452–484
75910	Amygdaloidal diabase. Melaphyre (?)	484–515
75911	.....do	515–556
75912	.....do	556–560
75913	.....do	560–750
75914	.....do	750–775
75915	.....do	750–775
75916	.....do	750–775
75917	.....do	750
75918	Dyke between hard rock and blue ground	750
75919	Hard blue ground	750

DE BEERS SHAFT.

Museum number.	Kind of rock.	Position in shaft.
75920	Quartzite	800
75921	.....do	1, 200
75922	Quartz porphyry	1, 400
75923	Amygdaloid dyke (?)	1, 440
75924	.....do	1, 480
75925	Quartz porphyry	1, 520
75926	.....do	1, 560
75927	Dyke	1, 600
75928	Dyke (?)	1, 640
75929	Quartz porphyry	1, 680
75930	Quartz porphyry dark	1, 720
75931	Snake rock. Blue ground matrix	300
75932	Soft blue	1, 720
75933	Hard blue	1, 720
75934	.....do	1, 720
75935	Biotite	([1])
75936, 75937, 75938	Concentrates	

[1] From crater, about 1,400-foot level.

KIMBERLEY SHAFT.

Museum number.	Kind of rock.	Position in shaft.
		Feet.
75939	Quartzite	1,000
75940	Altered shale	1,200
75941	Mixture, quartzite, etc	1,200
75942	Diabase with amygdaloid	1,520
75943	Quartz porphyry	1,520
75944	.....do	1,520
75945	Basalt dike	1,840
75946	Porphyry (?)	1,840
75947	Quartz porphyry	1,840
75948	.....do	2,160
75949	.....do	2,160
75950	Basalt dike	2,160
75951	Metamorphosed shale	2,470
75952	Shales	2,500
75953	Dyke	2,560
75954	Soft blue ground	2,000
75955	Hard blue ground	1,840
75956	.....do	2,520
75957 75958 75959	Concentrates	

BULLFONTEIN SHAFT.

75960	Peridotite	200
75961	Quartzite	600
75962	Olivine diabase	600
75963	Blue ground	400
75964	Blue ground north side of mine	600
75965	Blue ground south side of mine	600
75966 75967 75968	Concentrates	

PREMIER MINE.

75969	Blue ground south side of mine	500
75970	Blue ground north side of mine	500
75971	Blue ground open mine	300
75972 75973 75974	Concentrates	

3. GRANITE PEGMATITES AND THEIR ASSOCIATED MINERALS.

The term "pegmatite" is applied to an interesting and peculiar type of igneous rock which occurs in the form of intrusive dikes and sheets, and is characterized as a rule by a coarse and extremely variable crystallization. The granite pegmatites consist for the most part of the same minerals as compose ordinary granite—that is, of quartz and feldspar, with or without mica—but are often accompanied by a considerable number of accessory minerals, which make them favorite hunting grounds for the collector. Crystallization sometimes takes place on a gigantic scale, even to the formation of individuals several feet in length, though as a rule much smaller. At times the quartz and feldspar crystallize contemporaneously in long, parallel, skeleton, and enfolding prisms, giving rise to forms which when cut across resemble ancient Greek or Phoenician characters. Such forms are called *graphic granite*. The quartz and feldspar of the pegmatites are mined for use in pottery manufacture, the mica for electric and other purposes, while the beryls and the tourmalines, if of good color, are utilized as gems.

The pegmatites are common features of granitic rocks, and are found in greater or less abundance in nearly all of the states along the Appalachian chain, as well as in many of the regions west of the front range of the Rocky Mountains.

Two collections of these interesting rocks are shown, one from the Appalachians of the eastern United States, and one from the celebrated gem regions of southern California. Each comprises upward of 100 specimens showing the rocks in the rough and cut and polished conditions, and the associated minerals. In each case, and in the California series in particular, space is given to the decomposed and disintegrated material from the middle or "pay streak" portion together with examples of the same amount of material separated into its component minerals. The gem minerals from the California region, it should be mentioned, are mainly tourmalines of a pink and green color, and the variety of spodumene known as kunzite. Those from the Appalachians are mainly green tourmaline and the variety of beryl known as aquamarine.

A. THE APPALACHIAN PEGMATITES.

Among the more prominent objects in the Appalachian series are several large specimens showing (1) a pegmatite intrusion some 6 inches in width in gneiss, from Auburn, Maine (39058), (2) one of similar nature, 4 inches in width, bordered by a thin black tourmaline, in granite, from Cape Elizabeth, Maine (62508), (3) a thin zone of pegmatitic material with very obscure outlines in the Rockport, Massachusetts, granite (38757). There is also a large rough pegmatite from Amelia, Virginia (88983), and a fine large polished slab from Auburn, Maine (74795), cut across the grain, showing to advantage the "graphic" structure. Among the smaller and associated minerals are crystals of muscovite, showing the characteristic hexagonal outline (62377), masses of the lithia mica, lepidolite (90229), and the feldspar orthoclase or microcline (49700), amazonstone (48721), and albite (48723); also large masses of black tourmaline (89944); green radiating tourmaline in matrix (82268, 89939) and examples of beryl (90244), including the variety emerald in matrix from North Carolina (53778). The gem minerals (90223) occur associated mainly with the albitic feldspar and the lepidolite, as in the examples from Portland, Connecticut.

Other associated minerals shown are lithiophilite from Grafton, New Hampshire (88253); apatite from Strafford, New Hampshire (87435); allanite from Crown Point, New York (90262); gadolinite from Barringer Hills, Texas (88442); and uraninite from Mitchell County, North Carolina (59329).

B. THE MESA GRANDE, CALIFORNIA, PEGMATITES.

The California series was prepared with great care and elaboration by Dr. W. T. Schaller, of the United States Geological Survey and at the same time honorary custodian of gems and precious stones in the National Museum. The details of the collection as given by him are as follows:

The nearly flat-lying pegmatite dikes, from which most of the specimens shown were obtained, crop out on the hills north and east of Pala, San Diego County, California, and are of the compound, unsymmetrical type whose different parts are thought to be due to differentiation processes rather than to multiple injections of material into reopened fissures. The upper portion of the dike is locally known as the "top rock" (nos. 89549, 89550) and is a mixture of a coarse, granular aggregate of quartz and feldspar and of a graphic pegmatite. No gem stones are found in this "top rock." The lower portion of the dikes, locally called the "bottom rock" (no. 88551), is a much finer grained granular quartz-albite rock characterized by numerous wavy bands of brownish-red garnets. These bands lie nearly horizontal in their general trend, being parallel to the slight dip of the dike. The "bottom rock" is likewise free from gem stones, but both it and the "top rock" are of great interest from the scientific point of view. Between the "top rock" and the "bottom rock" is the middle portion, called the "pay streak" by the miners, in which the gem minerals of value are found. Here also occur the cavities or pockets which often yield an abundance of the well-crystallized minerals shown in the exhibit.

The top horizontal shelf on the south side of the exhibition case contains the granitic (no. 89871) and gabbro country rock (no. 88556) and also the partly altered gabbro—a loose, friable rock—and the completely altered gabbro (no. 89856), which as a brown iron-stained clay has been washed into the cracks and seams of the pegmatite rock. Where such a crack extends into a pocket the clay has coated the gems and associated minerals found therein. There are shown, for example, white feldspars of the pegmatite coated with the brown clay derived from the gabbro country rock. The origin of the clay of the gem pockets is thus explained.

The second horizontal shelf on the south side contains different varieties of the "top rock," consisting of graphic pegmatite and granular pegmatite. The third horizontal shelf shows the mineral aggregates of the middle part or "pay streak," which yields on decomposition the loose, friable material forming the gem pockets. This same shelf also shows examples of the banded "bottom rock."

The sloping shelf on the south side contains large specimens of the different varieties of the pegmatite rock, including granular, graphic, and banded pegmatites. Several of these larger specimens have been sawed and polished and are well adapted for use as an ornamental stone, especially when cut obliquely so as to form wavy lines and circular effects resembling bird's-eye wood. One specimen in particular consists of a large section of the entire pegmatite dike and shows the aggregate of lithium minerals in the upper portion or "top rock," the granular pegmatite of the middle portion, and the banded "bottom rock." (No. 88560.)

The sloping shelf on the north side of the case illustrates the mineral contents of the gem pockets. A sample of the gem-bearing clay or pocket material is first shown, below which is an equal amount of similar gem clay separated into its constitutent minerals; thus the relative proportions of the gem tourmaline, the clay washed into the pocket from the decomposed gabbro country rock, and the various minerals associated with the gem tourmaline are exhibited. For example, the pocket material from the Tourmaline King mine (no. 90312 and 90308), at Pala, shows much lepidolite, orthoclase, clay, and gem tourmaline (pink and green), and smaller amounts of muscovite and quartz. Similar gem-bearing clay from the Tourmaline Queen mine, at Pala (no. 90307), shows, in addition to much pink tourmaline, large amounts of clay, quartz, albite, and cookeite, but practically no orthoclase. A gem pocket from the Ed. Flethcher, jr., mine, at Pala (no. 90310), shows, in addition to much pink tourmaline, clay, and albite, a considerable amoumt of lepidolite, with only a little orthoclase. A gem pocket from the Pala Chief mine, at Pala (no. 90310), shows considerable gem kunzite, with lepidolite, quartz, clay, cookeite, and orthoclase, and smaller amounts of albite and muscovite. A similar pocket from the Caterina mine at Pala (no. 90311) shows only spodumene, pink clay, and quartz. The exhibit also includes a pocket containing an abundance of small blue tourmalines; a small pocket from the Tourmaline King mine, very rich in gem tourmalines; and several pockets free from any gem stones. Such pockets are known by the miners as "dead ones."

On this same sloping shelf are shown also several large specimens of the minerals associated with the gem pockets. Among these minerals may be noted a fine example of orbicular muscovite, an altered perthite (feldspar) crystal, a large amblygonite crystal, and several specimens of spodumene (kunzite) in the matrix. These kunzite specimens are very difficult to collect, as in general the matrix of the kunzite is so friable that it breaks to pieces when it is taken out of the mine.

The three horizontal shelves above the sloping shelf on the north side of the case contain well-developed and well-crystallized specimens of the different minerals found in the gem-pocket zone of the pegmatite dikes. Among these minerals may be noted in particular a good series of the various forms of lepidolite (nos. 88528, 88536) (including several well-crystallized specimens) (no. 89865), crystals of muscovite, fine tourmaline crystals (nos. 88165, 88166), albite and orthoclase in well-developed crystals, pink beryl (no. 89170), stilbite, cassiterite, a large crystal of lithiophilite bismuth, bismuthite, bismuthosphaerite, purpurite, hematite, and pyrite, apatite, pucherite, topaz, manganotantalite, a fine example of clear pink kunzite in the matrix (nos. 88538 and 90027), and the phosphate minerals first found in this locality, namely, palaite, salmonsite, and sicklerite.

THE CUTTING OF GEM STONES.

The cutting of gem stones is necessary for the complete development of those properties upon which their beauty largely depends. Rarely does the stone, as found in nature, present those qualities which make it attractive to the eye. In its natural state it is often opaque, dull, or flawed, and even if transparent and flawless its form is rarely adapted to the display of those characters which distinguish the fashioned stone. Occasionally a stone may, without artificial treatment, show to a sufficient degree those qualities which give it rank; but such cases are rare, and in order that its inherent beauty may be developed to the maximum it must be cut and polished.

The several styles of cut may all be brought under one or the other of the following heads: I. Those bounded by plane surfaces only. II. Those bounded by curved surfaces only. III. Those bounded by both curved and plane surfaces. The several examples under the above heads may be tabulated thus:

    I. Bounded by plane surfaces:
        Brilliant cut.
        Double brilliant or Lisbon cut.
        Half brilliant or single cut.
        Trap or split brilliant cut.
        Portuguese cut.
        Star cut.
        Rose cut, or briolette.
        Step brilliant or mixed cut.
        Table cut.
    II. Bounded by curved surfaces:
        Double cabochon cut.
        Single cabochon cut.
        Hollow cabochon cut.
    III. Bounded by curved and plane surfaces—mixed cabochon cut.

BRILLIANT CUT.

The brilliant cut may be described as two truncated pyramids, placed base to base. The upper pyramid is called the *crown*, and is so truncated as to give a large plane surface; the lower one, called the *pavilion*, terminates almost in a point. The line of union of the two pyramids is called the *girdle*, and is the widest part of the stone. This fashion of cut, though occasionally modified as to the size, mutual proportions, and even the number of facets, requires, when perfect, 58 facets. The uppermost facet is called the *crown*, and is formed by removing one-third of the thickness of the fundamental octahedron; the lowermost facet is called the *culet*, or *collet*, and is formed by removing one-eighteenth of the thickness of the stone (*a* and *b*, in text fig. 16). The triangular facets touching the table (s in *c*, fig. 16) are called *star facets;* those touching the girdle fall into two groups, *skill facets* (E in *c*) and *skew facets* (D in *c*). The corner facets touching the table and girdle on the crown (B in *c*), and the culet and girdle on the pavilion (Q in *d*) are called *quoins.* The facets between the quoins, and touching the table and girdle when on the crown, and the culet and girdle when on the pavilion, are called, respectively, *bezel*

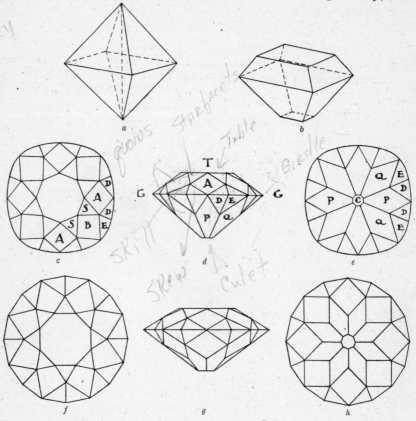

Fig. 16.—The Brilliant. *a* and *b*, manner in which the brilliant is derived from the funda-mental form; *c, d,* and *e*, top, side, and back views of brilliant with 58 facets; *f, g,* and *h*, top, side, and back views of modified brilliant with 66 facets.

facets (A in *c*) and *pavilion* facets (P in *d*). The total number of facets are distributed as follows: 1 table, 16 skill facets, 16 skew facets, 8 star facets, 8 quoins, 4 bezel facets, 4 pavilion facets, and 1 culet, as shown in *c, d,* and *e* of the text figures, representing the top, side, and bottom views of a brilliant with 58 facets. Occasionally the cut is modified by cutting extra facets around the culet, making 66 in all.

The brilliant cut is especially applied to the diamond, and when perfect should be of the following proportions: From the table to the girdle, one-third, and from the girdle to the culet two-thirds of the total. The diameter of the table should be four-ninths of the breadth of the stone. When applied to other stones these proportions are more or less modified to suit their individual optical constants.

DOUBLE BRILLIANT CUT.

The double brilliant, or Lisbon cut, is a form with two rows of lozenge-shaped facets, and three rows of triangular-shaped facets,

a   *b*   *c*

FIG. 17.—THE DOUBLE BRILLIANT. TOP (*a*), SIDE (*b*), AND BACK (*c*) VIEWS.

74 in all. The figure shows top (*a*), side (*b*), and bottom (*c*) views of this fashion.

HALF BRILLIANT CUT.

The half brilliant, single, or old English cut is the simplest form of the brillliant, and is generally employed for stones too small to admit

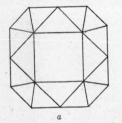 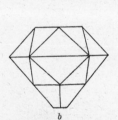 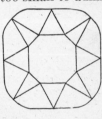

a   *b*   *c*

FIG. 18.—THE HALF BRILLIANT. TOP (*a*), AND SIDE (*b*) VIEWS OF THE HALF BRILLIANT. IN *c* THE TOP IS CUT IN THE FORM OF A STAR, THEN CALLED ENGLISH SINGLE-CUT.

of numerous facets. The figure shows top (*a*) and side (*b*) views of this style of cut. Occasionally the top is cut so as to form a star (*c* in fig. 18) and then called English single-cut.

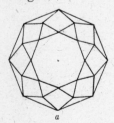  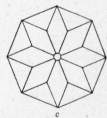

a   *b*   *c*

FIG. 19.—THE TRAP BRILLIANT. TOP (*a*), SIDE (*b*), AND BACK (*c*) VIEWS.

TRAP BRILLIANT CUT.

The trap brilliant, or split brilliant, differs from the full brilliant in having the foundation squares divided horizontally into two triangular facets, making 42 in all.

PORTUGUESE CUT.

The figures show the top, side, and bottom views of the Portuguese cut, which has two rows of rhomboidal and three rows of triangular facets above and below the girdle.

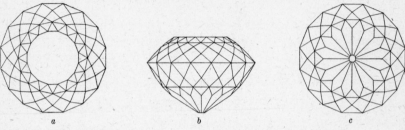

FIG. 20.—THE PORTUGUESE CUT. TOP (*a*), SIDE (*b*), AND BACK (*c*) VIEWS.

STAR CUT.

The figures show the front and back views of the star cut. The table is hexagonal in shape, and is one-fourth of the diameter of the

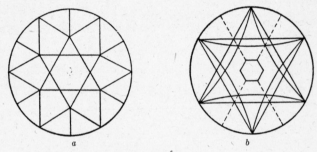

FIG. 21.—THE STAR CUT. FRONT (*a*), AND BACK (*b*) VIEWS.

stone; from the table spring six equilateral triangles, whose apices touch the girdle, and these triangles, by the prolongation of their points, form a star.

ROSE CUT.

The rose cut differs from the brilliant cut in that the crown consists of triangular or star facets, whose apices meet at the point or

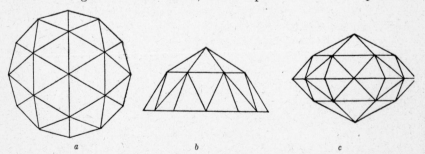

FIG. 22.—THE ROSE CUT (*a*) AND (*b*), TOP AND SIDE VIEWS; (*c*) SIDE VIEW OF DOUBLE ROSE.

crown of the rose. The base lines of these star facets form the base lines for a row of skill facets whose apices touch the girdle, leaving spaces which are each cut into two facets. The base may be flat or the bottom may be cut like the crown, making a double rose or briolette cut. The shape of a rose-cut stone may be circular, oval, or indeed any other that the rough gem may permit.

TRAP OR STEP CUT.

In the trap or step cut the facets run longitudinally around the stone from the table to the girdle and from the girdle to the culet. There are usually but two or three sets of step facets from the table

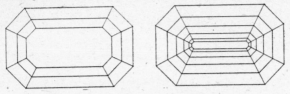

FIG. 23.—UPPER AND UNDER SIDES OF TRAP CUT.

to the girdle, while the number of steps from the girdle to the culet depends upon the thickness and color of the stone. The fashion is best adapted to emeralds and other colored stones.

STEP BRILLIANT OR MIXED CUT.

Here the form from culet to girdle is the same as that of the trap cut, while from the girdle to the table the stone is brilliant cut, or the opposite.

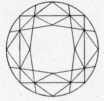

FIG. 24.—THE STEP BRILLIANT CUT.

TABLE CUT.

The table cut consists simply of a greatly developed table and culet meeting the girdle with beveled edges. Occasionally the 8 edge facets are replaced by a border of 16 or more facets.

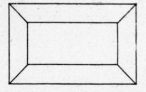
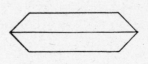

FIG. 25.—TOP AND SIDE VIEWS OF TABLE CUT.

CABOCHON CUT.

The cabochon cut is usually applied to opaque, translucent, deep colored, or chatoyant stones. The double cabochon is usually cut with a smaller curvature on the base than on the crown. The single cabochon is a characteristic cut for the turquoise. The hollow cabochon is adapted to very deep-colored transparent stones. The

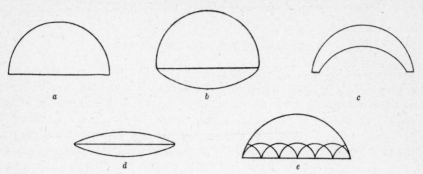

Fig. 26.—The cabochon cut. *a*, the single cabochon; *b*, the double cabochon; *c*, the hollow cabochon; *d*, flat or tallow top cabochon; *e*, mixed cabochon.

mixed cabochon has either the edge or side faceted, or both. In all of the cabochon cuts the arches may be of a varying degree of flatness, depending upon the nature of the stone.

CAMEO AND INTAGLIO.

The term "cameo" is applied to any engraving in relief upon the surface of a gem, usually upon a stone like onyx or a shell composed of layers of different colors, the engraving being of sufficient depth to expose the underlying layers and producing the desired contrast. An intaglio differs in being an incised engraving and usually upon a stone of uniform color throughout.

APPENDIX 2.

GEMS MENTIONED IN THE BIBLE.

The Bible contains three lists of gems. The first of these is an account of the jewels on the *ephod* of Aaron. The *ephod* is described as having a front part and a back part fastened at each shoulder with an onyx mounted in gold and engraved with the names of the children of Israel, six on each stone, to memorialize the Lord of the promise made to them. (Exodus xxviii, 6, 12, 29.) The breastplate was made of the same material as the *ephod*, and folded so as to form a kind of a pouch in which the Urim and Thummin were placed. (Exodus xxxix, 9.) The external part of this gorget, or "breastplate of judgment," was set with four rows of gems, three in each row, each stone set in a golden socket and having engraved upon it the name of one of the twelve tribes of Israel. (Exodus, xxviii, 17–20.)

The following lists taken from Biblical antiquities by Adler and Casanowicz [1] give the names of these stone in the original and in the Septuagint, together with the meaning adopted by most authorities, the rendering of the Revised Version, both in text and margin being added in parentheses:

1. *Odem* (*sardion*), carnelian (sardius, ruby).

2. *Pitdah* (*topazion*), topaz or peridot.

3. *Bareketh* (*smaragdos*), smaragd or emerald (carbuncle emerald).

4. *Nofek* (*anthrax*), carbuncle, probably the Indian ruby (emerald, carbuncle).

5. *Sappir* (*sapfeiros*), sapphire or lapis lazuli (sapphire).

6. *Yahalom* (*iaspis*), onyx, a kind of chalcedon (diamond, sardonyx).

7. *Leshem* (*ligyrion*), jacinth, others, sapphire (jacinth, amber).

8. *Shebo* (*achates*), agate.

9. *Achlamah* (*amethystos*) amethyst.

10. *Tarshish* (*chrysolithos*), chrysolite, others, topaz (beryl, chalcedony).

11. *Shoham* (*beryllion*), beryl (onyx, beryl).

12. *Yashpeh* (*onychion*) jasper.

In many instances the equivalent of the Biblical names of gems is uncertain in the nomenclature of modern mineralogy, and as a consequence there are several distinct lists of names given for the stones in the breastplate. In the Section of Comparative Religions in the United States National Museum is a very old silver breastplate employed as an ornament for the manuscript copy of the Torah, or Pentateuch, used in an ancient synagogue. The twelve stones, with the names of the

[1] Report of the U. S. National Museum, 1896, p. 943. A collection of these stones is on exhibition in the division of Old World Archaeology, Department of Anthropology.

147

twelve tribes, according to it are as follows: Garnet, Levi; diamond, Zebulon; amethyst, Gad; jasper, Benjamin; chrysolite, Simeon; sapphire, Issachar; agate, Naphthali; onyx, Joseph; sard, Reuben; emerald, Judah; topaz, Dan; beryl, Asher.

The second list is that given in the description of the ornaments of the Prince of Tyre (Ezekiel xxviii, 13):

1. *Odem.*	2. *Pitdah.*	3. *Yahalom.*
4. *Tarshish.*	5. *Shoham.*	6. *Yashpeh.*
7. *Sappir.*	8. *Nofek.*	9. *Bareketh.*

The third list is that given in the description of the Heavenly City (Revelations xxi, 19, 20). As in the preceding list, the word used in the original, or Greek, is followed by the rendering given by most authorities, that of the Revised Version in parentheses:

1. *Iaspis*, jasper.	2. *Sapfeiros*, sapphire or lapis lazuli.	3. *Chalkedon*, chalcedony.
4. *Smaragdos*, s m a r a g d (emerald).	5. *Sardonyx*, sardonyx.	6. *Sardios*, sardius.
7. *Chrysolithos*, chrysolite.	8. *Beryllos*, beryl.	9. *Topazion*, topaz.
10. *Chrysoprasos*, c h r y s o - prase.	11. *Hyakinthos*, j a c i n t h (sapphire).	12. *Amethystos*, amethyst.

In addition to the gems enumerated in these lists, there is mentioned the diamond by the Hebrew name of *shamir* (Jeremiah xvii, 1; Ezekiel iii, 9; Zechariah vii, 12); amber, Hebrew *Hashmal* (margin of Revised Version gives *electrum*) (Ezekiel i, 4); and crystal (quartz), Hebrew *qerah* and *gabish* (Ezekiel i, 22; Job xxviii, 18; Revelation iv, 6).

The complete list of gems mentioned being as follows:

Agate, Hebrew *shebo*.—One of the stones in the breastplate of judgment. (Exodus xxviii, 19.)

Amber, Hebrew *hashmal*.—Ezekiel i, 4. Some render the Hebrew *leshem* as amber, thus making it one of the gems in the breastplate. (Exodus xxvii, 19.)

Amethyst, Hebrew *ahlamah*.—One of the stones in the breastplate. (Exodus xxviii, 19). In Revelation xxi, 20, it is mentioned as garnishing the twelfth foundation of the heavenly Jerusalem.

Beryl, Hebrew *shoham*.—One of the stones in the breastplate. (Exodus xxviii, 20.) Mentioned as one of the ornaments of the King of Tyre. (Ezekiel xxviii, 13.) In Revelation it is spoken of as adorning the eighth foundation of the Holy City.

Carbuncle, Hebrew *nofek*.—One of the stones in the breastplate. (Exodus xxviii, 18; see also Ezekiel xxviii, 13). The word *nofek* has been rendered ruby.

Carnelian, perhaps the Hebrew *odem* of the breastplate (Exodus xxviii, 17), and the sardius in Revelation xxi, 20. In Revelation iv, 3, of the Revised Version, is the rendering sardius. In the Authorized Version the reading is: "And he that sat was to look upon like a jasper and a *sardine* stone." In the Vulgate: "Et qui sedebat similis erat aspectui lapidis jaspidis et sardinis." The Textus receptus (Greek) is: Καὶ ὁ καϑήμενος ἦν ὅμοιος ὁράσει λίϑῳ ἰασπίδι; καὶ σαρδίνιῳ. All other editions have for the last word, σαρδίω. It is evident that the Vulgate and the Authorized Version simply followed the Textus receptus, and that the correct rendering is "sardius" and not "sardine stone."

Chalcedony.—The Hebrew *tarshish* (Exodus xxviii, 20) has been rendered chalcedony. In Revelation xxi, 19, it is enumerated in the description of the foundation of the New Jerusalem.

Chrysolite.—(See Revelation xxi, 20.) The Hebrew *tarshish* (Exodus xxviii, 20) has been rendered chrysolite.

Chrysoprase.—One of the stones in the foundation of the Heavenly City. (Revelation xxi, 20.)

Diamond, Hebrew *shamir.*—(See Jeremiah xvii, 1; Ezekiel iii, 9; and Zechariah vii, 12, where it is spoken of as an object of extreme hardness. In the Authorized Version the Hebrew *yahalom* (Exodus xxviii, 18) is rendered diamond.

Emerald, Hebrew *bareketh.*—One of the stones in the breastplate. (Also see Revelation iv, 3.)

Jacinth, Hebrew *leshem.*—A stone in the breastplate. (Exodus xxviii, 19). The eleventh foundation of the Heavenly Jerusalem. (Revelation xxi, 20.)

Jasper, Hebrew *yashpeh.*—A stone in the breastplate. (Exodus xxviii, 20.) Mentioned as adorning the Prince of Tyrus (Ezekiel xxviii, 13.) One of the stones enumerated in the description of the Heavenly City. (Revelation xxi, 19.)

Onyx, Hebrew *shoham.*—One of the stones in the breastplate. (Exodus xxviii, 20; see also Genesis, ii, 12; and Ezekiel xxviii, 13.) According to certain renderings the *shoham* is beryl. *Shohams* set in gold were put on each of the two shoulder straps of the *ephod* of the high priest, and the two were engraved with the names of the twelve tribes, six on each. (Exodus xxviii, 12.)

Pearl.—It is thought that pearl is meant by the Hebrew *peninim,* a word often employed in the Old Testament as a figure of something valuable and precious. (See Proverbs, iii, 5; xxxi, 10, and Job xxviii 18.) Jesus uses the pearl for the same purpose in Matthew vii, 6, and xiii, 45.

Ruby, Hebrew *nofek* or *odem.*—One of the gems in the breastplate. (Exodus xxviii, 17; see also Ezekiel xxvii, 13.)

Sapphire, Hebrew *sappir.*—One of the stones in the breastplate. (Exodus xxviii, 18; also mentioned in Ezekiel xxviii, 13, and Revelation xxi, 19.) Some authorities render *sappir* as lapis lazuli, and not sapphire.

Sardonyx, Hebrew *yahalom.*—One of the stones in the breastplate. (Exodus xxviii, 18.)

Topaz, Hebrew *pitdah.*—One of the stones in the breastplate. (Exodus xxviii, 17; also mentioned in Ezekiel xxviii, 13, and in Revelation, xxi, 20.)

MYSTICAL PROPERTIES OF GEMS.

Man has endowed gems with talismanic, curative, and supernatural powers. Certain gems preserved him from incubi, vampires, and kindred terrors; others preserved him from the powers of sorcery or conferred the powers of witchcraft; by their aid he controlled the spirits of evil or was protected from their malign influence. With a suitable gem he could foretell the future, review the past, or conjure up pictures of events taking place at a distance. Protected by their mystic influences he feared neither plague nor poison, while his belief in the marvelous efficacy of their curative powers gave them a place among his most potent remedies.

The virtues of gems were diverse. Some procured the favor of the great; others rendered their possessors amiable, wise, strong, and brave; some protected him from fire, lightning, and tempests; others from danger and disease; some were preferred as talismans and charms; others were used as drugs, either alone or with electuaries, and with or without prayers, incantations, or other prescribed formulas.

Certain gems brought good or evil through the planetary influence of certain days. All yellow gems were appropriate for Sunday wear through the name giver, the sun. On Monday, the moon day, all white stones except the diamond were to be worn. Tuesday, the day of Mars, claimed garnets, rubies, and all red stones. Wednesday demanded blue stones. Thor's day, or Thursday, required amethysts and other stones of a sanguine tint. Friday, the day of Venus, had for its gem the emerald. Saturn's day claimed the diamond.

A particular stone was potent for good during a particular month, and, under the proper astrological control was supposed to have a mystical influence over the twelve parts of the human anatomy. Such a gem was the more potent if the natal day of the wearer corresponded with its particular sign, and when worn as a birth or month stone was supposed to attract at all times propitious influences and avert malign effects. The more important stones, their zodiacal control, and most potent periods of influence are:

Stone.	Zodiacal control.	Period.
Garnet	Aquarius	Jan. 21 to Feb. 21.
Amethyst	Pisces	Feb. 21 to Mar. 21.
Bloodstone	Aries	Mar. 21 to Apr. 20.
Sapphire	Taurus	Apr. 20 to May 21.
Agate	Gemini	May 21 to June 21.
Emerald	Cancer	June 21 to July 22.
Onyx	Leo	July 22 to Aug. 22.
Carnelian	Virgo	Aug. 22 to Sept. 22.
Chrysolite	Libra	Sept. 22 to Oct. 23.
Aquamarine	Scorpio	Oct. 23 to Nov. 21.
Topaz	Sagittarius	Nov. 21 to Dec. 21.
Ruby	Capricorn	Dec. 21 to Jan. 21.

A closely related idea is found in the 12 stones which, according to the Jewish cabalists, when engraved each with an anagram of the name of God, were supposed to have a mystical power over, and a prophetical relation to, the 12 angels.   Thus:

Ruby...Malchediel.
Topaz..Asmodel.
Carbuncle...Ambriel.
Emerald...Muriel.
Sapphire..Herchel.
Diamond...Humatiel.
Jacinth..Zuriel.
Agate..Barbiel.
Amethyst..Adnachiel.
Beryl..Humiel.
Onyx...Gabriel.
Jasper...Barchiel.

These stones also had reference to the Twelve Tribes of Israel, the 12 parts of the human body, 12 hierarchies of devils, etc.   By their aid a system of prognostication was practiced, based upon the change of hue or brilliancy of the stone, so that the cabalist was enabled to foretell future events.

The Twelve Apostles were represented symbolically by precious stones: Jasper, St. Peter; sapphire, St. Andrew; chalcedony, St. James; emerald, St. John; sardonyx, St. Philip; carnelian, St. Matthew; beryl, St. Thomas; chrysoprase, St. Thaddeus; topaz, St. James the Less; hyacinth, St. Simeon; amethyst, St. Matthias.

The superstitions connected with the 12 stones have persisted in one form or another from the times of the Magi to the present, and the belief in their virtues can still be traced in the wearing of "birthstones," as listed below:

BIRTH STONES.

January....Garnet (also hyacinth).
February...Amethyst (hyacinth and pearl occasionally used).
March.....Bloodstone (also jasper).
April.......Diamond (also sapphire).
May.......Emerald (chalcedony, carnelian, and agate occasionally used).
June.......Agate (chalcedony, turquoise, pearl, and cat's-eye occasionally used).
July........Ruby (carnelian, onyx, sardonyx, and turquoise occasionally used).
August.....Sardonyx (carnelian, moonstone, alexandrite, and topaz occasionally used).
September..Sapphire (also chrysolite and sardonyx).
October.....Opal (also beryl and aquamarine).
November..Topaz (also pearl).
December..Turquoise (ruby, bloodstone, and chrysoprase occasionally used).

In the *Sympathia Septem Metallorum ac Septem Selectorum Lapidum ad Planetas* is a list of stones recorded as being in sympathy with the planets, and as such were possessed of astrological and medicinal properties which, under the proper sign, rendered them of service to men. Thus—

[♄] Saturn..... Turquoise, sapphire.
[♃] Jupiter.... Carnelian, topaz, amethyst.
[♂] Mars....... Jasper, emerald.
[♀] Venus..... Emerald, amethyst, topaz.
[☿] Mercury... Crystal, agate, emerald.
[☽] Moon...... Moonstone, topaz, and all white stones.
[☉] Sun........ Diamond, ruby.

The Hindu propitiated hostile stars by the bestowal of gems. If the sun was hostile, a pure ruby; the moon, a good pearl; if *sani*, a star affecting to a powerful degree the destinies of men, a sapphire. He also averted the evil effects of adverse astral influences by wearing certain stones. If the sun was adverse, the cat's-eye; if the moon, the sapphire, etc.

The mystic ascribed a certain significance both to the gem and to its various colors. For example, white was the emblem of light, purity, faith, innocence, joy, and life; worn by women it was emblematic of chastity; by the ruler, of humility and integrity. Red signified pure love and wisdom; in other sense it signified passion, love of evil, hatred, etc. Blue was indicative of truth, constancy, and fidelity. Yellow in one sense was symbolical of marriage and faithfulness; in another sense of inconstancy, jealousy, and deceit. Green was the color of hope, especially that of immortality. Amethystine signified love, truth, passion, suffering, and hopefulness, and among the Rosicrucians was symbolical of the divine male sacrifice.

Stones of all sorts were engraved with the figure of a cockatrice, which, under the proper planetary influence, were preservatives against the evil eye. The names of Jesus, Mary, and Joseph were engraved on stones, chiefly amethyst, onyx, and bloodstone, which were worn as preventives of contagious diseases; the larger the stone, the greater its efficacy. Gems were also supposed to indicate the state of health of the donor or wearer. If the stone became dull, opaque, or colorless it was thought to be significant of danger and death. In a similar manner they lost or changed color in contact with poisons.

Dreaming of gems was usually fraught with good, while seeing or handling them on the eve of a journey, or at certain phases of the moon, was regarded as auspicious.

Supernatural influences have been attributed to gems which still pass current. For example, an onyx ring, supposed to be the espousal ring of Mary and Joseph, exhibited in the Duomo of Perugia, is thought to be efficacious in the cure of every disorder. Amber is still used as a prophylactic and curative for goiter, croup, and diseases of the throat. The opal is thought by many to bring ill luck to the wearer. The coral is still believed to be a charm against diseases of childhood, and is extensively worn in Italy as a protection against the "evil eye." Pearls are dreaded by some and favored by others. No French bride will wear them on her wedding day, since they would bring tears to her married life. In the East the believers are dogmatic in their faith, and it is heresy to assert that the use of gems has no practical influence over body or mind.

It is impossible here to do more than hint at the many beliefs concerning gems which were or are current, and the following notes merely suggest a few of the more prevalent beliefs on this subject:

Agate.—Emblematic of health and wealth. An enemy to all venemous things; assuages thirst when held in the mouth; gives victory to its wearer; repels storms; sharpens the sight; preserves and increases strength, and renders its wearer gracious and eloquent. (Camillus Leonardus, Speculum Lapidum, 1502.) Efficacious as an amulet against scrofula and skin diseases. (Albertus Magnus, De Vertutibus Herbarium, Lapidum, Animalum, etc.) Various properties are attributed to it by Mohammedan authorities. It cured insanity when administered with water or with the juice of the fruit *Sheu* (an apple?); a remedy for hemorrhage in the genital organs or in the rectum; for the spitting of blood; for the unusual discharge of the menstrual fluid. In conjunction with other medicines it cured hard boils and porous ulcers, gravel, spleen, and kidney troubles. It prevented bleeding of the gums and rendered them hard when applied to the parts as a calcined powder.

Agates having the reddishness of the water after washing raw flesh in the shape of finger rings prevent bleeding of all kinds. The wearer strikes terror to the heart of his enemies, obtains his heart's wishes from the gods, and becomes free from pain in the breast.

The *Akik* (agate) confers upon the wearer all the blessings that the use of the turquoise does. Its internal use may do harm to the stomach, but this can be avoided by mixing it with *Katira*, or, in its absence, with the *Basud* stone. (Views of Arabic and Persian writers on gems and stones.)

If taken internally, the agate drives away fear, increases the power of digestion, cures insanity and monomania of that kind which creates the impression of being beaten and abused by others. If worn, it cures stricture and the vomiting of blood coming from the chest; worn on the neck, it cures the spitting of blood issuing from the lungs at the time of coughing. Calcined, powdered, and administered with white wine in doses weighing 16 barleycorns, it cured the gravel. If tied about the thighs of a woman under painful labor, it helps to a speedy and easy delivery. The weight of the stone here prescribed should be about 120 barleycorns. (Ben Adloulah.)

The eye-agate was considered efficacious as an amulet in cases of scrofula and other skin diseases. In great repute to-day in Syria as a curative for "Aleppo" sores.

Pierre de Boniface, writing in 1315, said:

The agate of India or Crete renders its possessor eloquent and prudent, amiable, and agreeable.

Ben Jonson, in the Alchymist, speaking of the medicinal properties of gems, wrote:

My meat shall come in Indian shells, dishes of agate set in gold, and studded with emeralds, sapphires, hyacinths, and rubies. The tongues of carps, dormice, and camel's heels boiled in the spirit of Sol, and dissolv'd pearl, apicus diet 'gainst the epilepsy. And I will eat these broths with spoons of amber, headed with diamond and carbuncle.

Dioscorides, in his Materia Medica, recommends the use of the agate as a preventive of contagion.

Alabaster.—According to Leonardus it is the best for vessels to hold unguents, which are preserved in them without spoiling. Dioscorides and many other doctors account it good in physics. He who carries it will prove victorious in suits at law.

Amber.—Supposed to be "generated out of the urine of the lynx, and is hardened by time; that voided by the male, brown; by the female, saffron, inclining to a darkness." Amber assuaged pain in the stomach, cured jaundice, flux, and king's evil.

It naturally restrains the flux of the belly; is an efficacious remedy for all disorders in the throat (a belief still prevalent). It is good against poison. If laid on the breast of a wife when she is asleep, it makes her confess all her evil deeds. Being taken inwardly it provokes urine, brings down the menses, and facilitated a birth. It fastens teeth that are loosen'd, and by the smoke of it poisonous insects are driven away. (Camillus Leonardus, Speculum Lapidum. 1502.)

When buried in a moist soil it was supposed to generate a fungus, which was administered to those troubled with the gravel. It cured fits, dysentery, scrofula, and jaundice. Used as an amulet it charmed away toothache, asthma, croup, and diseases of the throat; supposed to be efficacious as a curative and prophylactic if rubbed on the parts or taken internally, after dissolving in white wine. (Dissertatio medica de Succino, 1682.) These beliefs are still current.

Thomas Nicols writes that the—

white odoriferous amber is esteemed the best for physic use, and thought to be of great power and force against many diseases, as against the *vertigo* and *asthmatic paroxysmes*, against *catharres* and *arthriticall* pains, against diseases of the stomach, and to free it from sluffings and putrefactions, and against diseases of the heart, against plagues, venoms, and contagions. It is used either in powder, or in oil, or in troches, either in distempers of men or of women, either married or unmarried, either with child or without, or in the distempers of children. (Arcula Gemmea, 1653.)

Olaus Worm, of Copenhagen, writing in 1640, says that amber was received as a panacea; a sovereign remedy for toothache, asthma, and dropsy.

In the work "De Proprietatibus Rerum," by Bartholomaeus Glanvilla, amber is reported to possess the property of driving away adders and of being contrary to friends.

The Shah of Persia is said to wear an amulet of amber reported to have fallen from heaven, and which has the property of rendering him invulnerable.

Amber is used to-day in Lombardy and the Piedmont as a cure for goiter—a belief that dates back to the time of Pliny.

Amethyst.—Emblematic of sincerity.

As an amulet it dispelled sleep, sharpened the intellect, prevented intoxication, gave victory to soldiers, and protected its wearer from sorcery.   (Leonardus.)

"The amethyst banishes the desire for drink and promotes chastity." (Art Magic; or Mundane, Submundane, and Supermundané Spiritism.)

Lost its color in contact with and was an antidote for all poisons. (Albertus Magnus.)

According to Pliny, the amethyst was an antidote to drunkenness, and it takes its name from this property.   Moreover, if the name of the moon or sun be engraved on it and it be thus hung about the neck from the hair of a baboon or the feathers of a swallow, it is a charm against witchcraft.   It is also serviceable to persons having petitions to make to princes.   With the assistance of a spell or incantation it kept off hailstorms and flights of locusts.

Porta, in his treatise on magic, says that the amethyst neutralizes magic incantations.

The Puranas hold that the amethyst "gives strength and cures morbid heat and fistula."

Beryl.—Used with incantations to foretell the future and review the past, was efficacious in detecting thieves, forewarned death, and was supposed to have power over and to be the abode of evil spirits that could be made to work the wearer's will by means of suitable ncantations.   It rendered its owner cheerful, preserved and increased conjugal love, cured diseases of the throat and jaws and disorders "proceeding" from the humidity of the head, and is a preservative against them."   (Camillus Leonardus, Speculum Lapidum.   1502.)

According to Freeman, who wrote in 1701—

The beryl disturbs devils beyond all others.   If it be thrown in water with the words of its charm sung it shews various images of devils and gives answers to those that question it.   Being held in the mouth, a man may call a devil out of hell and receive satisfaction to such questions as he may ask.

Browning, in one of his poems, makes use of this belief.

The beryl was largely used for divination in 1600.   The method was as follows: A bowl was filled with water and the ring suspended in it.   The answer to the question propounded was spelled out by the ring striking the sides of the vessel.   A modification of this, and one still in use, was to mark the edges of the bowl with the letters of the alphabet; the stopping of the ring at certain letters composed the answer.   Still another method, and one said to have been used by Napier, was to throw a sphere cut from the stone into a bowl of water.

The character of the circles formed announced whether the presiding demon was favorable or not. If favorable, the information desired was pictured on the surface of the bowl.

Prior to the seventeenth century the beryl was in some repute as a curative. Mixed with an equal weight of silver, its powder, taken internally, was thought to cure leprosy. Water in which the stone had stood was good for the eyes, and, taken internally, it dispelled flatulency and cured indisposition of the liver.

Nicols, in the "Arcula Gemmea," published in 1653, said:

Wurtzung, in his general practice, saith that the beryll is used in all distempers of the heart. But take this caution by the way: Beware of the use of gemms (unless you are sure they be true) in physick, by reason they are so frequently adulterated.

Bloodstone.—Symbolical of wisdom, firmness, and courage.

Used with the proper incantations, its owner was enabled to foretell the future, and if rubbed with the juice of the heliotrope, it rendered its wearer invisible. The stone brought safety and long life to its possessor, stopped the flow of blood, and was an antidote for poisons. (Camillus Leonardus, Speculum Lapidum. 1502.)

Albertus Magnus taught that it cured dyspepsia, strengthened the stomach, and, if "washed according to medicinal art," was a styptic. Mixed with honey or the white of an egg, its powder was held by him to be an excellent remedy for hard tumors, while its dust would cure proud flesh and running sores.

Pliny and Leonardus mention that if placed in a basin of water containing the juice of the heliotrope and set in the sun, the water will appear red and the sun bloody. After a time the water will apparently boil and overflow the basin. Taken out of the water, the sun and solar eclipses could then be viewed in the water as in a mirror.

In a "Booke of the Thinges that are brought from the West Indies," published in 1574, the statement is made:

They doo bring from the New Spain a stone of great virtue, called the stone of the blood. The Bloodstone is a kind of jasper of divers colours, somewhat dark, full of sprinkles like to blood, being of colour red, of the which stones the Indians dooth make certayne Hartes, both great and small. The use thereof both there and here is for all fluxe of bloode, and of wounds. The stone must be wet in cold water, and the sick man must take him in his right hand and from time to time wet him in cold water. And as touching the Indians, they have it for certayne that touching the same stone in some part where the blood runneth, that it doth restrain.

The bishop of Rennes, in the eleventh century, writing on the talismanic efficacy of stones, asserts that the bloodstone endows its bearer with the gift of prophecy and renders him proof against poison.

During the Middle Ages the belief was prevalent in Europe that the stone had its origin in a dark-green jasper which happened to lie at the foot of the cross at the time of the crucifixion, and upon which the blood of Christ fell, hence the red spots.

Carnelian.—According to Epiphanius it cured tumors and all wounds made by iron.

It preserved the strength, prevented hoarseness, and cleared the voice. (Camillus Leonardus.)

It cheered the soul, banished fear and enchantments, and preserved harmony. (Albertus Magnus.)

According to the work by Giov. B. Porta, the wearing of a carnelian insured victory in all contests save those of love.

As an amulet and as a powder it was supposed to be a sovereign remedy for hemorrhage. De Laet, in 1647, has described from a personal experience its power in stopping bleeding at the nose, and advises the wearing of rings cut entirely from the stone for this purpose. The belief in its efficacy in such cases still persists.

Cat's-eye.—The cat's-eye cheers the mind, cures pallor, brings on a safe delivery in case of protracted labor, especially if tied in the hair of a patient. Applied locally, it causes infants suffering from the croup to bring up phlegm.

Applied as an ointment to the eyes, it cures lachryma. Calcined, the powder applied to sores heals them, and will cause new flesh to appear in the place of proud flesh. (Ben Adoula.)

According to the Mani-Málá, "the cat's-eye is warm, sour, and curative of cold, chronic derangements of the spleen, and colic, and is generally auspicious when worn." The same authority says that the perfect cat's-eyes, which are "heavy, deliciously cool, flawless, smooth, and otherwise faultless," are considered very lucky; while those that are defective bring about loss of friends, ruin, and wasting of the body.

The Hindus group the cat's-eye in four castes, according to their quality, all of which are replete with lucky signs.

The Persians held that the stone ground to a fine powder, mixed with water and then dried in the sun, and the operation repeated until the powder soaks up four times as much water as was first put in, would cure dropsy and inflammation of the navel if applied locally.

The Assyrians dedicated the stone to the god *Belus*, and ornaments containing it would, after the proper religious ceremony, render its wearer invisible to his enemies.

Chalcedony.—Prevented and cured melancholy. Worn as an amulet and in contact with the hairs of an ass, it was a preventive of danger during tempests and sinister events. (Camillus Leonardus, Speculum Lapidum. 1502.)

Reported to drive away evil spirits, a preventive of melancholy and sadness, and would bring victory to its wearer. (Andrea Baccius, Armot. Super. 6, c. de Natur. gem.)

Chrysoberyl.—As an amulet it dispelled evil dreams, fear, and melancholy; in addition, it possessed the properties of the beryl. (The Mirror of Stones. 1750.)

The oriental chrysolite (chrysoberyl) dispelled pestilential vapors and infectious airs. Taken internally, it alleviated asthma. (Rulandus, Medicina Practica. 1564.)

It was said to cool boiling water when immersed in it, soften anger, lose its luster on contact with poison, and induce its wearer to repent of the faults he had committed. (Porta, Magiae Naturalis. 1561.)

According to the Mani-Málá, the chrysoberyl, when set in gold and worn about the neck or hand, removes disease and vicious habits, and increases family, life, and happiness.

Chrysolite.—Cardanus, in his "De subtilitate," says that he cured one C. Palavicinus of a fever and another person of the "falling sickness" by the administration of powdered chrysolite with wine.

The powder was prescribed as a remedy for asthma. Held under the tongue, it assuaged thirst in fever. (Arcula Gemmea. 1653.)

Chrysoprase.—Preserved the sight, banished covetousness, and rendered its wearer cheerful. (Mirror of Stones. 1750.)

Worn as an amulet, it assuaged the pains of gout. (Arcula Gemmea. 1653.)

Bound around the arm, it was supposed to become a diuretic, to expel gravel, and prevent the generation of the stone. (Rulandus, Medicina Practica. 1564.)

Citrini.—The citrini (yellow corundum) protected the wearer from danger while traveling, secured him from pestilential vapors, and procured him every courtesy. (Arcula Gemmea. 1653.)

Coral.—In the "Arcula Gemmea" is a rather interesting account of the coral, as follows:

This is a but of maratime beauty, and the delight of children, the best of nature's buds, as somewhat furthering the springtide of their growth. The corall is a plant of nature's setting in the sea, which, though being covered with the waters of the sea, it bee green and soft, yet so soon as it is elevated above the waves and discovered in the region of the aire it altereth its colour and changeth its nature; its colour from green to a very noble and beautifull red; its softnesse into the compacted firmness and solidnesse of a stone, beautifull and lasting; by the operation of the aire encompassing its sometimes soft and flaccid substance. It is (under the waters of a brinish sea) a thriving, growing plant, sprung by nature with the ornament of many pretty branches, which is no sooner violently forc'd from the place of its growth and brought to light above the overflowing of the waters, but it blushes at the injurious hand that offereth violence to its secret, silent, tender, spreading growth.

Ovid, the Roman poet, accounts for the origin of the coral in the "Metamorphoses" in the following manner:

Perseus, having cut off the head of the Medusa, placed it upon some twigs and leaves near the seashore. The twigs were turned to stone on contact with the head, were scattered far and wide beneath the sea by sea nymphs, and thus became the seeds of coral.

The coral was thought to be of greater beauty when worn by a man than by a woman. By its change of color it was thought to fore-

warn the approach of disease; and should the wearer become danger-
ously sick, the gem became spotted.   Worn as an amulet, it drove
away fear, kept men from the influence of sorcery and evil spirits.
It was a protection against poison, plague, and storm.   (Arcula
Gemmea.   1653.)

It secured women from *incubus* and men *succubus* and hindered
the delusions of the devil.   (Dioscorides, De Materia Medica.)

Coral was administered, according to the following prescription,
for vomiting, purging, and colic:

Tabellae Corallatae.

℞.   Corrallorum rubeorum praeparatorum, ℥ii; margaritar praeparator, ℥i; boli
armeni, ℨβ; light aloes, Эi.   Sacch. albissimi dissoluti in aqua rosaru cinnamomi
tenuioris quantum sufficit; fiat confectio in tabellis.   (Arcula Gemmea.   1653.)

According to the "Medicina Practica" of Rulandus, written in
1564, a half drachm of powdered coral was given as a cardiac stimulant; and in all contagious diseases, fevers, and poisonings the
"tinctura corallorum" and the "sal corallorum" were equally
efficacious.

Stopped every flux of blood; drove away ghosts, illusions, and
dreams; was a protection against lightning, wind, tempest, and
attacks of wild beasts.   (Methrodorus.)

It gave relief to pains in the stomach and heart and strengthened
those organs.   It made sound diseased gums, and cleansed putrid
sores.   The powder, taken with wine, was given for the gravel.   If
hung on fruit-bearing trees, it insured fertility and protected them
from hail and blighting winds.   A kind known as *Grogius* had the
power of stopping thunder and lightning.   (Leonardus, Speculum
Lapidum.   1502.)

Before the time of Pliny coral was held in great esteem, but during
his period it was apparently not so highly appreciated, since he
remarks "that formerly it was deemed a most excellent antidote for
poison."   During the Middle Ages, however, it was in great repute
throughout Europe both as a drug and as an amulet.   It was at that
time deemed a powerful astringent, and in demand as a talisman
against witchcraft, poison, epilepsy, etc.

Boetius de Boot, writing in 1636, says that he was cured of a
dangerous pestilential fever by taking 6 drops of tincture of coral.
A. de Villenevee prescribed 10 grains of coral for infants in order to
preserve them from epilepsy or any other fit through life.   It is still
in repute as a preservative against children's diseases and is not infrequently worn suspended from the neck for this purpose.   In India it
is occasionally given to children in the hope of ridding them of the
hives and kindred itches.

According to the Mani-Málá a deep red coral was worn as an imme-
diate cure for poisoning.   Kar, an oriental sage, says that any man
who wears an ugly discolored and rough coral courts death.

Sanskrit medical science taught that coral is sour, sweet, a specific for cold and biliousness, nutritious, and grace imparting; and the wearing of it very beneficial to women.

According to the Arabic and Persian writers, as given by Tagore in his Treatise on Gems, a dose of coral was considered to be a good astringent, a remedy for all bleedings, and an antidote for all poisons. Worn over the parts it cured all stomach complaints; worn around the neck it stopped crying in infants and protected them from fear and sudden starts while asleep. In Afghanistan the coral mixed with gold dust is given as a tonic. In Egypt it is used according to the following receipt:

Cut open a lemon and put a piece of coral inside, cover the opening with a paste of clay, and place the whole under a fire for some time until it gets white from burning; remove it and after grinding the stone use it as an ointment for the eyes. Mixed with electuaries and taken internally it will give great physical strength.

Porta, in his Magiae Naturalis, says that the coral will arrest the flow of blood and keep off evil spirits. This belief still persists in Italy, where a hand holding a branch of coral is not infrequently worn as a protection against the evil eye.

Diamond.—This stone, being of all gems the purest, hardest, and most brilliant, was considered to be the most powerful in spiritual influences and was consecrated to all that was holy and heavenly. It was symbolical of constancy, purity, and innocence, and hence early used in betrothal rings. It softened anger, strengthened love, and was considered an infallible test of conjugal fidelity. To the ancients the diamond represented inexorable justice and unchangeable fate, hence the judges of Hades were described as having hearts and bosoms of adamant.

According to the Talmud, a certain gem, supposed to have been the diamond, worn in the girdle of the high priest, if brought in contact with an accused man became dark and dim if the suspect was guilty; if innocent the stone shown with increased brilliancy.

In Europe as late as 1700 the diamond was thought to be the most potent talisman against poison, pestilence, witchcraft, etc. It was esteemed a safeguard to virtue; was used as a preventive of and a cure for lunacy. It was supposed to drive away lemures, incubi, and kindred terrors; and was considered a preservative against lightning. The gem was supposed to possess sex, and Boetius de Boot mentions two such diamonds which by their union produced others and thus left a numerous progeny.

Sir John Mandeville also bears witness to the procreative powers of diamonds:

They grow together, male and female, and are nourished by the dew of heaven; and they engender commonly, and bring forth small children that multiply and grow all the year.' I have oftentimes tried the experiment, that if a man keep them with a little of the rock, and wet them with May dew often, they shall grow every year and the small will grow great.

Speaking further concerning the diamond, Mandeville held that in order to secure the greatest good from a diamond it should be worn on the left side:

For it is of greater virtue than on the right side; for the strength of their growing is toward the north, that is the left side of the world, and the left part of a man is when he turns his face toward the east. He who so carries the diamond upon him, it gives him hardness and manhood, and it keeps the limbs of his body whole. It gives him victory over his enemies, if his cause is just; and it keeps him that bears it in good wit; and it keeps him from strife and riot; from sorrows and enchantments; and from phantasies and illusions of wicked spirits. It makes a man stronger and firmer against his enemies; and heals him that is a lunatic, and those whom the fiend pursues or torments. And if venom or poison be brought in presence of the diamond, anon it begins to grow moist and sweat. Nevertheless, it happens often that the good diamond loses its virtue by sin, and for incontinence of him who bears it; and then it is needful to make it recover its virtue again, or else it is of little value.

Pierre de Boniface, a fourteenth century alchemist, taught that one of the virtues of the diamond was to render its wearer invisible and invincible.

In this connection the Shah of Persia is the possessor of a diamond set in a scimitar which is believed to render him invincible so long as he has it by him. The shah also has a five-pointed star of diamonds which is thought to make conspirators instantly confess their crimes when in its presence.

A diamond ring was given to Mary, Queen of Scots, by Ruthven, as a talisman against danger and poison. The queen also possessed two other diamonds—"one medicinable and against poison," the other "medicinable for the collicke."

According to the Puranas, the diamond varies in the preponderance of one or the other of the five primal elements—

Earth, water, sky, energy, and air. The "airy" sort gives heart and gracefulness, the "skyey" diamonds bring about the possession of all kinds of wealth. The ownership and use of those kinds in which energy predominates adds to puissance, heroism, and hope. Those diamonds which are white like the jessamine flower, white clouds, or the moon, and are possessed of six or eight corners, sharp ridged, that have originated from water, and that shine in the darkness, lead to the instant cure of snake bites, and prove efficacious in neutralizing the effects of other poisons, and prove a panacea as soon as worn.

Like men, diamonds are divided into castes—Brahmins, Vaisya, Kshatriyas, and Súdras. The wearing of superior Brahmin diamonds gives favor in the eyes of the gods. The better sort of the Kshatriya class bring about uniform success, accession of power, and destruction of foes. The best stones of the Vaisya class are productive of fame, wisdom, and skill in the fine arts. The higher order of the Súdra caste induce benevolence in their owner and make him hale and wealthy.

As the promiscuous intercourse of one caste with another gives rise to mixed castes among men, so it is with diamonds. These mixed castes give rise to impurities and flaws in the stones, and which, according to their nature and kind, are fraught with grave trouble to man.   Such diamonds cause unchastity; brings destruction; renders man apprehensive of snake bites; creates fear; leads to ruin, loss of family dignity, and death.   Such stones are dangerous to pregnant women and contact with them may lead to abortion.

A shapeless diamond is fraught with danger; a dirty diamond with grief; a rough diamond with unhappiness, and a black diamond with various troubles.   A three-cornered diamond gives rise to quarrels; a four-cornered diamond occasions various fears; a five-cornered one brings death; but a six-cornered stone is productive of good.

Since the use of impure diamonds leads to danger, causes swelling in wounds, faintness, leprosy, pleurisy, jaundice, etc., it is highly advisable to refine and purify the stone before using it medicinally.

The process is as follows: On some auspicious day dip the diamond in the juice of *Kantakari* (solarium jaquiri) and then burn it in a fire made of dried cow or buffalo dung.   The burning should be carried on for a whole night.   In the morning the diamond should be put under horse's urine and again burnt.   These operations are continued for seven days.   The stone is then immersed in a gruel made of various leguminous seeds to which assafoedita and rock salt have been added and heated repeatedly twenty and one times.   By this means the diamond is purified and reduced to ashes.   The taking of a diamond so treated gives longevity, strength, energy, beauty, develops the parts, and effects a cure for every distemper. (Mani-Mála.)

The Brahmin diamond is useful in chemical operations, and brings about the acquisition of power, friends, wealth, position, and good luck to one's family.   A Kshatriya diamond wards off old age and premature death; a Vaisya one crowns every endeavor with success; while a Súdra one is a panacea.

The Hindu held that the diamond was masculine, feminine, or neuter according to its marking and appearance.   The masculine kinds were considered the best and were useful in medicine.   The feminine diamond was auspicious to women; but the neuter diamond was destructive of vigor and brought weakness and disappointment; as a medicine it was administered for impotency.

According to the views of Arabian and Persian authorities the diamond, if worn, imparted health and dispelled fear.   Tied around the thighs of a woman about to be confined it brought on a safe and speedy delivery and assuaged the pain of labor.   Cut into a hexagon and worn on the arm it cured epilepsy.   Combined with other ingredients and used as a dentifrice it rendered the teeth bright and hard; its use in this manner was attended with risks, for on too long a contact with the teeth it caused them to fall out; while the presence of a single particle in the stomach was liable to produce death.   It was a fatal poison if taken internally without electuaries; and—

if by accident one takes a quantity of it his life should not be considered safe until he is made to vomit it out by means of drinking a quantity of fresh cow's milk or some heated clarified butter, or by any other means, such as applying the fingers to the inside of the throat.   The soup of some fatty flesh is then to be given to the patient to complete the recovery. (Tagore, Treatise on Gems.)

The Burmese call the diamond and arsenic by the same name, *chein,* on the ground that they are both fatal poisons.

This idea was not unknown in Europe, for we find the diamond listed as one of the poisons given to Sir Thomas Overbury when a prisoner in the Tower; while Benvenuto Cellini, the famous goldsmith, writing about 1560, relates how his life was preserved by the roguery of an apothecary, who, being employed to pulverize a diamond intended to be mixed in a salad for Cellini with the intention of poisoning him, substituted a beryl as cheaper, thus saving the life of Cellini.

According to Sanskrit medicine the diamond combined all the six tastes, cured every disease, brought health and strength, and was very useful in chemical operations. (Mani-Málá.)

In Egypt the diamond, when set in gold, gives health and wealth to its wearer.

According to Porta, in his Magiae Naturalis, the diamond contends against sleeplessness, enchantments, and turns away wrath.

Rabbi Benoni, a fourteenth century mystic, held that the diamond was capable of producing somnambulism, and when used as a talisman with lodestone and sapphire it would attract such powerful planetary influences as to render its wearer almost invincible.

In Art Magic; or Mundane, Submundane, and Supermundane Spiritism, it is stated that the diamond is the most powerful of all means to promote spiritual ecstacy.

Emerald.—Emblematic of happiness. As an amulet it was a preserver of chastity, and betrayed or punished its violation by flying into pieces or losing color. It preserved women in childbirth and eased the pains of labor; water in which the stone had stood hastened the afterbirth. (Leonardus.) Applied to the lips it stopped hemorrhage. When hung around the neck it prevented epileptic attacks. (Albertus Magnus.)

Dedicated to Mercury.

Much used by astrologers for the purpose of divination. (Cardanus, De Lapidibus Preciosis.)

Albertus Magnus cites the case of a certain King of Hungary who, while wearing an emerald, had knowledge of his wife, upon which the stone broke in three parts.

There is such an enmity betwixt it and illegitimate venery, or the uncleanness of the flesh, as that if it do but touch the skin of an adulterer it will break, and that it doth bridle the reins of lasciviousness and much temper it. (Arcula Gemmea.)

Avenzoar held that it was an antidote for poisons, and that 6 grains of its powder taken in water made an excellent cordial.

Mundella, a sixteenth century physician, calls attention to the purchase of a fine emerald by Franciscus Maria, Prince of Urbine, for use as a remedy in the treatment of a disorder with which he was troubled. (Arcula Gemmea.)

Ahmed Ben Abdalaziz, in his Treatise on Jewels, says that if a serpent fix his eyes on the luster of emeralds he immediately becomes blind. Thus Moore in "Lalla Rookh":

> Blinded like serpents when they gaze
> Upon the emerald's virgin blaze.

The Shah of Persia has a small casket of gold studded with emeralds, said to have been blessed by Mahomet, which has the property of rendering the royal wearer invisible so long as he remains celibate.

The San Greal was a chalice made from a single emerald, and which possessed the power of preserving chastity, prolonging life, curing wounds and disease, and other wonderful properties. The Holy Grail was used at the Last Supper, and in it were caught the last drops of the blood of Christ as he was taken from the cross. In the legends and poetry of the Middle Ages are many notices of the Greal—a subject revived by Tennyson.

The Romans used it to rest, strengthen, and preserve the eyes, a practice which persisted through the Middle Ages, during which period water in which the stone had stood was used as a specific for ophthalmia.

Boetius de Boot gives directions for its treatment for use as a drug as follows:

Pound the emerald in an iron mortar, sift the powder through the muslin, then cover it with *spiritos urinae;* the spirit must be distilled off, leaving the powder of a gray color, but which will communicate that of the emerald to the spirits of wine.

This taken internally was considered a powerful remedy for many diseases, such as dysentery, epilepsy, venomous bites, fevers, etc.

According to Sanskrit medicine—

The emerald is cool, good in poisoning, sweet, and purgative, helps digestion, cures biliousness, removes disrelish, is nutritious, and wards off spectral influences. (Tagore, Treatise on Gems.)

The Hindu authorities held that the perfect emerald was an infallible remedy for all cases of poisoning; cleansed men from sin, brought about success in war, and rendered successful the rites performed according to the Atharva-Veda. The defective emerald led to sickness, injury, loss of male children, and rendered one liable to bites. (Mani-Málá.)

The Persian and Arabian sages taught that, whether worn or taken as a medicine, the emerald—

bestows contentment of mind; quickens the pulse; gives nourishment to the soul, heart, brains, and stomach; cures epilepsy; removes all bodily pain; stops the vomiting and purging of blood; is an antidote to poison; allays unnatural thirst; and is a panacea for jaundice, liver troubles, stricture, gravel, and leprosy.

If administered in doses weighing 8 wheat corns to a patient suffering from poison, it neutralizes its action, provided it be taken soon enough. To prevent vomiting of blood, the dose of the emerald should be the weight of 4 barleycorns. The powder, applied to the eyes, brings out all impurities therein and stops the flow of fluid substances. When set in a gold ring and worn on the forefinger or thumb it is prophylactic against cholera. The ashes of burnt emerald heals ulcers if applied locally.

According to the Rosicrucians, if at the time when Sol enters Libra an emerald be set in a gold ring of the same weight and worn on the finger, its wearer would attain his cherished object and could detect the presence of poisons by the sweating of the stone.

The possessor of an emerald would never become poor.

If a serpent looked at this stone, he was struck with blindness.

The Egyptians held that the best test for a genuine emerald was that a serpent immediately fell to licking it as soon as it came across it.

The Aztecs administered its powder as a remedy for venereal diseases.

Garnet.—Emblematic of constancy. Its virtue was to dispel "poisonous and infectious airs" (Leonardus). During the Middle Ages it was considered to possess the same marvelous and medicinal properties as the ruby, though to a less degree. It gave and preserved health, drove away vain thoughts, and reconciled differences between friends.

Suspended from the neck, it kept off plague and thunder, strengthened the heart, and increased riches and honors. (Giov. B. Porta, Magiae Naturalis. 1561.)

According to the Puranas—

A garnet which is colored like the conch, the lotus, the black bee, or the sun, and which is strung on a thread, is sound and auspicious, and heralds good fortune. A garnet which is colored like the crow, the horse, the ass, the jackal, the bull, or the blood-stained beak of a vulture holding a piece of flesh, brings on death.

Jacinth.—Procured sleep, riches, honor, and wisdom. A preservative against pestilence and foes. (Leonardus, Speculum Lapidum. 1502.)

Cardanus, in De Lapidibus preciosis, says that he was in the habit of carrying a jacinth about him for the purpose of inducing sleep, which he says "it did seem somewhat to confer, but not much."

Nicols, quoting Cardanus, says that jacinth procured sleep, cheered the heart, drove away plagues, brought protection from thunder, and increased wisdom and honor when worn on the finger or about the neck as an amulet. (Arcula Gemmea. 1653.)

Jade.—Worn as an amulet or administered internally, it was a curative of diseases of the kidney and loins.

Wecker, in the Antidotae speciale de Lapidibus minus preciosis Alterantibus, says that a nobleman, well known to him, had a fine "nephritick stone," which he wore on his arm—

by the power of which he voided a very great quantity of gravel, so great as that he feared lest he should suffer harm by so large an expulsion of it in so short a time.

Porta, in the Magiae Naturalis, says: It alleviates the pain of the kidneys, expels gravels from the bladder, and when worn as a charm is a preservative against venomous things.

Jasper.—Was a charm against scorpions and spiders. (Boot, Gemmarum et Lapidarum Historia. 1690.)

Checked the flow of blood; strengthened the chest, lungs, and stomach; cured fevers and dropsy; cleared the sight, and prevented conception. (Leonardus, Speculum Lapidum. 1502.)

In the list of valuables left by George, Earl Marischal, who died in 1620, is "ane jaspe stone for steming of bluid."

Mottled jasper, suitably engraved, was believed to prevent its wearer from death by drowning and to render him free from injury while on the water. (Arcula Gemmea. 1653.)

Burton, in the Anatomy of Melancholy, says:

If hung about the neck, or taken in drink, it much resisteth sorrow.

Nonus, a physician of the Middle Ages, reported of it that it cured epilepsy.

Galen asserted that a green jasper, worn as an amulet suspended from the neck so that it was above the navel, would cure dyspepsia and strengthen the stomach.

Jet.—Cardanus (De Subtilitate, lib. 5) says:

The wearing of this stone doth secure men from nocturnal fears, from incubus or succubus, or the nightmare, and from evil spirits; and that being drunk will show whether a maid hath her virginity or no.

Believed to dissolve spells and enchantments.

If burned as incense, its smoke drives away devils and relieves the dropsical. (Boetius, De Gagate.)

Bruised in water and given to a gravid animal, it brings forward the fetus. Its powder cures epilepsy and fastens loose teeth. Mixed with the marrow of a stag and taken internally it cures snake bites. (Speculum Lapidum. 1502.)

Used as a perfume it prevented irregularity in female periods. (Wurtz, Tab. gener. prac.)

Lapis-lazuli.—Believed to cure melancholia. (Speculum Lapidum.) Dioscorides, in De Materia Medica, suggests its use as a cure for melancholy, and states that it is a good purgative.

Cardanus advises its use in pectoral diseases of children and in epilepsy. The dose to be 5 grains. (De Subtilitate.)

Boetius (Tract. de Lapidibus et Gemmis) states that it is a good purgative. Unwashed, it purges by vomiting; washed, it purges by stool. Used for this purpose to-day in India, Chile, and Peru.

A. Mussa Brassavolus (Lib. de Med. purgant.) used it as a purgative according to the following prescription:

℞ Lapidis lazuli praeparati, ʒj. Camphorae, anisi, cinnamomi, zinziberis, mastiches ana, gr. 6. Misce, cum succo salviae vel diacatholico fiant pilulae quinq.

Dosis est à ℨij ad ℨj, aut in pilulis, aut in pulvere, aut in jure, aut in aqua Boraginis, aut in conserva Boraginis, aut in vino cretico.

According to Sanskrit medical science lapis-lazuli is cooling and a curative of biliousness.   (Mani-Málá.)

Lodestone.—Orpheus, in the Hymni et de Lapidibus, says:

It will confer strength, banish disease, and when worn constantly about the person ward off epidemics and plagues. Sitting before it and fixing the eyes earnestly upon it one has but to ask the gods for light on any subject, and the answer will come breathing out through the stone. The soul will hear it and the senses discover it clearly.

In great repute in Europe during the fifteenth, sixteenth, and seventeenth centuries for its numerous virtues as an amulet and drug.   Carried about the person it cured cramp and gout; held in the hand during the hour of travail it shortened the time and eased the pains of labor.   Bruised and taken internally with the juice of fennel it cured disorders of the spleen; applied as an ornament it prevented baldness.   A dram of the stone mixed with the fat of a serpent and the juice of nettles caused insanity.   The powder thrown over a household fire caused the inmates to flee in a panic, an artifice, according to the popular belief, made use of by thieves.   (The Mirror of Stones.   1750.)

It is good against the headache, convulsions, and poisons; and that it causeth easy delivery, and procureth love 'twixt man and wife, and preserveth peace and concord amongst friends, and that it driveth away fears and increases wisdom.   Galen and Dioscorides say it. (Arcula Gemmea.   1653.)

Lodestone is in repute to-day as a preventive and cure for cramps, colic, and rheumatism.   Among the American negroes it is used as a voodoo stone, and is thought to be a love charm; to possess phallic properties; to increase the strength of the body, and to cure lumbago, rheumatism, and hernia.

Malachite.—Thought to increase the strength and growth of children and ward from them all dangers and infirmities. (Pliny, Nat. Hist.; Solinus, Polyhist., C. 36; Baccius de Nat. gem., C. 29.)

It strengthened the stomach; preserved children from hurt and convulsions.   (Arcula Gemmea.)

Boetius states that 6 grains taken internally acts as an excellent purgative.   It will cure "cardialgia" and colic.   (Tract. de Lapidibus et Gemmis.)

Held to be a powerful local anaesthetic, for "being taken in drink or bruised in vinegar and applied to the members that are to be cut off and burnt, it makes them so insensible that they feel scarce any pain.   (Speculum Lapidum.)

Moonstone.—According to Pliny, "the image of the moon contained therein daily waxes or wanes according to the period of the lunar motion."

During the period of the increase of the moon it was a potent love charm; during the period of decrease it enabled its wearer to fortell the future. Carried in the mouth it became an aid to the memory. As a powder and amulet it was prescribed in case of epilepsy. (Camillus Leonardus.) It is still used for this purpose among the Basques. (Crevecoeur.)

Onyx.—Its origin, according to the Greek legend, was due to Cupid cutting the nails of the sleeping Venus with his arrow; these falling into the Indus were changed to onyx.

The stone was thought to be a powerful aphrodisiac; to increase spittle in children; hasten a birth; give rise to nightmare, and stir up strife. Used as an eyestone "it enters of its own accord, and if it found anything within that is noxious, it drives it out and tempers the hurtful and contrary humors." (Camillus Leonardus, Speculum Lapidum. 1502.)

The belief in its causing nightmare and strife was widespread. This belief was explained by Beononi on the assumption that "in the onyx is a demon imprisoned in the stone who wakes only of a night, causing terror and disturbance to sleepers who wear it."

Among the Persians the onyx is to-day administered as a drug for the cure of epilepsy.

Opal.—Symbolical of hope.

The gem was in great repute as an eyestone, and was used in all diseases of the eye. It partook of all the virtues of those stones whose colors it showed. (Camillus Leonardus, Speculum Lapidum. 1502.)

It stimulated the heart; preserves from contagious and infectious airs; drives away dispondency; prevents fainting, heart disease, and malignant affections. (Giov. B. Porta, Magiae Naturalis. 1561.)

The opal was supposed to indicate the state of health of its wearer by change of color, losing its brilliancy if the wearer was ill, and the opposite.

The idea that the opal is unlucky is based on a Teutonic superstition, and is comparatively modern. Mention of its supposed evil qualities is made in a work entitled "Art Magic; Mundane, Submundane, and Supermundane Spiritism," in which the opal is credited with being fatal to love and sowing discord between giver and receiver.

Pearl.—Emblematic of purity, beauty, and nobility.

Pliny states that pearls were supposed to be generated by a celestial dew falling on the shellfish, which, in the early mornings of certain seasons, left the bottom of the sea to draw in the air containing the dew from which the pearls were derived, the size and quality of the pearl depending upon the size of the dewdrop and the purity of the air.

Cloudy weather spoiled the color, lightning stopped the growth, and thunder ruined the gem.

According to the ancient Hindu authorities pearls were held to originate in elephants, clouds, boars, conch shells, fishes, frogs, oysters, and bamboos. Of these the oysters were the most productive. The pearls were formed by raindrops falling into the open shell of the mollusk, the finest gems being found during the period when the sun rested on Arcturus, the fifteenth lunar asterism.

In the Orient the pearl was and is extensively used as a medicine for syncope, hemorrhage, stomach troubles, etc. In China large quantities of seed pearls are made into an electuary and taken to restore manly vigor and as a stimulant.

According to Sanskrit medical science the pearl is "sweet in taste, very cool, and a specific for eye diseases, cures poisoning and atrophy, and brings strength to weak limbs." (Mani-Málá.)

The Arabian and Persian sages held that the use of pearls was conducive to contentment of body and soul; cured insanity and all mental diseases; all diseases of the heart, stomach, and bowels; piles, stricture, and excessive and insufficient menstruation. It was an antidote for poison, stopped bleeding from cuts, and cured leprosy and skin diseases.

Rambam recommends the use of the burnt powder as an ointment in the treatment of ulcers and diseases of the eye, such an conjunctivitis, cataract, etc. The burnt powder taken internally cured vomiting of blood and purging.

According to Egyptian medicine, pearl powder taken with electuaries strengthened the body and added luster to the eyes.

The Hindu authorities recognized four shades as belonging to pearls—yellow, honey, white, and blue. The first brings wealth, the second fosters understanding, the third brings fame, and the fourth good luck. If defective, according to the kind and degree, the pearl brought on leprosy, loss of male issue, loss of fortune, disgrace, slothfulness, insanity, and death. (Mani-Málá.)

According to Art Magic; or Mundane, Submundane, and Supermundane Spiritism, the wearing of pearls brought one en rapport with spirits and promoted chastity.

In Bengal bracelets of pearl are worn by virgins to preserve their virtue.

In Europe as late as the seventeenth century decoctions containing pearls were thought to be powerful mental stimulants and a cure for insanity. A decoction of pearl powder and distilled water was one of the remedies given to the insane Charles, King of Spain.

Leonardus states that pearls boiled in meat would cure the quartan ague; powdered and taken with milk, they healed ulcers and cleared the voice; they comforted the heart, gave relief in cramps and colic, cured epilepsy and dysentery; taken with sugar, they were of assistance in the cure of pestilential fevers, and that they rendered their wearers virtuous.

According to Nicols (Arcula Gemmea) pearls were—

good against syncopes, and cardiacall passions, that they do comfort the spirits, stop the fluxes of blood, cure lienteries and diarrheas, and that they are good for the sight.

Prase.—Supposed to possess all the properties of the emerald, but to a less degree. Lost its color on contact with poison or venom, but recovered it again on being washed. Reported to be an excellent cordial and cardiac stimulant. Applied to the eyes, it strengthened the sight. (Arcula Gemmea. 1653.)

Benoni states that the powder mixed with the milk of a ewe that has had but one lamb will, if applied locally, cure the gout; taken internally, it was a deadly poison.

Quartz.—The powder mixed with wine was given for dysentery in the north of England during the twelfth century. A crystal held against the tongue assuaged thirst. (Leonardus, Speculum Lapidum.)

Applied locally to-day in the mountains of Georgia for faintness, headaches, and bleeding at the nose. Used in parts of Virginia to cure styes; the sty is rubbed with the crystal three times a day for three days. In northern New York a so-called "vital ore," consisting entirely of quartz sand, is sold as a veritable panacea, curing sore eyes, piles, carbuncles, indigestion, sore throat, giddiness, and blood poisoning.

In the Middle Ages the clear, transparent quartz was believed to betray the presence of poison, either by becoming opaque or breaking. The powder, mixed with wine, was given in dysentery; held in the mouth, it assuaged thirst, cured headaches and faintness; powdered and taken with wine and honey, it filled the breasts of nursing women with milk. (Leonardus.)

Orpheus recommended its use as a medicine for diseases of the kidneys.

Andrea Bacci, writing in 1605, says:

It is used either in powder, or the salt of it, or the oil of it, against all obstructions of the bowels, against gouts, swoonings, and all cephalic diseases.

A drachm of the powder taken with oil of sweet almonds cures those that have taken sublimate. (Arcula Gemmea. 1653.)

Quartz balls were and are used by mystics, astrologers, and diviners to forestall the future, review the past, and conjure up distant scenes. The famous "show-stone" of Doctor Dee, a sphere 3 inches in diameter, was made of quartz. It is interesting to note that while the modern mystic and the mystic of the Middle Ages differ somewhat in their methods, each has the same end in view, and each has produced witnesses to show that he attained that end.

The methods used to induce a vision as practiced by the mystic of the Middle Ages are as follows: The crystal, according to Scot, in his Discovery of Witchcraft, when "charged" with the name of St. Helen, written on the stone with olive oil while the operator faced the east, and held in the hands of an innocent child born in wedlock, would, upon the recital of a prayer to the saint, become an oracle and answer any question put to it.

In an eighteenth century manuscript is the following statement:

Take a christall stone or glasse, most clear, without a craise, and wrape about it a pece of harte's lether, saying, "In the name of the Holy Trinity, and of the hey Deity Amen." Then holde the cristalle in the beam where the ☉ is most bright, at the hotest of the day, and say there con(jurations) subscribed, and by and by you shall sie the spirit peradventer, appeiring himselfe.

The spirit is then to be "charged," upon which he will point out the whereabouts of stolen property; the location of buried treasure; give information concerning relatives, friends, or enemies, or such other information as may be desired.

According to Hindu authorities the quartz is cool and cooling, cures hemorrhage from the nose and mouth, and when worn removes baneful astral influences.

The crystal gives strength and cures biliousness, morbid heat, and fistula. A specific for consumption, leprosy, and poisoning. It may enter into medicines as a substitute for diamonds. (Mani-Mālá.)

A good rock crystal is an infallible remedy in all cases of poisoning. Wild animals like the leopard, the elephant, the lion, and the tiger, can not approach this gem. It neutralizes snake, rat, and scorpion poisons, and the wearer need never fear drowning, fire, or a thief. A moss-colored, clouded, rough, yellow, dull, dirty, and discolored rock crystal the authorities shun from a distance. (Tagore, a Treatise on Gems.)

Ruby.—Emblematic of love.

A sovereign remedy and amulet against plague, poison, evil thoughts, nightmare, and diverted the mind from sadness and sensuality. (Leonardus, Speculum Lapidum.)

It forewarned the wearer of the approach of any misfortune by loss of color. In this connection Wolfgang Gabelchover gives his experience:

On December 5, 1600, as I was travelling from Studtgard in company with my beloved wife, Catherine Adelmann, of pious memory, I observed most distinctly during the journey that a very fine ruby, her gift, which I wore set in a ring upon my finger, had lost almost all its splendid color, and had put on dullness in place of brilliancy and darkness in place of light; which blackness and opacity lasted not for one or two days only, but for several. * * * Whereupon I warned my wife that some grievous mishap was impending over either her or myself, as I foreboded from the change of color in my ruby. Nor was I wrong in my anticipation, inasmuch as within a few days she was taken with a fatal sickness that never left her till the day of her death. And truly, after her decease, its former brilliant color returned spontaneously to my ruby.

Arabian and Persian writers taught that the wearer of the ruby obtained peace of mind and strength of brain.

A *durm* dose of it, taken internally, cures epilepsy, insanity, cholera, and the spitting of blood; causes free circulation of blood throughout the system, and prevents uneasiness of mind. It cures all kinds of poisonings from snake bite or from admininstration of poison by enemies. It frees the atmosphere from the pollution engendered by cholera. It purifies the blood and brings back to its normal state the fatally quick action of the pulse. The wearer of the ruby in the form of a finger ring obtains from the deity all the desires of his heart and becomes proof against thunder stroke and cholera. Worn over the eyes or applied to them as an ointment it cures all complaints of the vision; over the mouth it takes away the bad smell of it, allays thirst, and gives constant satisfaction to the mind. It brings honor to the wearer. The dose for internal use is from 1 kirat (4 barleycorns) to 1 dang (16 barleycorns). (See the work Karabadin Kabir, as cited by Tagore in his Treatise on Gems.)

The ruby enters into the Chinese pharmacopoeia as an ingredient in the "five precious fragments," supposed to consist of ruby, topaz, emerald, sapphire, and hyacinth.

The Hindu writers held that those rubies—

which are flawless and of approved color are auspicious, produce health, wealth, wisdom, and happiness. If flawed or offcolored they bring humiliation, loss of friends, liability to wounds, loss of wealth, and lightning stroke; are fatal to domestic animals, and are inimical to life, wealth, and fame. The man who treasures a ruby furnished with every perfection, and which when cast in a quantity of milk a hundred times its bulk, makes the white mass one entire sheet of red, or sends out a red flame, is as meritorious as the celebration of the *Aswamedha jajna*.[1] Such a stone leads to wealth success, happiness, and long life. (Mani-Málá.)

Sapphire.—Emblematic of wisdom. If placed on the heart it bestows strength and energy. St. Jerome states that the sapphire procures royal favors, softens anger, frees people from enchantment, obtains release from captivity, and prevents evil and impure thoughts.

Because of its extreme coldness it was thought to preserve the chastity of its wearer, hence especially suited for ecclesiastical rings.

Worn in a ring or in any other manner it is able to quench concupiscence, and for this reason it is proper to be worn by the priesthood and by all persons vowed to perpetual chastity. It is said to grow dull if worn by an adulterous or lascivious person.

It rendered its wearer chaste, virtuous, pious, devout, wise, amiable, and pacific. It cured boils, carbuncles, and headaches, rested and refreshed the body, and gave a color to the cheeks. Taken with milk it cured cramps. (Leonardus, Speculum Lapidum. 1502.)

Soaked in vinegar its vinegar extract was administered in fevers; powdered and soaked in vinegar for one phase of the moon, it was given to insure continency and conjugal love. (Galen.)

---

[1] The Horse Sacrifice, a celebrated ceremony, the antiquity of which dates back to the Vedic period.

Placed on the heart it cured fever; on the forehead it stopped bleeding at the nose. The powder taken with milk was a remedy for fevers, plague, and poison. (Albertus Magnus.)

The powdered sapphire used as an ointment cured inflammation and irritation of the eyes; it was also thought to be able to draw out any foreign substance that might be present in them. (Canones Medicinae.)

According to Giov. Porta the sapphire was of great service in necromancy and the magic arts, and a deadly enemy to all venomous reptiles and insects. (Magiae Naturalis. 1561.)

The Hindus regarded the stone as unlucky and as a bringer of misfortune. Thus:

A sapphire, the surface of which wears a micalike sheen * * * brings about loss of wealth and life. That mark in a sapphire which at first sight looks like a rift, * * * renders one liable to bites. That sapphire which is parti-colored causes loss of family dignity. The sapphire which contains dirt produces a variety of skin diseases like itching. That which contains gritty fragments is destructive; that which is rough causes banishment. (Mani-Málá.)

The same authority says, however, "that sapphire which when placed in a pot of milk darkens it all through, increases wealth, and is conducive to fame and increase of family," while "a flawless, sterling sapphire brings its wearer strength, fame, and length of days," and "the man who wears a sapphire of spotless chastity finds favor with *Narayana*,[1] and acquires longevity, family dignity, fame, understanding, and wealth."

According to the Sanskrit medical science the sapphire is bitter, warm, and good in cold and biliousness, and when worn alleviates the rage of *Sani*.[2]

In Egypt the sapphire is taken with *majoom* (electuaries) to add strength to the body. (Tagore, Treatise on Gems.)

The Buddhists esteem the sapphire above all gems, claiming that it produced tranquillity of mind, and when worn by one wholly pure and devoted to God insures protection against disease, danger, and venomous reptiles.

The saphire is of a cold and drie faculty, even as are most pretious stones; it is reported of it that it is good against feverish distempers, hence this old distick.

Corporis ardorem refrigerat interiorem
Sapphirus, & cypriæ languida vota facit.

The best of these are very comfortable to the eyes if they be often looked on. (Arcula Gemmea. 1653.)

It is reported of it that if it be worn by an adulterer, by loosing its splendor it will discover his adultery. (Cardanus, De Lapidibus preciosis.)

The sapphire is of so contrary a nature to poisons that if placed in a glass with a spider the insect will quickly die. (Arcula Gemmea. 1653.)

---

[1] The preserver of the Hindu Triad.
[2] One of the stars influencing the destinies of men.

St. Jerome wrote that the sapphire conciliates to its wearer the condescension of princes, quells his enemies, disperses sorcery, sets free the captive, and may even assuage the wrath of God.

In the inventory of the jewels of Charles V mention is made of a "bluestone with two clasps of gold, good for the gout."

In the church of Old St. Paul's, London, was a famous sapphire which was supposed to cure the infirmities of the eyes of all those thus afflicted who might resort to it.

The modern mystic holds it capable of attracting powerful planetary influences, and nearly equal to the diamond and quartz in inducing visions. (Art Magic; or Mundane, Submundane, and Supermundane Spiritism.)

The star sapphire was and is still reputed to be a potent love charm. The powder of this gem was taken as an aphrodisiac during the Middle Ages. Star sapphire as a powder was given for vertigo in the low countries as late as 1810.

Sard.—Said to possess sex.

The males shine brighter than the females; for the females are the fattest and glitter more obscurely. (Leonardus, Speculum Lapidum.)

The sard nullified the evil effects of the onyx when worn with it, sharpened the wit, gave cheerfulness, and prevented dysentery. (Albertus Magnus, Leonardus, and De Boot.)

Epiphanius, writing in 1565, says that the sard conferred upon its wearer a cheerful heart, courage, and presence, and protected him from witchcraft and noxious humors.

Baccius in his Annotations says that powdered sard taken in spirits stops the menses and prevents miscarriage.

Sardonyx.—Symbolical of conjugal bliss. It rendered its possessor virtuous, cheerful, and agreeable. (Leonardus, Speculum Lapidum. 1502.)

Spinel.—Reconciled differences between friends; gave health and strength to the body; cured disorders of the liver; restrained passion and fiery wrath; and was a preservative from lightning. (Leonardus.)

Powdered and taken with water Arnobis used it as a remedy for diseases of the eye. (Dissertatio Medica.)

Boetius held that the wearing of a balas ruby (spinel) restrained fury, wrath, and lust.

In the Arcula Gemmea, written in 1653, the author, Nicols, says:

Rulandus reporteth this of it: That if the four corners of a house, arbor, or vineyard be covered with this stone it will preserve it from lightning, tempests, and worms.

According to Arabian and Persian medicine, the wearing of the spinel gives contentment, prevents the spitting of blood, cures piles and all diseases caused by the increase of phlegm. The dose for internal use is from 1 *kirat* (4 barleycorns) to 1 *dang* (16 barleycorns). Applied as an ointment to the eyes the stone adds to their luster.

According to an Arabic work, entitled "Azaabul beldan," as cited by Tagore:

The sea cows get spinel stones from the Kokaf Mountains and put them on the ground when they come grazing toward Ceylon. The stone gatherers, who remain concealed all about, then come out in stealthy steps, carefully throw lumps of clay over the stones left, and then retire. When after grazing these animals go back to the sea, disappointed at not finding the stones and fretting and fuming with rage, those people came back and took away the precious stones.

Staurolite.—In Brittany, France, a superstitious reverence is attached to the cruciform crystals of this stone, based on a belief that they fell from heaven.

In Virginia and the Carolinas the staurolite, locally known as fairy stone, is worn as a lucky charm and is believed to bring good fortune and ward off danger and disease.

Sunstone.—According to Sanskrit authorities—

the sunstone is warm, flawless, and good in cold and defective oxidation, and sacred; it is an *elixir vitae*, and is the delight of the Sun. (Mani-Málá.)

Topaz.—Symbolical of friendship.

It cooled boiling water on being immersed in it; became opaque on contact with poisons; restrained anger and desire; cured insanity; checked the flow of blood; cleansed hemorrhoids; and averted sudden death. (Camillus Leonardus, Speculum Lapidum.)

Benoni states that the topaz is favorable for all hemorrhages and imparts strength and good digestion. Powdered and taken in wine it cured asthma and insomnia. (Dissertatio Medica.)

Rubbed on a hone the topaz gave a milky juice in quantities, and yet lost none of its original weight. The juice was taken internally in cases of dropsy and certain poisonings. Used as an ointment it was in repute as a curative for diseases of the eye. (Epiphanius.)

Worn as an amulet, so says Porta, it drove away sadness and nightmare; strengthened the intellect and bestowed courage. Mounted in gold and hung around the neck it dispelled enchantments; worn on the left hand it preserved its wearer from sensuality.

In the Honest Jeweller, written in the seventeenth century, the statement is made that—

the virtue and strength of the topaz is said to increase and decrease with the moon, and consist in the fact that when thrown into boiling water it at once deprives it of its heat.

According to the Sanskrit authorities, the—

topaz is sour, cool, and curative of abnormal oxidation, gives an appetite, and brings fame and wisdom.

The Hindu sages held that the medicinal properties of the topaz were similar to those of the coral, and in addition it prevented and cured sterility. (Mani-Málá.)

Like the ruby, the topaz was supposed to possess the power of emitting light to a great degree. A topaz given by the wife of Theodoric, count of Holland, to Adelbert, gave out so brilliant a light in the chapel where it was kept that prayers could be read by it.

Turquoise.—Emblematic of success. Highly valued by all orientals and worn by them to insure health and success. Supposed to preserve the wearer from injury through accidents. In the presence of poisons the stone sweated profusely, a property thought to be characteristic of many of the noble gems. Its color paled as its owner sickened and was lost entirely on his death, to be recovered only on its becoming the property of a healthy person.

The turquoise, according to Arabian and Persian authorities, as cited in the Mani-Málá, cured all diseases of the head and heart. A sovereign remedy for hernia, swellings, flatulence, dyspepsia, insanity, and cancerous sores. Whether taken alone, mixed with honey or with other drugs, it cures epilepsy, spleen, and stricture. In cases of poisoning or snake bite it was given with wine. Aristotle advises a similar dose for the same purpose. Applied as an ointment to the eyes it increased their luster, restored the vision, and prevented the fall of fluids therefrom. Worn as an amulet the turquoise brought happiness, dispelled fear, and rendered its wearer safe from drowning, lightning stroke, and snake bite. Seen after looking at the moon on the first day after the new moon it brought good luck.

In Egypt cure of a cataract is believed to be effected by the local application of a turquoise set in a silver ring and dipped in water, the application being accompanied by the chanting of the name of God.

Variolite.—Supposed to be a preventive and cure for variola (smallpox). (Castellani, History of Gems.)

Water sapphire or iolite.—A woman possessing a ring set with this stone as a signet, and on which was cut one-half of a fish, a mirror, a branch, and a nude female, procured any desire.

Zircon.—Supposed to bring riches, honor, and wisdom; a charm against plague and evil spirits; and afforded its wearer protection against thunderbolts. (Europe During the Middle Ages.)

According to the Mani-Málá—

The wearing of a weighty, lustrous, white, cool, tender, very old, and transparent gomèda (zircon) leads to prosperity. A light, discolored, exceedingly rough, delusion creating, and cool, yet dirty, gomeda blights happiness and saps the foundations of energy.

The same treatise, speaking of its medicinal value, says:

The zircon is sour, heating, and curative of unhealthy oxidation; sharpens the appetite, helps digestion, and takes away sin.

In conclusion, it would be expected to find the belief in the marvelous and medicinal properties of gems prevalent during the age of faith, while during the age of reason and inquiry it seems somewhat childish that they should still continue to exist.   In India, the land of occultism, the mystics still pursue their researches after the occult virtues of precious stones.   The modern Western spiritualist endeavors to discover and apply the occult knowledge of the East. He still believes in and teaches the virtues of gems, and is emphatic in his opinion that certain gems facilitate the rapport of a certain class of spirits with the wearers of those gems.

Swedenborg, the Swedish mystic, in his spirit revelations to L. A. Cahagnet, as cited in his Magic Magnetique (Paris, 1838), gives numerous categorical answers to questions asked by the medium concerning the spiritual and material powers of certain precious stones.

In Paris a school has been established which has for its object the study of the magnetic emanations, radiance, and crystals.   In Nice a Doctor de Lignieres has issued a prospectus of a work of 644 pages that seriously considers the medicinal properties and virtues of precious stones.

APPENDIX 4.

GEM AND MINERAL NAMES.[1]

The following list of gem names has been compiled from the literature and from correspondence with the producers of precious stones in the United States. The list is in two parts. Part I gives the name of the gem followed by the name of the mineral species to which the gem belongs. Part II aims to give all the names of the mineral species followed by the names of the corresponding gems.

Many of the names have been coined by the dealers in particular minerals for the evident purpose of increasing their sales. Many people who buy cheap gem stones under fanciful names probably would not buy the stones if they were offered under their true mineralogic names. The list herewith will enable those who are interested to look up the true mineral species of the gems offered.

The use of the name of a valuable gem mineral combined with another modifying word instead of the true name of a mineral of less value—for example, "Alaska diamond" instead of quartz, or "Arizona ruby" instead of garnet—is incorrect and should be avoided. The list does not contain all the names applied to gem minerals. Such self-evident names as "milky opal" and "blue beryl" are omitted. The object of the list is to show the mineral species forming the gem and not to list all possible names which have been used for gems.

A few names of substances not minerals but commonly used as gems have been included. Artificial products, however, many of them made of glass and fraudulently sold under mineral names—for example, glass sold as "fire agate"—have been excluded.

PART 1.—GEM NAMES.

A.

Achirite=dioptase from Siberia.

Achroite=colorless or white tourmaline.

Actinolite=green iron, calcium, and magnesium silicate (amphibole).

Adamantine spar=hair-brown corundum.

Adelaide ruby=blood-red pyrope (garnet) from South Africa.

Adularia=orthoclase (feldspar).

Aeroides=pale sky-blue beryl.

Agalmatolite=compact mica (aluminum and potassium hydrous silicate); also compact pyrophyllite (aluminum hydrous silicate).

Agate=variegated chalcedony.

---

[1] From Mineral Resources of the United States for 1917, by Dr. W. T. Schaller, of the United States Geological Survey and formerly custodian of gems and precious stones in the United States National Museum.

Agate jasper=intermediate between jasper and chalcedony with predominant translucent chalcedony; jasper with bands of chalcedony.

Agrite=brown, mottled, calcareous stone.

Alabandine ruby=red spinel of a violet tint.

Alabaster=white, fine-grained gypsum; also incorrectly applied to fine-grained and pure-white stalagmites of aragonite.

Alalite=diopside.

Alaska diamond=quartz.

Albite=aluminum and sodium silicate (feldspar).

Albite moonstone=iridescent albite.

Alençon diamond=quartz crystal from Alençon, France.

Aleppo stone=eye agate.

Alexandrite=emerald-green to dark-green chrysoberyl which changes in color to a columbine-red by artificial light.

Allanite=black hydrous aluminum, magnesium, cerium. and iron silicate and other elements.

Almandite (almandine)=columbine-red, or a deep crimson and violet garnet, aluminum and iron silicate.

Almandine spinel=violet-red spinel.

Alpine diamond=pyrite.

Amatrice=green, blue-green, and bluish variscite cut with its associated matrix.

Amazon stone=green microcline feldspar, aluminum and potassium silicate.

Amber=fossil resin.

Amber opal=opal colored brown by iron oxide.

Amberine=yellowish-green agate from the Death Valley region, California.

Ambroid=small pieces of inferior amber fused together.

American jade=californite (vesuvianite).

American ruby=blood-red garnet, mostly pyrope.

Amethiste basaltine=pale violet or reddish beryl.

Amethyst=purple and bluish-violet quartz, in crystals.

Amethystine quartz=quartz of an amethyst color, not necessarily in crystals.

Amphibole=group of minerals, aluminum, iron, calcium, magnesium silicates, and silicates of other elements.

Anatase=titanium oxide.   Another name for octahedrite.

Ancona ruby=quartz.

Andalusite=aluminum silicate; also trade name for brown tourmaline.

Andesine=aluminum, sodium, and calcium silicate (feldspar).

Andradite=garnet, iron and calcium silicate.

Anthracite=hard iron-black coal, harder than jet or cannel coal.

Apatite=calcium phosphate, with fluorine.

Aphrizite=black tourmaline.

Apophyllite=calcium and potassium hydrous silicate.

Apricotine=yellowish-red quartz pebbles from vicinity of Cape May, New Jersey.

Aquamarine=light bluish-green or sea-green beryl.

Aquamarine chrysolite=greenish-yellow beryl.

Aquamarine topaz=greenish topaz.

Aragonite=calcium carbonate in orthorhombic crystals.

Arizona ruby=deep-red pyrope (garnet) from Arizona and Utah.

Arizona spinel=deep-red pyrope (garnet) from Arizona and Utah.   Same as Arizona ruby.

Arkansas diamond=diamond from Arkansas; also quartz crystals from Arkansas.

Arkansite=brilliant iron-black, opaque brookite, oxide of titanium.

Armenian stone=(in part) lapis lazuli.

Arrow points=Indian arrowheads mostly made of quartz, more rarely of obsidian or other fine-grained rock.

Asparagus stone=pale-yellow apatite.

Asteria=asteriated sapphire; also any gem showing a six-ray star when cut cabochon.

Asteriated topaz=asteriated oriental topaz (yellow corundum).

Australian sapphire=deep inky blue sapphire (corundum).

Automolite=dark-green to nearly black zinc spinel.

Aventurine=opaque yellow, brown, or red massive quartz containing inclusions of minute scales of some other mineral, such as mica or iron oxide.

Aventurine feldspar=sunstone.

Axstone=nephrite.

Axinite=aluminum, calcium, iron, and manganese hydrous borosilicate.

Aztec stone=chalchihuitl.

Azure quartz=blue quartz.

Azure stone=lapis lazuli.

Azulite=pale-blue smithsonite.

Azurite=blue, copper hydrous carbonate.

Azurite malachite=azurmalachite.

Azurmalachite=combination of the copper carbonates azurite (blue) and malachite (green) from the copper mines of Arizona.

B.

Baffa diamond=quartz crystal.

Bahias=diamonds from Bahia, Brazil.

Balas ruby=rose-red or pink spinel.

Barite=barium sulphate.

Basanite=velvet black, flinty quartz.

Bastite=variety of bronzite.

Beckite=silicified coral shells or fossiliferous limestone replaced by silica.

Beekite=beckite.

Bemiscite=salmon-colored feldspar from Bemis, Maine.

Benitoite=blue barium and titanium silicate.

Beryl=aluminum and beryllium silicate with small amounts of other elements.

Beryllonite=beryllium and sodium phosphate.

Bishop's stone=amethyst.

Bixbite=red and rose-colored beryl from Utah.

Black amber=jet.

Black lava glass=obsidian.

Black opal=opal in a dark matrix; also opal with vivid colors.

Blood agate=flesh-red, pink, or salmon-colored agate from Utah.

Blood jasper=bloodstone.

Bloodstone=massive dark-green jasper (plasma) with red or blood-colored spots; also hematite (German usage).

Blue chrysoprase=chalcedony stained blue with chrysocolla.

Blue john=dark-blue fluorite, tinged with violet.

Blue malachite=azurite.

Blue moonstone=blue chalcedony from the Death Valley region, California.

Blue rock=lapis lazuli from California.

Blue white=diamond of highest grade.

Bobrowska garnet=grossularite (garnet).

Bohemian diamond=rock crystal (quartz).

Bohemian garnet=dark blood-red pyrope (garnet).

Bohemian topaz=yellow quartz.

Bohemian ruby=red or rose quartz.

Bonamite=translucent apple-green smithsonite from New Mexico.

Bone turquoise=teeth of fossil animals (mammoths, mastodons, etc.) stained blue by iron phosphate.

Bottle stone=moldavite.

Bowenite=unusually translucent serpentine of a cream color.

Brazilian aquamarine=greenish topaz.

Brazilian diamond=diamond from Brazil; also clear quartz from Brazil.

Brazilian emerald=green tourmaline.

Brazilian pebble=rock crystal (quartz).

Brazilian peridot=yellow-green tourmaline.

Brazilian ruby=rose-red or pink topaz, both naturally and artificially colored. Most of the pink or reddish topazes have been artificially colored by heating the dark-yellow ones.

Brazilian sapphire=light-blue or greenish topaz; also blue tourmaline.

Brazilian topaz=golden to reddish-yellow topaz; also smoky quartz artificially changed to yellow by heat.

Briançon diamond=quartz crystal from southeastern France, cut in Briançon.

Brighton emerald=green bottle glass purposely thrown on beach at Brighton, England.

Brilliant=diamond.

Bristol diamond=quartz crystal from Cornwall, England.

Bronzite=magnesium and iron silicate; variety of enstatite.

Brookite=hair-brown, yellowish, reddish, or ruby-red, transparent to translucent titanium oxide, in orthorhombic crystals.

Brown coal=brown or brownish-black coal, often retaining the original wood texture.

Brown jacinth=vesuvianite.

Brown spar=ankerite from Chester County, Pennsylvania.

Bull's-eye=labradorite with a dusky sheen.

Burma ruby=blood-red ruby (corundum).

Burmite=amber from Burma.

Burnt amethyst=purple amethyst changed to brownish-yellow by heat.

Burnt Brazilian topaz=burnt topaz.

Burnt topaz=yellow topaz from Brazil which has been changed to pink by heat.

Byssolite=fine greenish hair-like asbestos or actinolite, inclosed in quartz.

By-water=yellow-tinted diamond.

C.

Cabochon=any gem cut round, without facets.

Cacholong=opaque, procelain-like, milky-white opal.

Cacholong opal=feebly translucent common opal.

Caesium beryl=beryl containing several per cent of caesium, one of the rarer alkalies. The beryl is generally colorless or pink.

Cairngorm=yellow to smoky-brown, gray, or black quartz.

Calamine=zinc hydrous silicate. In England calamine is called smithsonite.

Calcite=calcium carbonate in rhombohedral (hexagonal) crystals.

Calcomalachite=mixture of calcium carbonate and malachite, from Arizona.

California cat's-eye=compact serpentine, sufficiently fibrous to show a silky luster and to yield a cat's-eye effect when cut cabochon, from Tulare County, California.

California iris=kunzite (spodumene).

California jade=californite (vesuvianite).

California moonstone=white or gray chalcedony.

California onyx=dark-brown aragonite.

California ruby=garnet.

California tiger-eye=California cat's-eye.

Californite=compact, translucent, green vesuvianite.

Callainite=translucent green aluminum hydrous phosphate (probably variscite).

Cameo=relief carving on a gem (the opposite of intaglio).

Canary=yellow diamond.

Canary beryl=greenish-yellow beryl.

Cancrinite=complex aluminum, calcium, and sodium hydrous silicate and the carbonate radicle.

Candle coal=cannel coal.

Cannel coal=dark grayish-black or brownish-black coal.

Cape chrysolite=green prehnite from South Africa.

Cape garnet=bright red-yellow almandite (garnet).

Cape May diamond=colorless and clear quartz crystal from Cape May, New Jersey.

Cape ruby=blood-red pyrope (garnet) from South Africa.

Cape=diamond having a yellowish tinge.

Carbonado=black diamond, not crystallized.

Carbuncle=clear deep-red almandite garnet; also any red, scarlet, or crimson garnet cut cabochon.   The term is also improperly applied to any red stone especially if cut cabochon.

Carmazul=oxidized copper ore showing red, brown, blue, and green colors, from Lower California, Mexico; composed of jasper, chalcedony, quartz, hematite, chrysocolla, and malachite.

Carnelian=translucent red chalcedony.

Carnelian-onyx=agate with red and white bands.

Cassinite=pearly, bluish-green aventurine feldspar from Delaware County, Pennsylvania.

Cassiterite=tin oxide.

Cat sapphire=dark-blue sapphire.

Catalinite=beach pebbles from Santa Catalina Island, California.

Catalina sardonyx=catalinite.

Catlinite=compact red clay.

Cat's-eye=any mineral having a changeable luster or showing opalescence without play of colors; also true cat's-eye (chatoyant chrysoberyl); also chatoyant quartz.

Celestial stone=turquoise.

Celestial precious stone=olivine from meteorite.

Cer-agate=chrome-yellow agate from Brazil.

Ceylon cat's-eye=chrysoberyl cat's-eye.

Ceylon chrysolite=yellowish-green or greenish-yellow tourmaline.

Ceylon hyacinth=garnet.

Ceylon opal=moonstone.

Ceylon peridot=honey-yellow or yellowish-green tourmaline.

Ceylon ruby=ruby from Ceylon; also deep-red almandine garnet from Ceylon; also any pale or pink ruby.

Ceylon sapphire=pale-blue sapphire (corundum).

Ceylonese zircon=fire-red cloudy zircon.

Ceylonite=black spinel.

Chalcedony=compact silica, transparent or translucent, with a waxy luster.

Chalcedony onyx=agate with white and pale bands.

Chalcedonyx=chalcedony with alternating stripes of gray and white.

Chalchihuitl=supposed to have been applied to blue, gray, or green calamine from Mexico, also to turquoise, emerald, prase, green jasper, and jadeite.

Chalchuite=green turquoise.

Changeant=labradorite.

Chert=compact silica, includes flint, hornstone, and jasper.

Chessy copper=azurite.

Chessylite=azurite.

Chesterlite=microcline feldspar from Chester County, Pennsylvania.

Chiastolite=variety of andalusite with crosslike marking.

Chinarump=petrified wood from Arizona.

Chlorastrolite=impure variety of prehnite or thomsonite.

Chloromelanite=dark-green to nearly black jadeite.

Chloropal=green opal from Silesia, Germany. Mineralogically, a hydrous iron silicate.

Chlorophane=variety of fluorite which phosphoresces with a greenish light on being slightly heated as by friction or by the heat of the hand.

Chlorospinel=green spinel.

Chlorutahlite=utahlite (compact variscite).

Chondrodite=silicate of magnesium and iron, with fluorine.

Chrome garnet=uvarovite (garnet).

Chromic iron=chromite.

Chromite=chromium and iron oxide.

Chrysoberyl=aluminum and beryllium oxide.

Chrysoberyllus=greenish-yellow, honey-yellow, or wine-yellow beryl.

Chrysocarmen=very similar to carmazul.

Chrysocolla=green to blue hydrous copper silicate.

Chrysolithus=pale yellowish-green beryl.

Chrysolite=olivine or peridot; also light-golden chrysoberyl (incorrect usage); also improperly applied to any light greenish-yellow to yellowish-green transparent gem.

Chrysoprase=apple-green, olive-green, or whitish-green, translucent chalcedony.

Cinnamon stone=essonite (garnet).

Citrine=golden-yellow quartz.

Cloudy chalcedony=chalcedony with dark cloudy spots in a light-gray transparent base.

Cobaltite=metallic cobalt and iron sulphide and arsenide.

Cobra stone=chlorophane.

Colophonite=brownish-black andradite (garnet), characterized by a resinous luster; iron and calcium silicate.

Colorado ruby=pyrope (garnet).   Same as Arizona ruby.

Colorado topaz=topaz from Colorado; also citrine (yellow quartz).

Common opal=translucent, only slightly colored opal without fire or play of colors.

Comptonite=thomsonite.

Congo emerald=dioptase from the Congo, Africa.

Copper emerald=dioptase.

Copper-ore gem=mixture of various copper minerals, such as green malachite, green or blue chrysocolla, blue azurite, red cuprite.

Copper-pitch ore=compact black or dark-brown mixture of iron and copper oxides.

Coral=hard calcareous structure secreted in or by the tissues of various marine zoophytes.   When fossilized, the calcareous matter is often replaced by silica (see beckite).

Coral agate=beckite (see coral).

Cordierite=aluminum, iron, and magnesium hydrous silicate.

Cornish diamond=quartz crystal from Cornwall, England.

Corundum=aluminum oxide.

Corundum cat's-eye=corundum with a bluish, reddish, or yellowish reflection of light of a lighter shade than the stone itself.

Cotterite=quartz having a metallic pearly luster.

Creoline=purplish epidotized trap rock from Massachusetts.

Creolite=banded jasper from Shasta County, California.

Crimson night stone=purple fluorite from Idaho.

Crispite=sagenite.

Crocidolite=fibrous hornblende of a bluish or greenish color, iron and magnesium hydrous silicate. The altered form consists of silica colored yellow and brown with oxide of iron and is called tiger-eye.

Cross stone=chiastolite (andalusite); also staurolite.

Crystal=colorless transparent quartz; also artificial flint glass.

Cupid's darts=quartz crystal with needle-like inclusions of goethite.

Cyanite=kyanite.

Cymophane=chrysoberyl having a bright spot of light which seems to float over the surface as the stone is moved.

Cyprine=sky-blue vesuvianite.

D.

Damourite=compact mica, a result of the alteration of some preexisting mineral.

Danburite=calcium borosilicate.

Datolite=compact massive calcium hydroborosilicate.

Dauphine diamond=rock crystal (quartz).

Davidsonite=greenish-yellow beryl from vicinity of Aberdeen, Scotland.

Delawarite=aventurine feldspar from Delaware County, Pennsylvania.

Demantoid=olive-green, brown, blackish-green, or light-green grossularite (garnet) from the Ural Mountains, Russia.

Dendrite=having the form of a tree.

Dendritic agate=mocha stone and moss agate.

Diallage=foliated variety of diopside.

Diamond=carbon, in isometric crystals.

Diaspore=aluminum hydrous oxide.

Dichroite=cordierite.

Diopside=calcium and magnesium silicate (pyroxene).

Dioptase=green hydrous silicate of copper.

Disthene=kyanite.

Doublet=consists of a real gem cemented to a piece of glass cut and colored to imitate the real stone.

Dravite=brown tourmaline.

Drop of water=rounded (water-worn), colorless, and transparent pebble of topaz.

Dumortierite=blue or lavender aluminum hydroborosilicate.

Dysluite=yellow or grayish-brown spinel.

E.

Edisonite=mottled blue turquoise.

Egyptian jasper=banded yellow, red, brown, or black jasper.

Egyptian pebble=Egyptian jasper.

Elaeolite=aluminum, sodium, and potassium silicate. Same as nephelite.

Eldoradoite=iridescent quartz from Eldorado County, California.

Elie ruby=red pyrope (garnet) from Elie in Fifeshire, Scotland.

Emerald=green beryl; also improperly applied to any green stone.

Emerald copper=dioptase.

Emerald malachite=dioptase.

Emeraldine=chalcedony artificially colored green.

Emeralite=green and bluish-green tourmaline from San Diego County, California.

Emerandine=dioptase.

Enhydros=hollow nodules of chalcedony partly filled with water.

Enstatite=magnesium silicate.

Epidote=greenish hydrous aluminum, iron, and calcium silicate.

Essonite=yellow variety of grossularite (garnet).

Euclase=bluish or greenish hydrous aluminum and beryllium silicate.

Evening emerald=peridot.

Euxenite=complex mineral containing columbium, titanium, and yttrium, and other elements.

Eye agate=concentric rings of agate with a dark center; also thomsonite.

Eyestone=thomsonite.

F.

Fairy stone=twinned crystal of staurolite, forming a cross.

False amethyst=purple fluorite.

False chrysolite=moldavite.

False diamond=quartz crystal.

False emerald=green fluorite.

False hyacinth=garnet.

False lapis=agate or jasper artificially colored blue.

False lapis lazuli=lazulite.

False ruby=red fluorite.

False sapphire=blue fluorite.

False topaz=yellow quartz; also yellow fluorite.

Fancy=term applied to stones having value other than intrinsic value.

Fancy agates=agates showing delicate markings and intricate patterns.

Fancy stone=unusual stone.

Fashoda garnet=dark brownish-red pyrope (garnet).

Feldspar=group of minerals, including orthoclase, microcline, albite, oligoclase, andesine, labradorite, aluminum and potassium, sodium, or calcium silicates.

Feldspar sunstone=sunstone.

Female sapphire=light-colored sapphire.

Feminine=term applied to stones of a paler color than masculine ones.

Fergusonite=black mineral composed chiefly of yttrium columbate.

Figure stone=agalmatolite.

Fire marble=dark-brown shell marble with brilliant firelike internal reflections.

Fire opal=red or yellowish-red opal.

First bye=diamond with a faint greenish tint.

First water=pure and colorless diamond.

Fish-eye=moonstone.

Fish-eye stone=apophyllite.

Flash opal=opal in which the color shows as a single flash.

Flêches d'amour=sagenite (quartz).

Fleurus diamond=quartz crystal.

Flint=compact silica, opaque, and of dull colors.

Floating light=cymophane.

Flos ferri=aragonite in shapes resembling coral.

Flowers of iron=flos ferri (aragonite).

Flower stone=beach pebbles (chalcedony) with flower patterns.

Fluorspar=fluorite.

Fluorite=calcium fluoride.

Fool's gold=pyrite.

Fortification agate=agate with parallel zigzag lines.

Fossil coral=coral replaced by silica (beckite).

Fossil pineapple=opal pseudomorph after glauberite, from New South Wales.

Fossil turquoise=bone turquoise.

Fowlerite=variety of rhodonite containing zinc.

Franklinite=black iron, manganese, and zinc oxide.

Frost stone=translucent gray chalcedony with pure-white patches or tufts, like snow-flakes, scattered through it, from the Mojave desert, California.

Fuchsite=green muscovite (mica).

G.

Gadolinite=velvety-black yttrium, beryllium, iron silicate, and silicates of other elements.

Gahnite=green zinc spinel.

Garnet=group of silicate minerals. The species are: Almandite, aluminum and iron silicate; andradite, iron and calcium silicate; grossularite, aluminum and calcium silicate; pyrope, aluminum and magnesium silicate; spessartite, aluminum and manganese silicate; uvarovite, chromium and calcium silicate.

Garnierite=green nickel and magnesium hydrous silicate.

Gem=cut and polished precious stone.

Gemstone=gem.

Geneva ruby=synthetic ruby made in Geneva, Switzerland.

Geyserite=siliceous deposit from a geyser.

Gibraltar stone=banded, mottled, or clouded calcium carbonate.

Girasol=corundum cat's-eye with a bluish, reddish, or yellowish reflection of light, lighter in shade than the stone itself, which moves on the surface of the stone like the lines of a starstone; also opal (see girasol opal); also moonstone (feldspar).

Girasol opal=fire opal.

Glass=artificial noncrystallized substance composed of silica and several bases, notably an alkali and lead.

Glass agate=obsidian.

Goethite=iron hydrous oxide.

Golconda diamond=diamond obtained from the regions watered by Krishna and Godavari Rivers but polished in Golconda, India.

Gold=metallic element, often mounted as found, as a nugget.

Gold opal=opal which shows yellowish light over a large area.

Gold quartz=massive quartz inclosing gold.

Golden beryl=clear bright-yellow beryl.

Golden stone=greenish-yellow chrysolite (olivine).

Golden topaz=topaz of a golden-yellow color; also golden-yellow citrine (quartz).

Goldstone=aventurine. An imitation of goldstone consists of glass with included metal filings (fraudulently sold as fire agate).

Gooseberry stone=brownish-green grossularite (garnet).

Goshenite=colorless, white, or bluish beryl from Goshen, Massachusetts.

Goutte d'eau=colorless topaz.

Goutte de sang=blood-red spinel.

Graphic granite=pegmatite composed of quartz and feldspar so arranged as to simulate writing.

Green agate=zonochlorite.

Green garnet=any green garnet; also incorrectly applied to green enstatite from South Africa.

Green starstone=chlorastrolite.

Greenstone=zonochlorite; also chlorastrolite; also californite (vesuvianite).

Grossularite=pale-green or yellow garnet.

· Guarnaccino=yellowish-red garnet. Same as vermeille.

Gypsum=calcium hydrous sulphate.

H.

Hair stone=quartz with inclusions of hairlike crystals or fibers of some other mineral. Same as sagenite.

Harlequin opal=opal in which the colors form a minute mosaic or are set in small squares.

Hatchet stone=nephrite.

Haüynite=complex aluminum, calcium, sodium, and potassium silicate with the sulphate radicle.

Hawk eye=quartz with inclusions of fine blue parallel fibers of crocidolite.

Heliodor=beryl from Rossing, Africa; contains a small amount of uranium and is weakly radioactive. By daylight gold-yellow, by artificial light a delicate blue-green.

Heliolite=sunstone (feldspar).

Heliotrope=bloodstone (quartz).

Hematite=iron oxide, either black or red.

Hemimorphite=calamine (English usage).

Hercynite=black to dark-green spinel composed of aluminum and iron oxides.

Herkimer diamond=clear quartz crystal from Herkimer County, New York.

Hessonite=variety of grossularite (garnet).

Hetaerolite=brilliant-black radiated mineral composed of the zinc and manganese oxides.

Hiddenite=green or yellowish-green spodumene.

Horatio diamond=colorless quartz from Arkansas.

Hornblende=aluminum, iron, calcium, magnesium silicate, and other elements.

Hornstone=compact form of silica, like flint but more brittle.

Hot Springs diamond=quartz.

Howdenite=chiastolite with fernlike markings, from South Australia.

Hungarian cat's-eye=quartz cat's-eye.

Hyacinth=red zircon; also wrongly applied to essonite or other light-colored garnets, to yellowish-red spinel from Brazil, and to red iron-stained quartz.

Hyacinth of Compostella=quartz, with red hematite inclusions.

Hyacinthozontes=sapphire-blue beryl.

Hyalite=clear and colorless opal.

Hyalosiderite=rich olive-green olivine, containing much iron.

Hydrophane=opal which becomes transparent in water.

Hypersthene=magnesium and iron silicate, variety of enstatite.

I.

Iceland agate=obsidian.

Iceland spar=clear calcite.

Iceland agate lava=obsidian.

Ichthyophthalmite=apophyllite.

Idocrase=vesuvianite.

Ilmenite=black iron and titanium oxide.

Image stone=agalmatolite.

Imperial jade (Chinese)=green, aventurine quartz.

Imperial yu-stone=green aventurine quartz.

Ilvaite=iron and calcium hydrous silicate.

Inca stone=pyrite.

Indian agate=moss agate.

Indian topaz=saffron-yellow topaz; also yellow quartz.

Indicolite=blue tourmaline.

Iolanthite=jasper from Crooked River, Crook County, Oreg.

Iolite=cordierite.

Iridescent quartz=rock crystal (quartz) filled with fine cracks containing air films which reflect the colors of the rainbow.

Iris=iridescent quartz; also applied to other iridescent minerals. California iris is spodumene.

Irish diamond=quartz crystal from Ireland.

Iron glance=hematite.

Isle of Wight diamond=quartz crystal.
Isle Royal greenstone=chlorastrolite.
Isopyre=very impure opal.
Italian chrysolite=vesuvianite.
Iztac Chalchihuitl=white or green Mexican onyx.

J.

Jacinth=yellow zircon, also improperly applied to essonite and other yellowish garnets.
Jade=two minerals, nephrite and jadeite. True jade is nephrite; many other minerals are also called jade, such as pectolite, vesuvianite, garnet, bowenite, serpentine, plasma, prehnite, agalmatolite, sillimanite, and saussurite (a rock).
Jadeite=greenish aluminum and sodium silicate (pyroxene).
Jager=bluish-white diamond of modern cut. Originally referred to diamond from the Jagersfontein mine, South Africa.
Jargon=white or grayish-white zircon.
Jargoon=jargon.
Jasp agate=intermediate between jasper and chalcedony with predominant opaque jasper.
Jasper=massive quartz, impure and opaque, containing more iron oxide than agate.
Jasper opal=deeply colored opal with many included impurities.
Jasperine=banded and variously colored jasper.
Jet=pitch-black or velvet-black coal sufficiently hard and compact to receive a brilliant polish.
Job's tears=local name for peridot from Arizona and New Mexico; also hyalosiderite, a rich olive-green olivine.

K.

Kashmir sapphire=cornflower-blue corundum.
Keystoneite=blue chrysocolla or chalcedony colored by copper silicate.
Kidney stone=nephrite.
Killiecrankie diamond=limpid topaz from Tasmania.
King topaz=clear pink, orange, red, yellow, or flesh-colored corundum.
Kinradite=jasper with spherulites of quartz, from the region around San Francisco, California.
Kornerupine=aluminum and magnesium silicate.
Kunzite=transparent lilac spodumene.
Kyanite=aluminum silicate.

L.

Labrador feldspar=labradorite.
Labrador hornblende=hypersthene.
Labrador spar=labradorite.
Labrador stone=labradorite.
Labradorite=feldspar, aluminum, sodium, and calcium silicate.
Lake George diamond=clear quartz crystal from Herkimer, New York.
Lake Superior greenstone=chlorastrolite.
Lapis lazuli=rock composed essentially of the minerals lazurite, haüynite, scapolite, calcite, pyroxene, amphibole, mica, and feldspar.
Lava=volcanic rock.
Lavendine=amethyst (quartz).
Lazulite=blue aluminum, iron, and magnesium hydrous phosphate.
Lazurite=blue aluminum, calcium, and sodium silicate, with the sulphate radicle.
Lechosos opal=opal showing deep-green flashes of color or specked with green and carmine; also used for milky opal.

Leelite=deep flesh-red orthoclase, having a waxy luster.

Lennilite=greenish feldspar from Lenni Mills, Delaware County, Pennsylvania.

Leopardite=porphyry with black spots of manganese oxide.

Lepidolite=mica, hydrous aluminum, lithium, and potassium silicate, with fluorine.

Leuco sapphire=white sapphire.

Lignite=brown coal showing the form and fiber of the original tree.

Lintonite=zeolite, probably thomsonite, with alternating bands of green and red.

Lithia emerald=green spodumene.

Lithoxyle=wood opal showing woody structure.

Lodestone=magnetite (iron oxide) which shows polarity.

Love arrows=sagenite (quartz).

Lucky stone=fairy stone (staurolite).

Lumachelle=fire marble.

Lydian stone=basanite (quartz).

Lynx sapphire=water sapphire (cordierite); also very dark-blue sapphire.

Lynx stone=cordierite.

M.

Macle=chiastolite.

Madeira topaz=citrine quartz.

Magic stone=hydrophane.

Magnetite=black magnetic iron oxide.

Mahogany ore=compact mixture of iron and copper oxides.

Malachite=green hydrous copper carbonate.

Malacolite=diopside.

Male sapphire=deep-colored sapphire.

Marble=recrystallized limestone or dolomite.

Marcasite=iron sulphide, in orthorhombic crystals. The same iron sulphide, in isometric crystals, is pyrite.

Marekanite=mottled brown and black obsidian.

Mariposite=green compact micaceous aluminum, magnesium, and potassium hydrous silicate.

Marmorosch diamond=quartz crystal from Marmaros Comitat, Hungary.

Masculine=term applied to stones of a deep and rich color.

Matara diamond=colorless or faintly smoky zircon from Ceylon; the pale-brown zircons are sometimes decolorized by heat.

Matrix=rock surrounding mineral.

Meerschaum=sepiolite.

Melanite=dull-black andradite (garnet).

Menaccanite=ilmenite.

Menilite=grayish-brown banded, sometimes concretionary, opal from vicinity of Paris, France.

Mesolite=zeolite similar to thomsonite in composition, aluminum, calcium, sodium, and potassium hydrous silicate.

Mexican onyx=banded, mottled, or clouded travertine.

Mica=group of silicate minerals, containing aluminum, and potassium, with water, and other elements.

Microcline=potash feldspar in triclinic crystals, aluminum and potassium silicate.

Microlite=essentially a calcium tantalate.

Mineral turquoise=true turquoise.

Mocha agate=translucent agate or chalcedony with brown, red, or black dendritic figures like trees or plants.

Mocha stone=chalcedony with brown, red, or black, treelike inclusions of manganese oxide.

Mohave moonstone=translucent, lilac-tinted chalcedony from the Mohave Desert, California.

Moldavite=dark-green to black glass resembling obsidian.

Monazite=cerium phosphate and other rare-earth elements.

Money stone=local name in Pennsylvania for rutile.

Montana agate=moss agate from Montana.

Montana jet=obsidian, from Yellowstone Park.

Montana ruby=garnet.

Montana sapphire=corundum; generally applied to dark-blue or greenish-blue sapphire (compare river sapphire).

Mont Blanc ruby=quartz.

Moonstone=feldspar (usually oligoclase or the adularia variety of orthoclase) showing a pearly opalescence; also commonly but erroneously applied to some white or gray chalcedony and to satin spar (gypsum).

Mora diamond=probably quartz crystal.

Morganite=rose-colored beryl from Madagascar.

Moriah stone=granular and spotted verd antique (serpentine).

Morion=deep-black almost opaque smoky quartz.

Moroxite=deep-green or blue-green apatite.

Mosaic agate=brecciated Mexican onyx.

Moss agate=chalcedony with greenish mosslike or treelike inclusions.

Moss jasper=opaque and translucent chalcedony crowded full with mosslike markings.

Moss opal=milky opal with black mosslike dendritic inclusions.

Mother of emerald=prase (quartz).

Mother-of-opal=rock matrix containing minute disseminated specks of precious opal.

Mother-of-pearl=the hard iridescent internal layer of various shells.

Mountain mahogany=banded obsidian.

Muller's glass=hyalite.

Myrickite=agate or chalcedony containing bright-red inclusions of cinnabar, from the Death Valley region, California.

N.

Nacre=mother-of-pearl.

Natrolite=zeolite, aluminum and sodium hydrous silicate.

Needle stone=sagenite (quartz).

Nephelite=aluminum, sodium, and calcium silicate.

Nephrite=true jade, a tough compact fine-grained tremolite (white) or actinolite (green).

Nevada diamond=obsidian, artificially decolorized.

New rock=bone turquoise (in distinction from "old rock"=true turquoise).

New Zealand greenstone=serpentine, richly colored, from New Zealand; also jade or nephrite from New Zealand.

Nicolo=onyx with a black or brown base and a bluish-white thicker wavy, top layer.

Nigrine=dark-brown to black rutile with some iron.

Noble opal=precious opal.

Novaculite=fine-grained hard chalcedonic silica.

O.

Obsidian=a glassy form of lava.

Ocean spray=satin spar (gypsum).

Occidental agate=agate less perfect than oriental agate.

Occidental amethyst=true amethyst (quartz).

Occidental cat's-eye=quartz cat's-eye.

Occidental chalcedony=somewhat opaque chalcedony; more opaque than oriental chalcedony.

Occidental diamond=rock crystal (quartz).

Occidental topaz=yellow quartz.

Occidental turquoise=bone turquoise.

Octahedrite=titanium oxide in tetragonal crystals, with slightly different properties from rutile.

Odontolite=bone turquoise.

Oeil de boeuf=labradorite.

Old rock=turquoise from Persia.

Oligoclase=feldspar, aluminum, sodium, and potassium silicate.

Olivine=magnesium and iron silicate. The word olivine is used as a trade name for green garnet (demantoid from the Ural Mountains), and is also improperly applied to any green stone. The following distinctions are sometimes applied to the mineral olivine: Chrysolite, inclining to yellow; peridot, inclining to yellowish green; olivine, inclining to green.

Onegite=quartz with inclusions of hair-like crystals of goethite.

Onyx=banded chalcedony with alternating bands of cloudy milk-white and another color, usually black.

Oolite=concretionary massive limestone (calcium carbonate) made up of minute spherical grains.

Opal=amorphous massive form of hydrous silica.

Opal agate=banded opal having alternate layers of opal and agate.

Opal jasper=jasper opal.

Opal onyx=alternate layers of precious and of common opal.

Opalescent chrysolite=chrysoberyl.

Opaline=opal matrix.

Opaline feldspar=labradorite.

Ophiolite=serpentine.

Orange topaz=same as Spanish topaz, smoky quartz changed to yellow by heat.

Oregon jade=californite (vesuvianite).

Oriental=variety of corundum (not necessarily found in the Orient).

Oriental agate=finely marked and very translucent agate.

Oriental alabaster=travertine.

Oriental amethyst=purple corundum.

Oriental aquamarine=light-green corundum.

Oriental cat's-eye=chrysoberyl cat's-eye; also smoky corundum.

Oriental chalcedony=very translucent chalcedony (compare with occidental chalcedony).

Oriental chrysoberyl=yellowish-green corundum.

Oriental chrysolite=greenish-yellow corundum; also chrysoberyl.

Oriental emerald=green corundum.

Oriental garnet=almandine (garnet).

Oriental girasol=girasol (corundum).

Oriental hyacinth=rose-colored corundum.

Oriental hyacinth=aurora-red corundum.

Oriental jasper=bloodstone (quartz).

Oriental lapis=lapis lazuli.

Oriental moonstone=pearly corundum.

Oriental onyx=banded, mottled, or clouded travertine.

Oriental opal=Hungarian opal carried to the Orient by merchants and then shipped back to Europe.

Oriental peridot=green corundum.

Oriental sapphire=(in part) blue corundum.

Oriental smaragd=green corundum.
Oriental sunstone=girasol (corundum).
Oriental topaz=yellow corundum.
Oriental turquoise=turquoise.
Orthoclase=potash feldspar in monoclinic crystals, aluminum and potassium silicate.
Orthose=moonstone (feldspar).
Ouachita stone=novaculite (whetstone); quartz.
Ouvarovite=emerald-green garnet colored by chromium.
Ox-eye=labradorite (feldspar).

P.

Pagoda stone=agalmatolite.
Pagodite=agalmatolite.
Paphos diamond=quartz.
Parisite=cerium carbonate (and other rare elements), with fluorine.
Paste=artificial lead glass used to imitate gems.
Paulite=hyperstene.
Pealite=opal-like variety of geyserite (silica).
Pearl=lustrous calcareous concretion with animal membrane between successive
  layers, deposited in the shells of various mollusks. Not a mineral but an animal
  product.
Pearlite=a form of obsidian.
Pebble=rock crystal (quartz).
Pecos diamond=quartz from Pecos River, Texas.
Pectolite=calcium and sodium hydrous silicate.
Pegmatite=coarsely grained rock composed of quartz and feldspar.
Pelhamite=variety of serpentine.
Peliom=cordierite.
Pennsylvania diamond=iron pyrite.
Peridot of Ceylon=same as Ceylon peridot, honey-yellow tourmaline.
Peridot=olivine. (See Olivine.)
Peristerite=iridescent albite (feldspar).
Persian lapis=lapis lazuli.
Perthite=potash feldspar (orthoclase or microcline) with laminae of soda feldspar
  (albite).
Peruvian emerald=the best emeralds from Muzo, Colombia.
Petoskey agate=cemented portions of fossil coral (beckite).
Petrified honeycomb=beckite.
Petrified wood=wood replaced by silica.
Phenacite=silicate of beryllium.
Phenomenal gem=one which shows a play or change of color by artificial light, or
  shows a movable line of light.
Piedmontite=brownish-red variety of epidote.
Pin fire opal=opal in which the area of the individual colors is very small.
Pink topaz=topaz either naturally pink or artificially colored pink by heating the
  yellow or brown varieties.
Pink wollastonite=lilac-colored pyroxene (diopside) from the region of San Francisco,
  California.
Pipestone=catlinite (compact red clay).
Pisolite=concretionary massive limestone, similar to oolite but made up of larger
  spherical grains.
Pistacite=greenish epidote.
Pitch opal=brown opal with a pitchy luster.
Pitchstone=obsidian of a pitchy luster.

Plasma=massive translucent quartz, dark grass-green in color, sometimes with white or yellow inclusions of celadonite or of delessite.

Pleonaste=black spinel.

Polycrase=black mineral similar in composition to euxenite.

Porcelain jasper=a naturally indurated clay.

Porphyry=rock, variegated in structure, with individual crystals much larger than the fine-grained matrix.

Potstone=soapstone (impure talc).

Prase=massive, translucent, and spotted quartz of a green to leek-green color caused by inclusions of minute crystals of actinolite or other minerals.

Prase opal=apple-green translucent opal.

Precious coral=red coral.

Precious opal=opal showing a play of colors.

Precious schorl=tourmaline.

Prehnite=greenish aluminum and calcium hydrous silicate.

Prismatic moonstone=clouded chalcedony (quartz) from Mohave Desert, California.

Prismatic quartz=cordierite.

Prosopite=aluminum and calcium hydrous fluoride.

Pseudochrysolite=moldavite.

Pseudodiamond=quartz crystal.

Pseudoemerald=malachite.

Pyrite=iron sulphide in isometric crystals.

Pyrope=blood-red garnet, aluminum and magnesium silicate.

Pyroxene=group of complex silicates of aluminum, iron, calcium, magnesium, and other elements.

Q.

Quartz=crystallized silica.

Quebec diamond=quartz crystal.

Quinzite=rose-colored common opal.

R.

Radio opal=opal of a smoky color caused by organic inclusions or impurities.

Radiumite=mixture of black pitchblende, yellow uranotile, and orange gummite.

Rainbow agate=agate which shows iridescence when cut across the concentric structure.

Rainbow quartz=iridescent quartz.

Rattle boxes=limonite geodes.

Realgar=orange arsenic sulphide.

Reconstructed gem=one artificially made by fusing and recrystallizing fragments of natural gems.

Red stone=ruby.

Resin opal=opal with a resinous luster.

Rhinestone=rock crystal (quartz).

Rhodochrosite=pink manganese carbonate.

Rhodolite=rose-colored garnet, between pyrope and almandite; aluminum, iron, and magnesium silicate; from Macon County, North Carolina.

Rhodonite=pink manganese silicate.

Riband agate=agate with parallel layers.

Riband jasper=jasper with differently colored alternating bands.

Ribbon agate=banded agate.

Ring agate=agate with differently colored bands arranged in concentric circles.

Ripe diamond=true diamond (see unripe diamond).

River agate=moss-agate pebbles found in brooks and streams.

River sapphire=light-colored sapphire from Montana.

Rock crystal=clear quartz crystal.

Rock ruby=red garnet (pyrope).

Rocky Mountain ruby=garnet.

Romansovite=brown grossularite (garnet), aluminum and calcium silicate.

Rosaline=thulite (pink zoisite).

Rose quartz=massive rose-red to pink quartz.

Rose topaz=pink topaz.

Roselite=pink garnet. Mineralogically a calcium and cobalt hydrous arsenate.

Royal topaz=blue topaz.

Rubasse=quartz artificially stained red.

Rubellite=pink and red tourmaline.

Rubicelle=yellow or orange-red spinel.

Rubino-di-rocca=red garnet having a tinge of violet.

Rubolite=red opal from Texas.

Ruby=red corundum.

Ruby spinel=deep-red spinel.

Ruin aragonite=brecciated Mexican onyx.

Rutile=titanium oxide.

S.

Sabalite=yellowish to greenish banded phosphatic material, similar to or inclosing variscite, from Utah.

Sacred turquoise=pale-blue smithsonite.

Sagenite=transparent quartz with inclusions of hairlike or needle-like crystals or fibers of some other mineral, generally rutile.

Samarskite=black mineral of complex composition, essentially a yttrium, uranium, and iron columbate.

Sandy sard=sard dotted with darker spots (quartz).

Saphir d'eau=water sapphire (blue cordierite).

Sapparé=transparent kyanite.

Sapphire=blue corundum. The name is also applied to colorless and colored (except red) corundum.

Sapphire quartz=blue quartz.

Sapphirine=blue chalcedony, blue quartz; also blue spinel; aluminum and magnesium silicate.

Sard=chalcedony of a rich brown color, with a reddish tint; brownish-red or dark-brown carnelian (sardoine).

Sardoine=brownish-red or dark-brown carnelian.

Sardonyx (sard-onyx)=white and brown banded chalcedony.

Satelite=serpentine cat's-eye.

Satin spar=finely fibrous gypsum having a pearly opalescence; also finely fibrous calcite having a silky luster; also finely fibrous aragonite having a silky luster.

Saussurite=greenish to white or gray rock composed chiefly of zoisite.

Saxon chrysolite=pale wine-yellow or greenish-yellow topaz tinged with green.

Saxon topaz=pale wine-yellow topaz; also citrine (quartz).

Scapolite=group of minerals composed of aluminum, calcium, and sodium silicates, with the chloride, carbonate, or sulphate radicles.

Scarab=precious stone inscribed with symbols, engraved like a beetle.

Schaumberg diamond=quartz crystal from Schaumberg, Hesse, Germany.

Schiller quartz=quartz cat's-eye.

Schiller spar=bastite (enstatite).

Schnecken topaz=Saxon topaz.

Schorl=black tourmaline.

Schorlomite=black garnet containing considerable titanium.

Scoopstone=amber collected from seaweed.

Scotch topaz=smoky quartz.

Seastone=amber cast upon shore by sea.

Selenite=colorless, transparent gypsum.

Semicarnelian=yellow agate.

Semiopal=colorless to strongly colored somewhat opaque, common opal.

Semiturquoise=soft pale-blue turquoise.

Sepiolite=magnesium hydrous silicate.

Serpentine=magnesium hydrous silicate.

Serpentine cat's-eye=serpentine showing when cut a changeable luster or opalescence without play of colors.

Siam=dark-red ruby.

Siam ruby=dark-red ruby from Siam; also red spinel.

Siberian amethyst=rich or dark-colored amethyst.

Siberian aquamarine=very light greenish-blue beryl.

Siberian chrysolite=demantoid (garnet).

Siberian ruby=red tourmaline.

Siberian topaz=very pale blue or bluish-white topaz.

Siberite=violet-red tourmaline.

Siderite=sapphirine (blue quartz).   Mineralogically, an iron carbonate.

Siliceous malachite=green chrysocolla.

Silicified wood=wood replaced by silica.

Sinople=quartz having red hematite inclusions.

Slave's diamond=colorless topaz.

Smaragdite=green variety of amphibole, like actinolite; also applied to other green stones, as the emerald, fuchsite, etc.

Smaragdus=smaragdite.

Smithsonite=zinc carbonate.   In England this zinc carbonate is called calamine.

Smoky quartz=quartz crystals of a smoky or brown color.

Smoky topaz=true topaz of a smoky color; also more commonly smoky quartz.

Sobrisky opal=opal from the Lead Pipe Spring district in the Death Valley region, California.

Sodalite=aluminum and sodium silicate, with chlorine, generally blue.

Soldier's stone=amethyst.

Spanish emerald=emerald of the finest quality (presumably from South America).

Spanish lazulite=cordierite.

Spanish topaz=smoky quartz changed to yellow by heat.

Specular iron ore=hematite.

Spessartite=yellow, brown, or red garnet, aluminum and manganese silicate.

Sphaerulite=variety of obsidian.

Sphalerite=zinc sulphide.

Sphene=titanite.

Spinel=group of minerals composed of aluminum, iron, chromium, magnesium, or zinc oxides.   The name spinel is also applied to the species of this group which consists chiefly of aluminum and magnesium oxides.

Spinel ruby=red spinel.

Spinel sapphire=blue spinel.

Spodumene=aluminum and lithium silicate.

St. Stephen stone=translucent chalcedony with round blood-red spots through it.

Stalactite=calcium carbonate in pendent masses deposited in caverns by evaporating water.

Stalagmite=calcium carbonate deposited from evaporating water on the floors of caverns.

Star stone=starolite (quartz).
Star ruby=ruby (corundum) showing a star of light.
Star sapphire=grayish-blue sapphire (corundum) showing a star of light.
Star topaz=asteriated oriental topaz (yellow corundum).
Starolite=asteriated quartz.
Staurolite=aluminum, iron, and magnesium hydrous silicate.
Steinheilite=cordierite.
Stibiotantalite=antimony tantalate.
Succinite=amber; also amber-colored grossularite (garnet).
Sulphur diamond=pyrite.
Sun opal=fire opal.
Sunstone=feldspar (usually oligoclase or labradorite) containing inclusions of minute
    scales of iron oxide.
Swiss lapis=agate or jasper artificially colored blue.
Synthetic gem=one artificially made from chemicals.
Syrian garnet=almandite (garnet) of a violet shade.

T.

Tabasheer=amorphous opal-like silica deposited in the joints of bamboo.
Tauridan topaz=very pale blue topaz.
Taxoite=serpentine from Chester County, Pennsylvania.
Test stone=basanite (jasper).
Texas agate=agate jasper from Texas.
Thetis hairstone=transparent quartz with inclusions of hairlike crystals of green
    actinolite.
Thomsonite=zeolite, aluminum, calcium, and sodium hydrous silicate.
Thulite=rose-red zoisite.
Tiger-eye=yellow to brown, altered crocidolite.
Titanite=calcium and titanium silicate.
Toad's-eye tin=concentric cassiterite. Same as wood tin but on a smaller scale.
Topaz=aluminum silicate, with fluorine. Most of the ordinary topaz of commerce
    is "false topaz" or yellow to brown quartz. Much of the "yellow quartz" is smoky
    quartz artificially changed from brown to yellow by heat. The term topaz is also
    improperly applied to any yellow stone.
Topaz cat's-eye=yellow corundum showing an elongated or round patch of opalescent
    light.
Topazolite=colorless, yellowish, or greenish andradite (garnet).
Touchstone=basanite (jasper).
Tourmaline=group of closely related minerals which are complex hydroboro-silicates
    of aluminum and one or more other bases, such as iron, manganese, calcium, mag-
    nesium, sodium, or lithium.
Trainite=impure banded variscite.
Tree agate=mocha stone.
Tree stone=mocha agate.
Trenton diamond=quartz crystal from Herkimer County, New York.
Trilobite=fossil.
Triphane=yellow or greenish-yellow spodumene.
Troostite=pink to gray willemite containing some manganese.
Turquoise=aluminum and copper hydrous phosphate.
Turkis=turquoise.
Turtle back=chlorastrolite; also matrix turquoise; also matrix variscite.

U.

Unripe diamond=quartz.
Ural chrysoberyl=alexandrite.

Uralian emerald=Siberian demantoid (green garnet).
Utahlite=compact variscite.
Uvarovite=green garnet containing chromium.

V.

Vallum diamond=quartz crystals from the Tanjore district, Madras Presidency, India.
Variolite=dark-green orthoclase (feldspar) containing lighter-colored globular particles.
Variscite=green hydrous phosphate of aluminum.
Vegetable fossil=amber.
Verd antique=variegated serpentine.
Verdite=green rock, composed chiefly of fuchsite (green muscovite containing chromium) or talc.
Verdolite=talcose-dolomitic breccia rock from New Jersey.
Vermeille=orange-red almandite (garnet); also orange-red spinel.
Vermilion opal=milky opal impregnated with cinnabar.
Vermilite=vermilion opal.
Vesuvian gem=vesuvianite.
Vesuvianite=complex silicate, chiefly of aluminum and calcium.
Vinegar spinel=yellowish-red spinel.
Violane=dark violet-blue diopside (pyroxene), from Piedmont, Italy.
Violet stone=cordierite.
Violite=compact purple chalcedony from San Diego County, California.
Volcanic chrysolite=vesuvianite.
Volcanic glass=obsidian.
Vulpinite=anhydrite.

W.

Wabanite=banded cream to black and gray to purple chocolate-colored slate from Massachusetts.
Wardite=aluminum hydrous phosphate.
Water agate=shell of chalcedony containing bubble of water.
Water chrysolite=moldavite.
Water opal=moonstone (feldspar).
Water sapphire=true water sapphire is cordierite; also white topaz.
Water stone=hydrolite (opal).
Wax agate=yellow agate, with a pronounced waxy luster.
Wax opal=yellow opal with a waxy luster.
Wernerite=scapolite.
White carnelian=cloudy, milk-white, or very pale reddish or yellowish chalcedony.
White emerald=caesium beryl.
White jade=white nephrite; also compact white garnet; also white californite (vesuvianite).
White sapphire=colorless corundum; also quartz.
White topaz=colorless topaz; also quartz.
Willemite=zinc silicate.
Williamsite=variety of serpentine of a rich blackish oil-green color.
Wiluite=green vesuvianite; also yellowish-green to greenish-white garnet.
Wilsonite=purlpish-red scapolite.
Wolf's eye=moonstone (feldspar).
Wolf's eye stone=crocidolite.
Wollastonite=calcium silicate.
Wood agate=wood petrified or replaced by agate.
Wood opal=wood silicified by opal.

Wood stone=silicified wood.
Wood tin=cassiterite with a concentric structure.
World's eye=hydrophane (opal).

X.

Xanthite=dark yellowish-brown vesuvianite from Amity, New York.

Y.

Yogo sapphire=dark-blue corundrum from Yogo Gulch, Montana.
Yu stone=jade.

Z.

Zincite=zinc oxide, mostly red.
Zircon=zirconium silicate.
Zoisite=aluminum and calcium hydrous silicate.
Zonite=variously colored chert or jasper, from Arizona.
Zonochlorite=banded prehnite, similar to chlorastrolite.

PART 2.—MINERAL NAMES.

A.

Allanite.
Amphibole=actinolite, axstone, byssolite, crocidolite, hawk's-eye, hornblende, jade, kidney stone, nephrite, New Zealand greenstone, smaragdite, smaragdus, tremolite, wolf's-eye stone.
Anatase.
Andalusite=chiastolite, cross-stone, macle, howdenite.
Anhydrite=vulpinite.
Ankerite=brown spar.
Apatite=moroxite, asparagus stone.
Apophyllite=fisheye stone, ichthyophthalmite.
Aragonite=alabaster, California onyx, flos ferri, flowers of iron, Gibraltar stone, iztac chalchihuitl, Mexican onyx, mosaic agate, oriental alabaster, oriental onyx, ruin aragonite, satin spar, stalactite, stalagmite, verd antique. (See also calcite.)
Axinite.
Azurite=blue malachite, chessy copper, chessylite.
Azurmalachite.

B.

Barite.
Benitoite.
Beryl=aeroides, amethiste basaltine, aquamarine, aquamarine chrysolite, bixbite, caesium beryl, canary beryl, chalchihuitl, chrysoberyllus, chrysolithus, david-sonite, emerald, golden beryl, goshenite, heliodor, hyacinthozontes, morganite, Peruvian emerald, Siberian aquamarine, smaragdite, Spanish emerald, white emerald.
Beryllonite.
Bone turquoise=fossil turquoise, new rock, occidental turquoise, odontolite.
Brookite=arkansite.

C.

Calamine=Aztec stone, chalchihuitl, hemimorphite.
Calcite=agrite, calcomalachite, fire marble, Iceland spar, lumachelle, marble, Mexican onyx, onyx marble, Oriental alabaster, oolite, pisolite, satin spar.
Cancrinite.
Cassiterite=toad's-eye tin, wood tin.

Chondrodite.

Chromite=chromic iron.

Chrysoberyl=alexandrite, cat's-eye, Ceylon cat's-eye, chrysolite, cymophane, floating light, opalescent chrysolite, oriental cat's-eye, Ural chrysoberyl.

Chrysocolla=keystonite, siliceous malachite.

Clay=catlinite, pipestone, porcelain jasper.

Coal=anthracite, black amber, brown coal, candle coal, cannel coal, jet, lignite.

Cobaltite.

Copper ore gem=carmazul, chrysocarmen, copper pitch ore, mahogany ore.

Cordierite=dichroite, iolite, lynx-stone, peliom, prismatic quartz, saphir d'eau, Spanish lazulite, steinheilite, violet stone, water sapphire.

Corundum=adamantine spar, asteria, asteriated topaz, Australian sapphire, Burma ruby, cat sapphire, Ceylon ruby, corundum cat's-eye, female sapphire, girasol, Kashmir sapphire, king topaz, leuco-sapphire, lynx sapphire, male sapphire, Montana sapphire, oriental, oriental amethyst, oriental aquamarine, oriental cat's-eye, oriental chrysoberyl, oriental chrysolite, oriental emerald, oriental girasol, oriental hyacinth, oriental moonstone, oriental peridot, oriental sapphire, oriental smaragd, oriental sunstone, oriental topaz, red stone, river sapphire, ruby, sapphire, star ruby, star sapphire, Siam, star topaz, topaz cat's-eye, white sapphire, Yogo sapphire.

D.

Danburite.

Datolite.

Diamond=Bahia, blue-white, brilliant, by-water, canary, cape, carbonado, first bye, first water, Golconda, jager, ripe-diamond.

Diaspore.

Dioptase=achirite, Congo emerald, copper emerald, emerald copper, emerald malachite, emerandine.

Dumortierite.

E.

Epidote=piedmontite, pistacite.

Euclase.

Euxenite.

F.

Feldspar=adularia, albite, albite moonstone, amazonstone, andesine, aventurine feldspar, bemiscite, bull's-eye, cassinite, Ceylon opal, changeant, chesterlite, delawarite, fisheye, girasol, heliolite, Labrador spar, Labrador stone, labradorite, leelite, lennilite, microcline, moonstone, oeil de boeuf, oligoclase, opaline feldspar, orthoclase, orthose, ox-eye, peristerite, perthite, sunstone, variolite, water opal, wolf's eye.

Fergusonite.

Fluorite=blue john, chlorophane, cobra stone, crimson night stone, false amethyst, false emerald, false ruby, false sapphire, false topaz, fluorspar.

Fossil=beckite, beekite, fossil coral, Petoskey agate, petrified honeycomb, trilobite.

Franklinite.

G.

Gadolinite.

Garnet=Adelaide ruby, almandite, American ruby, andradite, Arizona ruby, Arizona spinel, Bobrowska garnet, Bohemian diamond, Bohemian garnet, California ruby, Cape ruby, carbuncle, Ceylon hyacinth, Ceylon ruby, chloromelanite, chrome garnet, cinnamon stone, colophonite, Colorado ruby, demantoid, Elie ruby, essonite, false hyacinth, Fashoda garnet, gooseberry stone, grossularite, guarnaccino, hessonite, hyacinth, jacinth, jade, melanite, Montana ruby, olivine, oriental garnet, ouvarovite, pyrope, rhodolite, rock ruby, Rocky Mountain ruby, romansovite, roselite, rubino-di-rocca, schorlomite, Siberianchrys olite, spessartite, succinite, Syrian garnet, topazolite, Uralian emerald, uvarovite, vermeille, white jade, wiluite.

Garnierite.

Goethite.

Gold.

Gypsum=alabaster, moonstone, ocean spray, satin spar, selenite.

H.

Haüynite.

Hematite=bloodstone, iron glance, specular iron ore.

Hetaerolite.

I.

Ilmenite=menaccanite.

Ilvaite.

K.

Kornerupine.

Kyanite=cyanite, disthene, sapparé.

L.

Lapis lazuli=Armenian stone, azure stone, blue rock, oriental lapis, Persian lapis.

Lazulite=false lapis lazuli.

Lazurite.

Limonite=rattlebox.

M.

Magnetite=lodestone.

Malachite=pseudo-emerald.

Marcasite.

Mesolite.

Mica=agalmatolite, damourite, figure stone, fuchsite, image stone, lepidolite, mariposite, pagoda stone, pagodite, smaragdite, verdite.

Microlite.

Moldavite=bottle stone, false chrysolite, pseudo-chrysolite, water chrysolite.

Monazite.

N.

Natrolite.

Nephelite.

O.

Obsidian=arrow points, black lava glass, glass agate, Iceland agate, Iceland agate lava, marekanite, Montana jet, mountain mahogany, Nevada diamond, pearlite, pitchstone, sphaerulite, volcanic glass.

Octahedrite=anatase.

Olivine=celestial precious stone, chrysolite, evening emerald, golden stone, hyalosiderite, Job's-tears, peridot.

Opal=amber opal, black opal, cacholong opal, common opal, fire opal, flash opal, flash fire opal, fossil pineapple, girasol opal, gold opal, harlequin opal, hyalite, hydrophane, isopyre, jasper opal, lechosos opal, lithoxyle, magic stone, menilite, moss opal, mother-of-opal, Muller's glass, noble opal, opal agate, opal jasper, opal onyx, opaline, oriental opal, pealite, pin fire opal, pitch opal, prase opal, precious opal, quinzite, radio opal, resin opal, rubolite, semiopal, Sobrisky opal, sun opal, tabasheer, vermilion opal, vermilite, water stone, wax opal, wood opal, world's eye.

P.

Parisite.

Pectolite=jade.

Phenacite.

Pitchblende=radiumite.

Polycrase.

Prehnite=Cape chrysolite, chlorastrolite, green agate, green star stone, greenstone, Isle Royal greenstone, Lake Superior greenstone, turtleback, zonochlorite. (See also thomsonite.)

Prosopite.

Pyrite=alpine diamond, fool's gold, Inca stone, Pennsylvania diamond, sulphur diamond.

Pyrophyllite=agalmatolite.

Pyroxene=alalite, bastite, bronzite, chalchihuitl (jadeite), diopside, enstatite, green garnet (enstatite), hypersthene, jade, jadeite, Labrador hornblende, malacolite, New Zealand greenstone, paulite, pink wollastonite, Schillerspar, violane, yu stone.

Q.

Quartz=agate, agate jasper, Alaska diamond, Alençon diamond, Aleppo stone, amberine, amethyst, amethystine quartz, Ancona ruby, apricotine, Arkansas diamond, arrow points, aventurine, azure quartz, Baffa diamond, basanite, beckite, beekite, bishop's stone, bloodstone, blood jasper, blue chrysoprase, blue moonstone, Bohemian diamond, Bohemian topaz, Bohemian ruby, Brazilian diamond, Brazilian pebble, Brazilian topaz, Briançon diamond, Bristol diamond, burnt amethyst, cacholong, cairngorm, California moonstone, Cape May diamond, carnelian, carnelian-onyx, catalinite, Catalina sardonyx, cat's-eye, cer-agate, chalchihuitl, chalcedony, chalcedony onyx, chalcedonyx, chert, china, rump, chloropal, chrysoprase, Colorado topaz, Cornish diamond, cotterite, creolite, crispite, crystal, cupid's darts, Dauphiné diamond, dendritic agate, Egyptian jasper, Egyptian pebble, eldoradoite, emeraldine, enhydros, eye agate, false diamond, false lapis, false topaz, fancy agate, feminine carnelian, flêches d'amour, Fleurus diamond, flint, flower stone, fortification agate, fossil coral, frost stone, geyserite, gold quartz, golden topaz, hairstone, heliotrope, Herkimer diamond, Horatio diamond, hornstone, Hot Springs diamond, hyacinth, Hungarian cat's-eye, hyacinth of Compostella, Imperial jade, Imperial yu stone, Indian agate, Indian topaz, iolanthite, iridescent quartz, iris, Irish diamond, Isle of Wight diamond, jasp-agate, jasper, jasperine, kinradite, Lake George diamond, lavendine, love arrows, lydian stone, Madeira topaz, Marmorosch diamond, masculine carnelian, milky quartz, mocha stone, Mohave moonstone, Montana agate, Mont Blanc ruby, moonstone, Mora diamond, morion, moss agate, moss jasper, mother of emerald, myrickite, needlestone, nicolo, novaculite, occidental agate, occidental amethyst, occidental cat's-eye, occidental chalcedony, occidental diamond, occidental topaz, onegite, onyx, orange topaz, oriental agate, oriental chalcedony, oriental jasper, ouachita stone, Paphos diamond, pebble, Pecos diamond, petrified wood, plasma, prase, prismatic moonstone, pseudo diamond, Quebec diamond, rainbow agate, rainbow quartz, rhinestone, riband agate, riband jasper, ribbon agate, ring agate, river agate, rock crystal, rose quartz, rubasse, sagenite, sandy sard, sapphire quartz, sapphirine, sard, sardoine, sardonyx, Saxon topaz, Schaumberg diamond, Schiller quartz, Scotch topaz, semicarnelian, Siberian amethyst, siderite, sinople, silicified wood, smoky quartz, smoky topaz, soldier's stone, Spanish topaz, St. Stephen stone, star stone, starolite, Swiss lapis, test stone, Texas agate, Thetis hairstone, tiger-eye, topaz, touchstone, tree agate, tree stone, Trenton diamond, unripe diamond, Vallum diamond, Venus hairstone, violite, water agate, wax agate, white carnelian, white sapphire, white topaz, wood agate, woodstone, zonite.

R.

Realgar.

Rhodochrosite.

Rhodonite=fowlerite.

Rock=agrite, catlinite, clay, creoline, graphic granite, lapis lazuli, lava, leopardite, matrix, mother-of-opal, novaculite, obsidian, pegmatite, pipestone, porcelainjasper, porphyry, potstone, saussurite (jade), verdolite, volcanic lava, wabanite.
Rutile=money stone, nigrine.

S.

Samarskite.
Sapphirine.
Scapolite=wernerite; wilsonite.
Sepiolite=meerschaum.
Serpentine=bowenite, California cat's-eye, California tiger-eye, jade, moriah stone, New Zealand greenstone, ophiolite, pelhamite, satelite, serpentine cat's-eye, taxoite, verd antique, williamsite.
Sillimanite=jade.
Smithsonite=azulite, bonamite, sacred turquoise.
Sodalite.
Sphalerite.
Spinel=Alabandine ruby, almandine spinel, automolite, balas ruby, ceylonite, chlorospinel, chromite, dysluite, franklinite, gahnite, goutte de sang, hercynite, hyacinth, magnetite, pleonaste, rubicelle, ruby spinel, sapphirine, Siam ruby, spinel ruby, spinel sapphire, vermeille, vinegar spinel.
Spodumene=California iris, hiddenite, kunzite, lithia emerald, triphane.
Staurolite=cross stone, fairy stone, lucky stone.
Stibiotantalite.

T.

Talc=verdite.
Thomsonite=comptonite, eye agate, eyestone, lintonite.
Titanite=sphene.
Topaz=aquamarine topaz, Brazilian aquamarine, Brazilian ruby, Brazilian sapphire, Brazilian topaz, burnt Brazilian topaz, burnt topaz, drop of water, golden topaz, goutte d'eau, Indian topaz, Killiecrankie diamond, pink topaz, royal topaz, Saxon chrysolite, Saxon topaz, Schnecken topaz, Siberian topaz, slave's diamond, tauridian topaz, water sapphire.
Tourmaline=achroite, andalusite, aphrizite, Brazilian emerald, Brazilian peridot, Brazilian sapphire, Ceylon chrysolite, Ceylon peridot, dravite, emeralite, indicolite, peridot of Ceylon, precious schorl, rubellite schorl, Siberian ruby, siberite.
Turquoise=celestial stone, chalchihuitl, chalchuite, edisonite, mineral turquoise, old rock stone, oriental turquoise, semiturquoise, turkis, turtleback.

V.

Variscite=amatrice, callainite, chlorutahlite, sabalite, trainite, turtleback, utahlite.
Vesuvianite=American jade, brown jacinth, California jade, californite, cyprine, greenstone, idocrase, Italian chrysolite, jade, Oregon jade, Vesuvian gem, volcanic chrysolite, volcanic scoria, white jade, xanthite.

W.

Wardite.
Willemite=troostite.
Wollastonite.

Z.

Zincite.
Zircon=Ceylonese zircon, hyacinth, jacinth, jargon, jargoon, matara diamond.
Zoisite=rosaline, thulite.

APPENDIX 5.

INDUSTRIAL USES OF PRECIOUS STONES.[1]

In the following paragraphs are mentioned some industrial uses of minerals of gem quality. In addition to ornamentation, all gem minerals are of value as specimens for collections, for use in standardization (for example, fluorite and quartz as standards of densities and of refractive indices), and as sources of material for investigation, both industrial and scientific. These uses are therefore not always repeated under the different mineral names. Ornamentation itself covers a variety of utilization, such as for jewelry, knife handles, paper weights, and pipes (meerschaum).

Agate.—Mechanical bearings and supports, scale bearings, balls for water meters, mortars for laboratory use, spatulas, paper knives, playing marbles, and small ornaments.

Azurite.—Ore of copper; pigment for paint.

Azurmalachite.—Ore of copper.

Calcite.—See Iceland spar.

Chromite.—Ore of chromium.

Chrysocolla.—Ore of copper.

Cobaltite.—Ore of cobalt.

Corundum.—See Sapphire.

Diamond.—Cutting, grinding, engraving, boring, and polishing material; supports for bearings and pivots; dies for wire drawing; tips for phonograph needles.

Epidote.—For coloring artificial slate and roofing material.

Fluorite.—See Optical fluorite.

Franklinite.—Ore of manganese and zinc.

Garnet.—Abrasive; for watch jewels or jeweled bearings; as tared weights.

Garnierite.—Ore of nickel.

Gypsum.—Used in manufacture of artificial pearls—the so-called "Roman pearls."

Hematite.—Ore of iron.

Iceland spar.—Iceland spar is a variety of calcite, clear and transparent and unusually free from imperfections and impurities. Transparent crystals or cleavage pieces of calcite of any appreciable size are very rare, and as Iceland has furnished almost all of such material used the name Iceland spar has been given it.

Elongated cleavage rhombohedrous of Iceland spar are used in the manufacture of nicol prisms, which are an essential part of optical instruments requiring plane polarized light, as, for example, certain microscopes, dichroscopes, and saccharimeters. The material, on account of its simple chemical composition and purity, finds application in chemical standardization. Iceland spar is also used in the manufacture of some kinds of glass, and some of it is sold as mineral specimens.

Pieces of Iceland spar, either in single untwinned crystals or parts of such crystals or in homogeneous untwinned cleavage rhombohedra, which are large enough to yield a rectangular prism at least 1 inch long and half an inch thick each way and which possess the properties described below, are suitable for optical purposes. The colorless material must be so clear and transparent that it is limpid and pellucid.

---

[1] Dr. W. T. Schaller, Mineral Resources of the United States, 1918.

It must not be partly opaque on account of numerous cracks or fractures, must not show any internal, iridescent, or rainbow colors due to incipient cracks along fracture lines, nor any cleavage, nor twinning planes. Neither can there be any capillary or larger tubelike cavities, nor cavities or bubbles of any shape, nor inclusions, as isolated particles, veins, or clouds, composed of minute crystals of some other mineral or of any kind of foreign substance. The spar should not be discolored or stained by the presence of any clay, iron oxide, or other material. It should be noted that many of the inclusions and imperfections of Iceland spar are not always scattered irregularly through the mineral or even segregated in distinct masses, but frequently lie in a distinct but very thin plane which can hardly be seen if looked at on edge. In examining a piece of Iceland spar for defects the piece should therefore be turned in all directions while held to the light.

The material suitable for optical uses naturally brings the highest prices, as it has to be at least of the dimensions already given. Specimen material is generally of a larger size. The material used for standardization, chiefly chemical, need be of no special size, and the smaller pieces are as usable as the larger ones. [1]

Although calcite is, next to quartz, the commonest mineral, the only locality outside of Iceland known to produce the variety Iceland spar in commercial quantity is in Montana, about 9 miles from Gray Cliff, Sweet Grass County, on the main line of the Northern Pacific Railway. The spar occurs in a nearly vertical fissure vein from 3 to 8 feet thick, which strikes northwest, traversing a gneissic rock for several miles.

Jasper.—See Agate.

Malachite.—Ore of copper, pigment for paint.

Mariposite.—Pigment for paint.

Meerschaum.—Pipe bowls; cigar and cigarette holders.

Optical fluorite.—Fluorite, commonly called fluorspar, is a common mineral but is very seldom found in pieces clear enough and large enough to be of special use in the manufacture of certain optical lenses and prisms. Fluorite of the requisite qualities, as described below, suitable for such use is known as "optical fluorite." Any deposit of fluorite may yield a small quantity of such material, but at present about the only localities known to produce it are southern Illinois; Meiringen, Switzerland; and Obira, Bungo, Japan. Optical fluorite is cut into lenses and placed between glass lenses. It forms the apochromatic objective for microscopes and similar optical instruments, the fluorite lens correcting the spherical and chromatic errors of the glass lens systems. This result is due to the low refractive power, weak color dispersion, and single refraction of fluorite. These apochromatic lenses represent the finest type of microscope objectives made. The use of such a fluorite lens greatly increases the value of a microscope and if optical fluorite were more abundant many more microscope objectives would be equipped with such lenses.

Optical fluorite is also used in the lenses of certain telescopes, in making prisms for spectrographs in ultra-violet work, and in other optical apparatus where transparency in the ultra-violet and infra-red parts of the spectrum is necessary.

---

[1] The optical variety of Iceland spar produced in the United States, sold, a pound, for $3 to $4 in 1914, about $8 in 1915, and as high as $20 in July, 1918. The specimen variety sells for considerably less, and material for standardization sells for from $1 to $2 a pound.

The following firms are buyers of Iceland spar suitable for optical use: Bausch & Lomb Optical Co., Purchasing Department, Rochester, New York; Central Scientific Co., 460 Ohio Street east, Chicago, Illinois; Gilbert S. Day, Superintendent Optical Department, Eastman Kodak Co., Rochester, New York.

The market for specimen spar is irregular, as the demand is usually very light. The best market will probably be found with some of the larger mineral dealers.

Standardization material may be sold to large dealers in general chemicals as well as to mineral dealers.

Optical fluorite must yield or contain pieces at least one-fourth of an inch in diameter, which must be clear and colorless and free from all defects.   Defects consist of internal cracks or cleavage planes, bubbles, or inclusions of dirt or mineral matter. The presence of faintly developed or incipient cleavage planes or fracture surfaces usually may be determined, if not readily visible, by moistening the specimen with kerosene.   The material must not show any anomalous double refraction. Absolutely clear-water material is of the highest value, but very faint tints of green, yellow, or purple do not render the material useless.[1]

Suitable material has been obtained from several of the fluorite mines in Hardin County, Illinois, and may also occur in the extension of this fluorite belt in western Kentucky.   Although fluorite is found in many other States, practically none of them is known to contain any "optical fluorite."

Quartz.—See Rock crystal.

Rock crystal.—The perfectly clear and colorless variety of quartz is called rock crystal. It furnishes the material for certain special glasses and fused silica ware; and it is used in wedges for microscopic work, as spectographic prisms for special researches and as mechanical bearings.   A use in connection with certain sounding boxes has recently been developed.

Sepiolite.—See Meerschaum.

Sapphire.—The variety of gem corundum used for other purposes than jewelry is called sapphire, irrespective of its color.   It is used for mechanical bearings and pivot supports, especially in watches and phonograph needles (mostly artificial sapphire).

Topaz.—Abrasive.

Tourmaline.—In the tourmaline tongs or in polarizing forceps, a very simple form of polariscope.

Fluorite suitable for optical use is valued at from $1 to $10 a pound, according to the size of the piece suitable for cutting as well as to its quality.   The present yearly requirement is not large—perhaps several hundred pounds—but under proper conditions and with a dependable steady supply this requirement may be increased.

Possible buyers of optical fluorite are: Bausch & Lomb Optical Co., Rochester, New York; Spencer Lens Co., Buffalo, New York; Ward's Natural Science Establishment, Rochester, New York; United States Bureau of Standards, Washington, District of Columbia.

APPENDIX 6.

TABLES FOR THE IDENTIFICATION OF PRECIOUS STONES.

The accurate identification of a precious stone, even by an expert, is often a matter of considerable difficulty, and, indeed, sometimes rendered quite impossible by the manner in which the stone is mounted. The task, as a rule, is quite beyond the skill of the untrained. The method given below has been prepared by Dr. Edgar T. Wherry, formerly in charge of the Division of Mineralogy. The appliances needed comprise:

Sharp-pointed fragments of the minerals diamond, corundum, and quartz, preferably set in wooden handles the size of ordinary lead pencils.

Cleavage pieces or crystals, with good bright surfaces, of the minerals corundum, quartz, and feldspar (microcline).

Some means for determining specific gravity, such as picnometer, fine platinum-wire cage to be hung on chemical balance, small Nicholson hydrometer, etc. Liquids with high specific gravities, upon which stones of lower gravity will float, such as methylene iodide, specific gravity 3.30; acetylene tetrabromide, specific gravity 2.95; and bromoform, specific gravity 2.85, are also useful.

A microscope provided with nicol prisms, and a small, round-bottomed glass dish to be placed in the center of its stage, in which the stone can be immersed in a high-refracting liquid such as α-mono-brom-naphthalene, $n=1.66$.

The stone is:

I. Colorless, white, or very pale tinted.
  A. Transparent or nearly so.
    (a) Hardness 9 or greater; not scratched by corundum point.
      1. Scratches corundum surface; not scratched by diamond point....Diamond.
      2. Does not scratch corundum surface............Corundum (white sapphire).
    (b) Hardness 8 to 7; scratched by corundum, but not by quartz.
      1. Specific gravity very high, 4.5......................................Zircon.
      2. Specific gravity high, 3.5..Topaz.
      3. Specific gravity medium, 2.65.......................Quartz (rock crystal).
        (Colorless varieties of beryl, chrysoberyl, garnet, spinel, spodumene, and tourmaline, and the rare minerals danburite and phenakite, belong here.)
    (c) Hardness less than 7; scratched by quartz.
      1. Isotropic between crossed nicols under the microscope.....Glass (artificial).
      2. Anisotropic...Feldspar (varieties).
        (The rare minerals beryllonite and datolite belong here.)
  B. Opaque or nearly so.
    (a) Hardness greater than 6; scratch microcline.
      1. Luster waxy; not scratched by quartz.........................Chalcedony.
      2. Luster greasy; scratched by quartz......................................Jade.
        (Compact white vesuvianite (californite) belongs here.)
    (b) Hardness less than 6; do not scratch microcline.
      (White agalmatolite, serpentine, opal, and opaque glass belong here.)

II. Color violet, red-violet, and related hues.
 A. Transparent or nearly so.
   (a) Hardness 9 or greater; not scratched by corundum.
     1. Does not scratch corundum surface..........Corundum (oriental amethyst).
       (The rare violet-colored diamond belongs here; it scratches corundum.)
   (b) Hardness 8 to 7; scratched by corundum, but not by quartz.
     1. Specific gravity very high, 4..............Garnet (almandine and rhodolite).
     2. Specific gravity high, 3.6...Spinel.
     3. Specific gravity rather high, 3.2.....................Spodumene (kunzite).
     4. Specific gravity medium, 2.65...........................Quartz, amethyst.
       (The rare violet-colored varieties of iolite, tourmaline, and zircon, and
       the rare mineral axinite, belong here.)
   (c) Hardness less than 7; scratched by quartz.
     1. Isotropic..Glass (artificial).
       (The rarely used violet varieties of apatite belong here.)
 B. Opaque or nearly so.
   (a) Hardness greater than 6; scratch microcline.
       (The rare violet chalcedony and the rare mineral dumortierite belong here.)
   (b) Hardness less than 6; do not scratch microcline.
       (The rarely used lepidolite, pyroxene variety violan, and opaque violet
       glass belong here.)
III. Color blue and related hues.
 A. Transparent or nearly so.
   (a) Hardness 9 or greater; not scratched by corundum.
     1. Does not scratch corundum surface....................Corundum, sapphire.
       (The rare blue-colored diamond belongs here; it scratches corundum.)
   (b) Hardness 7; scratched by corundum, but not by quartz.
     1. Sp. gr. 4.6; color pale blue, essential................................Zircon.
     2. Sp. gr. 3. 6; color deep green-blue, essential..........................Spinel.
     3. Sp. gr. 3.5; color pale blue, disperse................................Topaz.
     4. Sp. gr. 3.1; color deep smoky or green-blue, essential.Tourmaline (indicolite).
     5. Sp. gr. 2.7; color pale blue or green-blue, disperse........Beryl, aquamarine.
     6. Sp. gr. 2.6; pleochroic, blue to yellow.................................Iolite.
       (The rare mineral euclase belongs here.)
   (c) Hardness less than 7; scratched by quartz.
     1. Isotropic...Glass.
       (The rare blue-colored varieties of apatite, fluorite, kyanite, and opal, and
       the rare minerals benitoite and hauynite, belong here.)
 B. Opaque or nearly so.
   (a) Hardness greater than 6; scratch microcline.
     1. Luster waxy (in part artificially colored by dyes)..............Chalcedony.
     2. Luster glassy; color due to inclusions................................Quartz.
   (b) Hardness 6 or less; do not scratch microcline.
     1. Sp. gr. 3.8; color deep blue; effervesces with acid....................Azurite.
     2. Sp. gr. 2.8; color pale green-blue; luster waxy.....................Turquois.
     3. Sp. gr. 2.4; color mottled and showing pyrite dots.............Lapis-lazuli.
       (Several little-used minerals belong here, such as calamine (copper-
       stained), chrysocolla, crocidolite, smithsonite (copper-stained), sodalite, etc.;
       also glass imitations of turquois.)
IV. Color green.
 A. Transparent or nearly so.
   (a) Hardness 9 or greater; not scratched by corundum.
     1. Does not scratch corundum surface.............Corundum, oriental emerald.
       (The rare green-colored diamond belongs here; it scratches corundum.)

IV. Color green—Continued.
  A. Transparent or nearly so—Continued.
    (b) Hardness 8 to 7; scratched by corundum but not by quartz.
      1. Sp. gr. 3.7; color yellow-green, in artificial light red.Chrysoberyl, alexandrite.
      2. Sp. gr. 3.2; color pale brown-green or yellow-green...............Andalusite.
      3. Sp. gr. 3.1; pleochroic, pale to deep green.................Tourmaline.
      4. Sp. gr. 2.7; color pale blue-green, faintly pleochroic.................Beryl.
      5. Sp. gr. 2.7; color deep green, moderately pleochroic........Beryl, emerald.
      6. Sp. gr. 2.65; color pale, cloudy green, not pleochroic........Quartz, prase.
          (The rare green-colored varieties of euclase, topaz, and zircon belong here.)
    (c) Hardness less than 7; scratched by quartz.
      1. Sp. gr. 3.8; color deep yellow-green; isotropic..........Garnet, demantoid.
      2. Sp. gr. 3.5; pleochroic, deep green-yellow to brown.................Epidote.
      3. Sp. gr. 3.4; pleochroic, yellow-green to green-yellow......Titanite, sphene.
      4. Sp. gr. 3.4; faintly pleochroic; color green-yellow........Chrysolite, peridot.
      5. Sp. gr. 3.3; not pleochroic; color pale green............Pyroxene, diopside.
      6. Sp. gr. 3.2; pleochroic, pale to deep green...........Spodumene, hiddenite.
      7. Sp. gr. 2.5; color dark brown-green; isotropic..........Obsidian, moldavite.
      8. Sp. gr. mostly below 3; isotropic............................Glass (artificial).
          (The rarely used minerals dioptase and prehnite and the rare green-colored
            varieties of apatite, enstatite, fluorite, and vesuvianite belong here.)
  B. Opaque or nearly so.
    (a) Hardness greater than 6; scratch microcline.
      1. Sp. gr. 3.3; luster rather vitreous; color yellow-green.
                                                    Vesuvianite, californite.
      2. Sp. gr. 3.3; luster rather greasy; color green or greenish gray..Jade (jadeite).
      3. Sp. gr. 2.6; luster rather waxy; color pale blue-green.
                                                    Chalcedony, chrysoprase.
      4. Sp. gr. 2.6; luster rather dull; color dark blue-green...Chalcedony, plasma.
          (When plasma is spotted with red it is known as bloodstone.)
    (b) Hardness 6 or less; do not scratch microcline.
      1. Sp. gr. 4; color intense green; luster rather silky.................Malachite.
      2. Sp. gr. 3, color green or greenish gray; luster greasy........Jade (nephrite).
      3. Sp. gr. 2.8; color pale blue-green; luster rather waxy..............Turquoise.
      4. Sp. gr. 2.6; color pale or deep green; luster greasy...............Serpentine.
      5. Sp. gr. 2.6; color blue-green, streaky; luster vitreous.
                                                    Microcline, amazonstone.
      6. Sp. gr. 2.6; color green-blue-green; luster waxy....................Variscite.
      7. Sp. gr. mostly below 3; isotropic; luster vitreous...........Glass (artificial).
          (Several little-used minerals belong here, such as calamine (copper-
            stained), chlorastrolite, chrysocolla, fuchsite, smithsonite (copper-
            stained), etc.)
V. Color yellow.
  A. Transparent or nearly so.
    (a) Hardness 9 or greater; not scratched by corundum.
      1. Scratches corundum surface; not scratched by diamond point....Diamond.
      2. Does not scratch corundum surface.............Corundum (oriental topaz).
    (b) Hardness 8 to 7; scratched by corundum but not by quartz.
      1. Sp. gr. very high, 4.5......................................Zircon, hyacinth.
      2. Sp. gr. high, 3.7..Chrysoberyl.
      3. Sp. gr. fairly high, 3.5...Topaz.
      4. Sp. gr. medium, 2.7.......................................Beryl, golden.
      5. Sp. gr. 2.65...Quartz, citrine.
          (The rare yellow varieties of chrysolite, danburite, garnet, spinel, and
            tourmaline belong here.)

V. Color yellow—Continued.
  A. Transparent or nearly so—Continued.
    (c) Hardness less than 7; scratched by quartz.
      1. Sp. gr. fairly high, 3.4; pleochroism distinct..............Titanite, sphene.
      2. Sp. gr. mostly less than 3; isotropic.......................Glass (artificial).
      3. Sp. gr. very low, 1.1...Amber.
          (The rarely used yellow forms of apatite, chrysolite, fluorite, microlite,
          sphalerite, spodumene, vesuvianite, and willemite belong here.)
  B. Opaque or nearly so.
    (a) Hardness greater than 6; scratch microcline.
      1. Sp. gr. medium, 2.6 (in part artificially colored)................Chalcedony.
      2. Like preceding, but more opaque.......................Chalcedony, jasper.
      3. Luster silky..Quartz after crocidolite.
    (b) Hardness less than 6; do not scratch microcline.
      1. Sp. gr. mostly below 3; luster glassy.......................Glass (artificial).
          (The rare yellow varieties of serpentine and smithsonite, and the little
          used mineral cancrinite belong here.)
VI. Color brown (including orange-color).
  A. Transparent or nearly so.
    (a) Hardness 9 or greater; not scratched by corundum.
        (The rare brown-colored diamond belongs here.)
    (b) Hardness 8 to 7; scratched by corundum but not by quartz.
      1. Sp. gr. high, 4.5; double refraction strong, very brilliant...........Zircon.
      2. Sp. gr. high, 4.1; isotropic.....................Garnet, essonite, spessartite.
      3. Sp. gr. fairly high, 3..Tourmaline.
      4. Sp. gr. medium, 2.7..Quartz, smoky.
          (The rarely used mineral staurolite, and the rare brown-colored varieties
          of andalusite, chrysoberyl, spinel, and topaz belong here.)
    (c) Hardness less than 7; scratched by quartz.
      1. Sp. gr. fairly high, 3.4; pleochroism distinct.....................Titanite.
      2. Sp. gr. medium, mostly less than 3; isotropic.............Glass (artificial).
      3. Sp. gr. very low, 1.1...Amber.
          (The rarely used minerals axinite, epidote, fluorite, chondrodite,
          sphalerite, staurolite, and vesuvianite belong here.)
  B. Opaque or nearly so.
    (a) Hardness greater than 6; scratch microcline.
      1. Sp. gr. high, 3.7; color deep brown ....Staurolite.
      2. Sp. gr. medium, 2.6; in part artificially colored...............Chalcedony.
      3. Same, banded...Chalcedony, agate.
      4. Same, but more opaque ....Chalcedony, jasper.
      5. Same, but luster highly silky.....................Quartz after crocidolite.
    (b) Hardness less than 6; do not scratch microcline.
      1. Sp. gr. medium, 2.6..Obsidian.
      2. Sp. gr. mostly less than 3....................................Glass (artificial).
          (Some rarely-used varieties of feldspar and altered staurolite belong here.)
VII. Color red or pink.
  A. Transparent or nearly so.
    (a) Hardness 9 or greater; not scratched by corundum.
      1. Does not scratch corundum surface......................Corundum, ruby.
          (The rare pink colored-diamond belongs here; it scratches corundum.)

VII. Color red or pink—Continued.
  A. Transparent or nearly so—Continued.
    (b) Hardness 8 to 7; scratched by corundum but not by quartz.
      1. Sp. gr. high, 3.9; color intense red; isotropic.........Garnet, pyrope, (etc.).
      2. Sp. gr. fairly high, 3.6; color intense red; isotropic......Spinel, balas-ruby.
      3. Sp. gr. fairly high, 3.5; color orange-red to pink; anisotropic........Topaz.
      4. Sp. gr. fairly high, 3.1, color pink; pleochroism strong..Tourmaline, rubellite.
      5. Sp. gr. medium, 2.7; color pink; pleochroism faint.....Beryl, "morganite."
        (The rare pink grossularite garnet and the red variety of zircon belong
          here.)
    (c) Hardness less than 7; scratched by quartz.
      (The little used mineral piedmontite, and the rare red-colored varieties
        of amber, and pink-colored varieties of fluorite and spodumene-kunzite
        belong here; also opal and artificial glass.)
  B. Opaque or nearly so.
    (a) Hardness greater than 6; scratch microcline.
      1. Sp. gr. fairly high, 3.3; color dull red or violet red.........Zoisite, thulite.
      2. Sp. gr. medium, 2.6; color pink, cloudy......................Quartz, rose.
      3. Same, but color red...............................Chalcedony, carnelian.
      4. Same, but more opaque ....Chalcedony, jasper.
      5. Same, but banded.....................................Chalcedony, agate.
    (b) Hardness less than 6; will not scratch microcline.
      (The little used minerals lepidolite, rhodonite, and rutile belong here;
        also coral and artificial glasses.)
VIII. Color black.
  (a) Hardness 9 or greater; not scratched by corundum.
    (Black diamond or carbonado belongs here; it scratches corundum.)
  (b) Hardness 8 to 7; scratched by corundum but not by quartz.
    1. Sp. gr. 2.7...Quartz, smoky.
    2. Same, more opaque; artificially colored.........................Chalcedony.
    3. Same, banded...Chalcedony, agate.
    (The rarely used black varieties of spinel and tourmaline belong here.)
  (c) Hardness less than 7; scratched by quartz.
    1. Sp. gr. very high, 5.3; "streak" (powder) red....................Hematite.
    2. Sp. gr. medium, 2.5; glassy.......................................Obsidian.
    3. Sp. gr. medium; glassy.....................................Glass (artificial).
    4. Sp. gr. low..Jet (and coal).
    (The little used minerals allanite, chromite, gadolinite, ilmenite, mag-
      netite, rutile, and samarskite belong here.)
Possessing internal colors:
  A. Transparent or nearly so.
    (a) Hardness 9 or greater; not scratched by corundum.
      1. Does not scratch corundum surface; int. refl. silvery, 6-rayed.
                            Corundum, asteria.
    (b) Hardness 8 to 7; scratched by corundum but not by quartz.
      1. Sp. gr. 2.7; int. refl. silky, forming fine sharp line...Chrysoberyl, cat's-eye.
      2. Sp. gr. 2.7; int. refl. silky, forming broad band...........Quartz, cat's-eye.
      (The rare tourmaline-cat's-eye belongs here.)
    (c) Hardness less than 7; scratched by quartz.
      1. Sp. gr. medium, 2.6; int. refl. blue to silvery-white...Feldspar, moonstone.
      2. Sp. gr. rather low, 2.2; int. refl. various brilliant colors................Opal.
      (Some amber, feldspar variety sunstone, obsidian, and various kinds of
        artificial glass belong here.)

Possessing internal colors—Continued.
  B. Opaque or nearly so.
    (a) Hardness greater than 6; scratch microcline.
      1. (Some asteria corundum is practically opaque; see A. *a* 1.)
                                        Corundum, asteria.
      2. Int. refl. silky, forming broad band; color brown-yellow...Quartz, tiger-eye.
      3. Int. refl. silky, forming broad band; color gray, green, etc..Quartz, cat's-eye.
      4. Int. refl. spangled; color various........................Quartz, aventurine.
    (b) Hardness 6 or less; do not scratch microline.
      1. Sp. gr. 3.4; int. refl. bronzy; color dark brown.
                                    Hypersthene (including bronzite).
      2. Sp. gr. 2.7; shows pearly luster and delicate color-play.......Calcite, pearl.
      3. Sp. gr. 2.7; color gray; int. refl. blue, green, red, etc..Feldspar, labradorite.
      4. Sp. gr. 2.7; color gray; int. refl. red, spangled...........Feldspar, sunstone.
      5. Sp. gr. 2.5; color dull green; int. refl. silky, gray.......Serpentine, satelite.
      6. Sp. gr. 2.3; very soft, color white; int. refl. strongly silky.
                                        Gypsum, satin-spar.

APPENDIX 7.

STATISTICS OF PRODUCTION.[1]

Value of precious stones produced in the United States, 1913–1919.

	1913	1914	1915	1916	1917	1918	1919
Beryl	$1,615	$2,395	$1,675	$2,031	$2,178	$1,906	(a)
Copper-ore gems	2,350	1,280	1,120	1,713	2,857	2,299	(a)
Corundum	238,835	61,032	88,214	99,180	54,204	42,414	$40,304
Diamond	6,315	765	608	2,680	4,175	1,910	(a)
Feldspar	1,285	449	368	305	(b)	(b)	(b)
Garnet	4,285	1,760	4,523	1,542	624	1,277	1,630
Hematite			126	(b)	(b)	138	(b)
Jade		300					
Opal	15,130	1,114	1,850	1,838	805	6,304	(a)
Peridot	375	100	(b)	455	(b)	1,018	
Pyrite	50		1,042	2,075	(b)	(b)	
Quartz	16,861	18,838	35,724	25,707	28,273	15,211	17,632
Rhodonite	165	1,050	85	(b)	(b)	515	160
Smithsonite	50	50	(b)		(b)		
Spodumene	6,520	4,000	(b)	(b)	(b)	281	(b)
Thomsonite		21	(b)	47	(b)	(b)	(b)
Topaz	736	1,380	862	1,005	230	907	210
Tourmaline	7,630	7,980	10,969	50,807	12,452	6,206	17,700
Turquoise	8,075	13,370	11,691	21,811	14,171	20,667	22,750
Variscite	6,105	5,055	3,867	3,140	2,350	753	925
Vesuvianite	152	1,425	1,535	(c)	2,765	320	
Beryl, copper-ore gems, diamond, opal	(c)	(c)	(c)	(c)	(c)	(c)	8,832
Miscellaneous gems	2,920	2,287	d 6,172	e 3,457	f 5,928	g 4,397	h 1,620
	319,454	124,651	170,431	217,793	131,012	106,523	111,763

a Less than 3 producers; figures combined with others to avoid disclosing confidential information.
b Small production included under "Miscellaneous gems."
c For value of production in this year, see above.
d Includes apatite, calamine, chlorastrolite, crocidolite, datolite, fossil coral, Iceland spar, kyanite, lapis lazuli, obsidian, peridot, phenacite, rutile, smithsonite, spodumene (kunzite), staurolite, thomsonite, titanite, and zircon.
e Includes chlorastrolite, datolite, epidote, fossil coral, hematite, kyanite, lazulite, rhodonite, rutile, sepiolite, serpentine, spodumene, staurolite, and vesuvianite.
f Includes andalusite, chlorastrolite, datolite, epidote, feldspar, fossil coral, hematite, Iceland spar, lapis lazuli, obsidian, peridot, phenacite, pyrite, rhodonite, rutile, sepiolite, smithsonite, spodumene, staurolite, thomsonite, willemite, and zoisite.
g Includes andalusite, calamine, chlorastrolite, datolite, epidote, feldspar, fluorite, Iceland spar, lapis lazuli, mariposite, meerschaum, obsidian, phenacite, pyrite, satin spar (gypsum), staurolite, thomsonite, willemite, and zoisite.
h Includes chlorastrolite, datolite, feldspar, fossil coral, hematite, jet, lapis lazuli, meerschaum, spinel, spodumene (kunzite), thomsonite, and Iceland spar.

[1] From Mineral Resources of the United States, 1919. Pt. 2, 1921.

APPENDIX 8.

SELECTED BIBLIOGRAPHY.

The very full bibliographies given in Tagore's "Mani-Málá," Feuchtwänger's "Treatise on Gems," Wodiska's "Book of Precious Stones," and Pogue's "The Turquoise" seemingly render unnecessary a reference here to any but a few of the more general treatises.

BAUER, MAX. Edelsteinkunde.
Leipzig, 1896.
English translation by L. J. Spencer. Lippincott & Co., Philadelphia.

BOUTAN, M. E. Le diamant.
Paris, 1886.
Contains a very full bibliography up to date of issue.

BURNHAM, S. M. Precious stones in nature, art, and literature.
Boston, 1886.

CATTELLE, W. R. Precious stones. A book of reference for jewelers.
Philadelphia and London, 1903.

CHURCH, A. H. Precious stones, considered in their scientific and artistic relations.
London, 1882.

CLAREMONT, L. Precious stones.
Philadelphia and London. J. B. Lippincott Co., 1903, 224 pp., xix plates, 8°.

DIEULAFAIT, L. Diamonds and precious stones; a popular account of gems.
New York, 1874.

DOELTER, C. Edelsteinkunde. Bestimmung und Untersuchung der Edelsteine und Schmucksteine; Kuenstliche Darstellung der Edelsteine.
Leipzig, 1893.

EMANUEL, H. Diamonds and precious stones.
London, 1865.
Contains a very full bibliography to date of publication.

ESCARD, J. Les pierres precieuses (precious stones), 520 pp., illustrated with colored plates.
Paris, H. Dunod et E. Pinat, 1914. (About $7.)

FARRINGTON, O. C. Gems and minerals. 229 pp., illustrated with colored plates.
Chicago, A. W. Mumford Co., 1903. ($3.)

FEUCHTWANGER, L. A popular treatise on gems in reference to their scientific value.
New York, 1872.

FURTWÄNGLER, A. Die antiken Gemmen. Geschichte der Steinschneidekunst im klassischen Altertum.
Leipzig, Berlin: Gieseck and Devrient, 1900. 3 vols, illustrations, plates.

GOODCHILD, W. Precious stones. 309 pp., illustrated. Archibald Constable and Co. Ltd. ($2.)
London, 1908.

HAMLIN, A. C. The tourmaline.
Boston, 1873.

HINDMARSH, R. Precious stones,, being an account of the stones mentioned in the Sacred Scriptures.
London, 1851.

JANETTAZ, N. and E. FONTENAY, EM. VANDERHEGEN, and A. COUTANCE. Diamant et pierres precieuses.
Paris, 1880.

JAZEK, BOH.   Aus dem Reiche der Edelsteine (In the domain of the precious stones), 171 pp., 8 pls., figs.
> Prague, Austria, E. Weinfurter.
KING, C. W.   The natural history of gems or decorative stones.
> London, 1867.
KUNZ, GEORGE F.   Gems, jewelers' materials, and ornamental stones of California, 2d ed.: California Min. Bureau, Bull. 37, 171 pp., illustrated (4 colored plates), 1905. (Price and postage, 58 cents.)
—— The curious lore of precious stones, 406 pp., 61 pls. (6 in color), figs.
> Philadelphia, J. B. Lippincott Co., 1913. ($5.)
—— Gems and precious stones of North America, 367 pp., illustrated with colored plates.
> New York, Scientific Publishing Co., 1890. ($10.)
—— (CHARLES H. STEVENSON).   The Book of the Pearl.
> New York City, 1908, The Century Co.
—— The fresh-water pearls and pearl fisheries of the United States. (In Bulletin of the United States Fish Commission, 1897, p. 375.)
LIESEGANG, R. E.   Die Achate (Agates), 118 pp., illustrated.
> Dresden and Leipzig, 1915.
LOWN, CLARENCE, and BOOTH, HENRY.   Fossil Resins, a compilation.
> New York, 1891, N. D. C. Hodges.
MAWE, JOHN.   A treatise on diamonds and precious stones, including their history, natural and commercial. To which is added some account of the best method of cutting and polishing them.
> London, 1813.
POGUE, J. E.   The Turquoise: A study of its history, mineralogy, geology, ethnology, archeology, mythology, folklore, and technology. Nat. Acad. Sci., Mem., vol. 12, pt. 2, No. 3, 206 pp., 22 pls. (1 colored), figs., 1915.
> Contains full bibliography to date.
ROSENMÜLLER, E. F. C.   Mineralogy of the Bible. Translated by Repp and Morren.
> Edinburgh, 1840.
ROTHSCHILD, M. D.   Handbook of precious stones.
> New York, 1890.
SMITH, G. F. H.   Gem stones and their distinctive characters. 312 pp., illustrated with colored plates.
> London, 1912, Methuen and Co. Ltd. ($2.10.)
SCHALLER, W. T.   The production of precious stones. Mineral Resources of the United States, 1915–1919.
STERRETT, D. B.   The production of precious stones.
> Washington, D. C., 1907. Mineral Resources of the United States, 1906–1914.
STREETER, E. W.   Precious stones and gems.
> London, 1877.
—— Great diamonds of the world.
> London, 1892.
TAGORE, S. M.   Mani-Málá, a treatise on gems. 2 vols.
> Calcutta, 1879.
> Contains a bibliography of Sanskrit, Persian, Arabic, and other oriental works on gems.
WILLIAMS, G. F.   The diamond mines of South Africa. 2 vols., 359 and 353 pp., illustrated.
> New York, B. F. Buck and Co., 1905.
WODISKA, JULIUS.   A book of precious stones. 363 pp., illustrated with colored plates.
> New York, 1910, G. P. Putnam's Sons.

INDEX.

This index is restricted to the gem and mineral names used in this bulletin.

219

#716